Symbolic Logic
and
the
REAL NUMBER SYSTEM

An Introduction to the Foundations of Number Systems

A. H. LIGHTSTONE

Queen's University
Kingston, Ontario, Canada

HARPER & ROW, Publishers   **New York**

SYMBOLIC LOGIC AND THE REAL NUMBER SYSTEM:

An Introduction to the Foundations of Number Systems

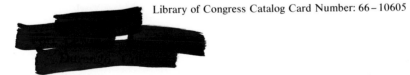

58621

Contents

Preface

This book is intended for students with enough mathematical maturity to tackle abstract mathematics. Generally, two years of university mathematics prepares a student for this sort of mathematics, where it is the mathematics itself, as contrasted to applications, that is under scrutiny.

One purpose of this book is to draw to the attention of the undergraduate, quite early in his career, the impact of symbolic logic on mathematics. A working knowledge of the logical connectives, including the universal and existential quantifiers, makes possible a remarkable precision of expression and enables the student to handle complicated mathematical statements. In short, symbolic logic facilitates communication. For these reasons, Chapter 1 is devoted to the logical connectives. Applications to syllogisms and to the design of switching networks are worked out in detail. The main purpose of Chapter 1 is to develop a language in which mathematical statements can be expressed with precision.

The notion of a mathematical object is presented in Chapter 2. In particular, sets and ordered n-tuples are considered from an intuitive viewpoint. Many mathematical concepts can be formulated in terms of these basic objects; for example, mappings, operations, and relations are sets of ordered n-tuples and are discussed in detail. The important idea of partitioning a set by using an equivalence relation is worked out. Throughout Chapter 2 the logical connectives are used freely; this gives the student some training in handling logical connectives in a simple setting. Properties of sets are demonstrated by applying the algebra of propositions, which is discussed in Chapter 1.

The ground is now ready for an elementary discussion of abstract algebra. The axiomatic method is discussed in terms of algebraic systems. Many examples are presented in order to bring to life the important mathematical object called an *algebraic system* and to give the student some experience in handling algebraic systems, binary operations, and binary relations. In short, Chapter 3 is an introduction to modern abstract algebra, which provides the necessary algebraic background for a study of number systems.

In Chapter 4 the usual number systems are constructed on the basis of the Peano Postulates. The Peano System is presented axiomatically, and is followed by the natural number system, which is constructed from the Peano System. Next, the system of integers is developed; this is followed by the rational number system. Logical connectives are used freely throughout this chapter. The mathematical statements that appear here are somewhat more complicated than those of the earlier chapters, thereby providing some preparation for Chapters 5 and 6, in which quite complicated statements must be handled.

In Chapter 5 we come to grips with the real number system. Here we meet one of the goals of this book: to develop the real number system on the basis of ordinary arithmetic. In high school the student learned that a real number is an infinite decimal; moreover, he mastered a complicated technique for computing the sum or product of two infinite decimals, a technique based on the operations of *rounding off, deleting digits*, and *normalizing* (i.e., eliminating a block of 9's). Accordingly, in Chapter 5 these fundamental operations are studied and are used to define addition and multiplication. With this approach the real number system is constructed from the rational number system by formalizing the student's own ideas on the subject. Thus, at each step the student can draw on his experience in handling real numbers. This makes for a meaningful discussion. There are two other well-known approaches to the real number system. One is attributed to R. Dedekind and is based on Dedekind cuts; the other is attributed to G. Cantor and uses Cauchy sequences. For a lucid exposition of these theories, see F. Waismann, *Introduction to Mathematical Thinking*, New York, Harper, 1959.

In Chapter 6 the limit concept, the basic idea of analysis, is developed. It is shown that the operations of *rounding off* and *deleting digits* are fundamental to the limit operation; this suggests that the R, D, and DR operations are well worth studying in their own right.

The two appendixes contain elementary discussions of cardinal numbers and of the complex number system.

The exercise lists are an integral part of this book and serve two functions: first, to provide some practice in handling the concepts and techniques of the text; secondly, to penetrate further into the topic by presenting additional material and notions.

The first three chapters of this book have grown out of the corresponding chapters of *The Axiomatic Method: An Introduction to Mathematical Logic*, © 1964, Prentice-Hall, Inc., Englewood Cliffs, New Jersey. The author is grateful to the publisher for permission to use this material here. In that book the chapters on symbolic logic and set theory were relatively condensed, serving to review the material from an advanced standpoint. In the present work, however, these topics are considered to be introduced to the student for the first time, and the treatment is accordingly fuller. There is a corresponding difference in the approach to abstract algebra. In *The Axiomatic Method* it is assumed that the reader has a basic knowledge of the subject, so that attention can be fixed on the axiomatic method itself. In this book the treatment is introductory; indeed, the major effort is to develop an appreciation for the concepts of modern algebra.

Chapter 2 has appeared in essentially its present form in the author's *Concepts of Calculus* (Harper & Row, 1965).

The author is indebted to Professor Dennis C. Russell, who read the manuscript and made many helpful suggestions.

A. H. LIGHTSTONE

Kingston
August, 1965

Symbolic Logic

and

the

REAL NUMBER SYSTEM

Chapter 1

Symbolic Logic

1.1 The Logical Connectives

Symbolic logic has its roots in the study of language. Any developed language, English, say, possesses a number of words and phrases with a distinct function — namely, these special words and phrases have a bearing on the truth or falsity of the sentences in which they occur. In particular, these special words and phrases indicate that the truth of the sentence in which they are used depends upon the truth or falsity of certain other statements. Such words or phrases are aptly called *logical connectives*. Some of the more important logical connectives are "not", "or", "and", "if . . . then", "if and only if".

Let us see how "and" functions as a logical connective. Consider the sentence: "It is cold and the sun is shining". This sentence is obtained by joining the two sentences "It is cold" and "The sun is shining" with the word "and". The resulting sentence, called a *compound* proposition, is true provided that each of the two component sentences is true.

Here, we shall be concerned only with declarative sentences which possess a definite and unique truth-value, i.e., are either true or false; any sentence of this type is called a *proposition*.

DEFINITION 1.1.1. A proposition is a declarative sentence which is true or else is false (but not both).

Thus, a proposition which is known to be not true must be false, and a proposition which is not false is true. Also, a proposition which is true is not false, and a proposition which is false is not true.

Let us consider the logical connective "or". This word is unusually sensitive in the sense that its meaning changes with the context. It is possible to interpret the compound proposition "p or q" in two ways:

1. "p or q, or both",
2. "p or else q", i.e., "p or q, but not both".

The first sense of "or" is called the *inclusive* "or", and the second interpretation of "or" is known as the *exclusive* "or". In mathematics, it is customary to interpret "or" in the inclusive sense. Thus, in mathematics, "p or q" means "p or q, or both".

To illustrate the use of the exclusive "or", consider the following situation: A university student on a limited budget says to his friend, "Saturday I shall go to the football game in the afternoon, or I shall go to the dance in the evening". Here, he means that he shall attend precisely one of the two events, and so he uses the exclusive "or".

Now consider the logical connective "if and only if", which it is convenient to abbreviate by writing "iff". The compound proposition "p iff q" is regarded as true provided that p and q have the *same* truth-value.

The logical connective "not" has the function of changing the truth-value of a proposition to which it is attached. Thus, the compound proposition "not p" is true in case p is false, and is false in case p is true. In other words, "not p" is true iff p is false.

In order to avoid the ambiguities mentioned above and to emphasize the intended meaning of the logical connectives, it is customary to introduce special symbols to denote the more important logical connectives. The symbols are as follows: $\sim$ (not), $\wedge$ (and), $\vee$ (inclusive "or"), $\underline{\vee}$ (exclusive "or"), $\leftrightarrow$ (iff), $\rightarrow$ (if . . . then).

The logical connectives are really functions with one or two arguments ($\sim$ has one argument, the other connectives have two arguments). The value of each of these functions is either "true" or "false". Denoting "true" by "T" and "false" by "F", the logical connectives are conveniently defined by means of a truth-table which spells out the truth-value of a compound proposition in each of the possible truth-value cases.

For example, to define "$\vee$", we let p and q be any propositions and we consider the truth-value of "$p \vee q$" in each of the possible truth-value cases. There are four truth-value cases:

1. p is true, q is true.
2. p is true, q is false.
3. p is false, q is true.
4. p is false, q is false.

The four truth-value cases are gathered together in Table 1.1.1. It remains to insert the truth-value of "$p \vee q$" in each of the four cases. For example, a "T" has been entered in line 3 of Table 1.1.2, under the heading "$p \vee q$". This means that "$p \vee q$" is true in case p is false and q is true.

The remaining connectives are defined by truth-tables in a similar way.

TABLE 1.1.1

	p	q	$p \vee q$
1.	T	T	
2.	T	F	
3.	F	T	
4.	F	F	

TABLE 1.1.2

	p	q	$p \vee q$
1.	T	T	T
2.	T	F	T
3.	F	T	T
4.	F	F	F

We present the truth-table definitions of $\sim$, $\vee$, $\underline{\vee}$, $\wedge$, $\leftrightarrow$; these truth-tables are obtained by considering the meaning (at least at an intuitive level) of "not", "or", "or else", "and", "iff" (see Table 1.1.3).

TABLE 1.1.3

p	q	$\sim p$	$p \vee q$	$p \underline{\vee} q$	$p \wedge q$	$p \leftrightarrow q$
T	T	F	T	F	T	T
T	F	F	T	T	F	F
F	T	T	T	T	F	F
F	F	T	F	F	F	T

We now examine the important logical connective $\rightarrow$. Considering the import of a proposition of the form "If p, then q", it is clear that the connective $\rightarrow$ differs from each of the connectives given in Table 1.1.3. To illustrate this point, consider the proposition "If I receive a bonus, then I shall have a holiday in Spain". This proposition cannot be expressed by any of the following propositions:

1. "I receive a bonus *and* I shall have a holiday in Spain";
2. "I receive a bonus *iff* I shall have a holiday in Spain";
3. "I shall have a holiday in Spain".

Let us agree, then, that "$p \rightarrow q$" is different from each of "$p \wedge q$", "$p \leftrightarrow q$", "q". We are now in a position to work out the truth-table for "$p \rightarrow q$". Bearing in mind the meaning of the compound proposition "if p, then q", we note that this proposition is true in case p is true and q is true; furthermore, our proposition is certainly false in case p is true and q is false.

We thus obtain the partial truth-table for $\rightarrow$, which is displayed in Table 1.1.4. There are exactly four ways of completing this truth-table; these are displayed in Table 1.1.5. But a is $p \wedge q$, b is $p \leftrightarrow q$, and c is q; since "if p,

TABLE 1.1.4

	p	q	$p \to q$
1.	T	T	T
2.	T	F	F
3.	F	T	
4.	F	F	

TABLE 1.1.5

p	q	a	b	c	d
T	T	T	T	T	T
T	F	F	F	F	F
F	T	F	F	T	T
F	F	F	T	F	T

then q" is not rendered by any of "p and q", "p iff q", "q", we conclude that d is the only possible interpretation of "if p, then q" – from our logical standpoint. This means that the truth-table definition of $\to$ is given by Table 1.1.6.

TABLE 1.1.6

p	q	$p \to q$
T	T	T
T	F	F
F	T	T
F	F	T

In mathematics, then, the compound proposition "if p, then q" is regarded as true provided that q is true or p is false.

Finally, we point out that there are many ways of expressing the proposition "if p, then q". For example, the proposition "If I receive a bonus, then I shall have a holiday in Spain" is rendered by each of the following:

(i) "*If* I receive a bonus, I shall have a holiday in Spain";
(ii) "My receiving a bonus *entails that* I shall have a holiday in Spain";
(iii) "I shall have a holiday in Spain *if* I receive a bonus";
(iv) "I shall have a holiday in Spain *provided that* I receive a bonus";
(v) "Receiving a bonus is a *sufficient condition* for a holiday in Spain".

Another connective of some importance is the phrase "only if". Consider the sentence "I shall have a holiday in Spain *only if* I receive a bonus". To determine the meaning of this connective, we ask ourselves when the given sentence is true and when it is false. Observing that this sentence can be interpreted as saying that the only route to a holiday in Spain is via the receipt of a bonus, we see that the sentence is false in case I have a holiday in Spain without receiving a bonus and that it is true in all other cases. In particular, note that the sentence is true in case I receive a bonus and yet do not have a holiday in Spain. This is so because the given sentence says that receiving a bonus is the first requirement for a holiday in Spain; there may be other conditions which must be met before having a holiday in Spain. Thus, the given sentence asserts that receiving a bonus is a *necessary* condition for a holiday in Spain — but this may not be a *sufficient* condition. On the other hand, the sentence considered before — "If I receive a bonus, I shall have a holiday in Spain" — can be interpreted as saying that receiving a bonus *guarantees* my having a holiday in Spain, so that receiving a bonus is a *sufficient* condition for a holiday in Spain.

We shall say that a compound proposition has been expressed symbolically if each component sentence has been replaced by an appropriate symbol. For example, denoting "It is raining" by "a" and "The sun is shining" by "b", the compound proposition "If it is raining, then the sun is not shining, and if the sun is shining, then it is not raining" is expressed symbolically by

$$(a \rightarrow \sim b) \wedge (b \rightarrow \sim a),$$

where parentheses have been inserted to indicate the punctuation. This can be worked in reverse. The compound proposition $\sim a \wedge \sim b$ is rendered in English by "It is not raining and the sun is not shining", which is usually expressed by "Neither is it raining nor is the sun shining".

To further illustrate the flexibility of our logical connectives, consider the sentence: "Hard work is a *sufficient* condition for a happy life". Denoting the proposition "I work hard" by "w", and the proposition "I shall have a happy life" by "h", the above proposition is expressed symbolically by "$w \rightarrow h$". This is so because the given sentence can be rendered by "If I work hard, I shall have a happy life". On the other hand, the sentence "Hard work is a *necessary* condition for a happy life" asserts that an indispensable requirement for a happy life is hard work, and so this sentence is expressed by "$h \rightarrow w$".

EXERCISES

Denoting the proposition "I study" by "s", and the proposition "I shall pass" by "p", express the following compound propositions symbolically:

1. I do not study.   (*Answer:* $\sim s$)
2. If I study I shall pass.   (*Answer:* $s \rightarrow p$)
3. I shall pass only if I study.   (*Answer:* $p \rightarrow s$)

4. I shall pass if I study.   (*Answer:* $s \to p$)
5. I study or I shall not pass.   (*Answer:* $s \lor \sim p$)
6. I study and I shall pass.   (*Answer:* $s \land p$)
7. I do not study and I shall pass.   (*Answer:* $(\sim s) \land p$)
8. If I study I shall not pass.   (*Answer:* $s \to \sim p$)
9. I neither study nor shall I pass.   (*Answer:* $(\sim s) \land \sim p$)
10. I shall pass if and only if I study.   (*Answer:* $p \leftrightarrow s$)
11. I study or else I shall not pass.   (*Answer:* $s \underline{\lor} \sim p$)
12. I study; otherwise I shall not pass.   (*Answer:* $(\sim s) \to \sim p$)
13. It is not the case that I study.   (*Answer:* $\sim s$)
14. I shall pass!   (*Answer:* p)
15. It is not the case that I do not study.   (*Answer:* $\sim(\sim s)$)

Denoting the proposition "It is cloudy" by "c", and the proposition "It is raining" by "r", express the following compound propositions symbolically:

16. It is raining if it is cloudy.   (*Answer:* $c \to r$)
17. It is raining only if it is cloudy.   (*Answer:* $r \to c$)
18. Neither is it raining nor is it cloudy.   (*Answer:* $(\sim r) \land \sim c$)
19. If it is not cloudy than it is not
    raining.   (*Answer:* $(\sim c) \to \sim r$)
20. A necessary condition for rain is that
    it be cloudy.   (*Answer:* $r \to c$)
21. A sufficient condition for rain is that
    it be cloudy.   (*Answer:* $c \to r$)
22. A necessary and sufficient condition
    for rain is that it be cloudy.   (*Answer:* $r \leftrightarrow c$)
23. If it is raining and is cloudy then
    neither is it not raining, nor is it not
    cloudy.   (*Answer:* $(r \land c) \to (\sim(\sim r)) \land \sim(\sim c))$)

Assuming that "l" stands for the proposition "Logic is easy", and "m" stands for the proposition "Mathematics is easy", express the following symbolic propositions in English:

24. $l \land m$.   29. $(\sim l) \to \sim m$.
25. $\sim l$.   30. $((\sim l) \land \sim m) \lor (l \land m)$.
26. $(\sim m) \land \sim l$.   31. $\sim(l \land m)$.
27. $l \to m$.   32. $(\sim l) \lor \sim m$.
28. $l \leftrightarrow m$.   33. $\sim(l \to m)$.

34. Define the logical connective "neither. . . . nor" by stating the truth value of the compound proposition "neither p nor q", in each of the four possible cases.

35. Define the logical connective "but" by stating the truth value of the compound proposition "p but q", in each of the four possible cases.

36. Define the logical connective "whenever" by stating the truth value of the compound proposition "p whenever q", in each of the four possible cases.

37. Define the logical connective "implies" by stating the truth value of the compound proposition "p implies q", in each of the four possible cases.

Compute the truth values of the following, given that p is true and q is false:

38. $p \wedge q$

39. $p \wedge \sim q$

40. $\sim (p \vee q)$

41. $p \vee ((\sim p) \wedge q)$

42. $q \rightarrow p$

43. $\sim (p \rightarrow q)$

44. $p \leftrightarrow q$

45. $q \rightarrow (p \vee q)$

46. $(\sim q) \rightarrow (p \vee q)$

47. $\sim [q \rightarrow (p \vee q)]$

48. $\sim (p \leftrightarrow q)$

49. $(p \wedge q) \rightarrow \sim p$

50. $p \rightarrow ((\sim p) \wedge q)$

51. $(p \leftrightarrow q) \vee \sim p$

52. $(p \leftrightarrow \sim q) \vee (p \wedge q)$

1.2 Truth-Table Analysis

Consider the compound proposition: "If logic is difficult and if music is difficult or logic is not difficult, then logic is not difficult". What is being said? Perhaps, by studying this proposition and absorbing its meaning, you can determine just what it states. There is, however, an easy and mechanical method of solving this problem. First, we express the given proposition symbolically. Let "l" denote the proposition "Logic is difficult", and let "m" denote the proposition "Music is difficult". Then the given compound proposition is expressed symbolically by "$[l \wedge (m \vee \sim l)] \rightarrow \sim l$". One point must be made clear: if we know the truth-values of the propositions l and m, we can easily work out the truth-value of "$[l \wedge (m \vee \sim l)] \rightarrow \sim l$". However, we have not been given the truth-values of l and m, and we have no right to judge the truth or falsity of these propositions. Accordingly, we shall consider each of the four possible truth-value cases in turn, working out the truth-value of the compound proposition "$[l \wedge (m \vee \sim l)] \rightarrow \sim l$" for each truth-value case; this proposition is said to be *compound* because it is constructed from the simpler, *atomic* propositions l and m; moreover, l and m are said to be the *independent* propositions of the compound proposition "$[l \wedge (m \vee \sim l)] \rightarrow \sim l$" because the truth-value of the compound proposition is computed in terms of the truth-values of l and m. The calculations are conveniently displayed in Table 1.2.1.

TABLE 1.2.1

l	m	[l	∧	(m	∨	~l)]	→	~l
T	T	T	T	T	T	F	F	F
T	F	T	F	F	F	F	T	F
F	T	F	F	T	T	T	T	T
F	F	F	F	F	T	T	T	T
1	2	3	4	5	6	7	8	9

Note that the body of this table consists of four lines, one for each of the possible truth-value cases. The essential thing we are after in constructing a truth-table is to obtain the truth-value of the given proposition in each of the truth-value cases. We shall always insert the resulting column of "T"'s and "F"'s under the *main* connective of the given proposition, "→" in this example, and we shall call this column the *main* column of the truth-table. Thus, the vital information contained in a truth-table consists of the main column and the columns under the independent propositions. In fact, we shall regard a truth-table as consisting of columns headed by the independent propositions, the main column, and any other columns which are required to compute the main column.

It should be pointed out that Table 1.2.1 is *not* read from left to right, as most tables are. To show how this table is to be read, let us consider how it was constructed. The first step in constructing this truth-table is to fill in columns 1 and 2, so that each possible combination of truth-values of the independent propositions is displayed. In a very real sense, these entries are part of the heading of the table, rather than part of the body of the table. The second step is to compute columns 3, 5, 7 and 9; this is easy. Thirdly, we compute the truth-values of "$m ∨ {\sim}l$", inserting this information in column 6, directly under "∨" — the main connective of the proposition involved. The fourth step is to compute the truth-value of "$l ∧ (m ∨ {\sim}l)$", which is easily accomplished since the truth-values of the two components of this proposition are displayed in columns 3 and 6; the resulting truth-values are entered in column 4, directly under "∧" — the main connective of "$l ∧ (m ∨ {\sim}l)$". Finally, we compute the truth-values of "$[l ∧ (m ∨ {\sim}l)] → {\sim}l$": this proposition has the form "$A → B$", where the truth-values of A are listed in column 4 and the truth-values of B in column 9; hence, the entries in the main column are obtained by considering the entries in columns 4 and 9. In this way, we obtain column 8, which is entered under "→" — the main connective of "$[l ∧ (m ∨ {\sim}l)] → {\sim}l$". Denoting this proposition by "C", we have shown that Table 1.2.2 is a truth-table for C. But

TABLE 1.2.2

l	m	C
T	T	F
T	F	T
F	T	T
F	F	T

it is easy to find a proposition which is false when l and m are both true and which is true in all other cases. Such a proposition is "$\sim l \vee \sim m$". Since we are concerned only with the truth or falsity of propositions, it follows that the given compound proposition is expressed by the simpler proposition: "Logic is not difficult, or music is not difficult". Thus, the given compound proposition asserts that "logic is easy or music is easy".

Referring to Table 1.2.1, notice that we can do without columns 3 and 5, since they are identical with columns 1 and 2; moreover, the entries in columns 7 and 9 can be computed mentally as they are needed, so these columns can be eliminated also.

We have observed that the truth-value of C is computed in terms of the truth-values of l and m; indeed, the truth-value of C depends upon the truth-values of l and m. This means that the truth-value of C is a function of the truth-values of l and m. Now, from the logical viewpoint, it is the truth-value of a proposition that interests us. Accordingly, we shall regard C as being a *truth-function* of the truth-values of l and m. Notice that this function is displayed in Table 1.2.2.

Now, any proposition can be regarded as a truth-function (if the proposition is not a compound proposition, then the function involved is the *identity* function). Accordingly, we may reduce a proposition to its truth-table, where only the heading and main column of the truth-table are displayed. For example, the proposition C is displayed in the truth-table of Table 1.2.2. By always listing the various possible truth-value cases in the same order, we can reduce a truth-table to its main column. For this reason, we shall regard a proposition as being a name of a column of "T"'s and "F"'s appearing in a truth-table.

What have we gained? Clarity for one thing. It is a simple matter, now, to compare two propositions—we simply construct their truth-tables! The truth-table *is* the proposition. Furthermore, if two propositions possess the following properties: (1) they involve the same independent propositions, (2) they take the same truth-value for each combination of truth-values of the independent propositions, then we know that these propositions are names of the same object—namely, a column of "T" 's and "F" 's —and so are equal. For example, the propositions "$[l \wedge (m \vee \sim l)] \rightarrow \sim l$" and "$\sim l \vee \sim m$" possess these properties; hence, we write $[l \wedge (m \vee \sim l)] \rightarrow \sim l = \sim l \vee \sim m$. This is the first occurrence of the symbol "$=$" in this book, and so deserves some comment. Here and throughout this book, we agree to write "$a = b$" only if "a" and "b" refer to the same object or are names of the same object. Notice the use of quotation marks! Usually, an object is referred to by writing down a name of the object. In case we wish to discuss a *name* of an object, rather than the object itself, we require a convention to indicate that we are *not* referring to the object. This is achieved by inserting quotation marks around the name in question. For example, consider the following sentences:

1. The Amazon is the longest river in South America.
2. The first letter of "Amazon" is the first letter of the alphabet.

In sentence 1 the name "Amazon" is used to refer to an object—namely, a certain river. This, of course, is the usual use of names. In sentence 2 it is the name, rather than the object possessing the name, that is mentioned. Therefore, in sentence 2 we place quotation marks around the name. In this way, we distinguish between *using* a name and *referring to* a name.

Another subtle point worth mentioning here is the distinction between the following, where p and q are propositions: (1) $p = q$, (2) $p \leftrightarrow q$. At first sight, (1) and (2) may appear to be the same. Taking a closer look, however, we see that (1) and (2) differ in the following way: (1) is a statement *about* the propositions p and q, whereas (2) is itself a compound proposition.

The point is this: at one level we have the fundamental objects treated in symbolic logic—namely, propositions; for example, "$p \leftrightarrow q$" is a proposition. We may also wish to discuss propositions—to make statements *about* propositions; this activity is on a higher level of abstraction than the former. For example, "$p = q$" is an assertion about the propositions p and q. To summarize, we recognize that it is one thing to assert particular propositions; it is a different matter to make statements *about* propositions.

In a similar way, there are two levels of activity in mathematics. At the first level, we have mathematics itself; here, people *do* mathematics. At the second level, we have statements *about* mathematics; this discipline is known as *metamathematics*. Here, the subject of discussion is the activity at the lower level.

The technique of carrying out a truth-table analysis is so important that it warrants a second illustration. We construct a truth-table (Table 1.2.3) for the proposition "$[(p \wedge q) \vee (p \leftrightarrow q)] \wedge \sim q$". Thus "$[(p \wedge q) \vee (p \leftrightarrow q)] \wedge \sim q$" is a name for the column F, F, F, T. But it is easy to see that

"$\sim p \wedge \sim q$" is also a name for this column. This establishes that $[(p \wedge q) \vee (p \leftrightarrow q)] \wedge \sim q = \sim p \wedge \sim q$.

TABLE 1.2.3

p	q	$[(p \wedge q)$	$\vee$	$(p \leftrightarrow q)]$	$\wedge$	$\sim q$
T	T	T	T	T	F	F
T	F	F	F	F	F	T
F	T	F	F	F	F	F
F	F	F	T	T	T	T

E X E R C I S E S

1. **a.** Construct a truth-table for the compound proposition $[(p \wedge q) \vee p] \rightarrow \sim q$.
   b. Construct a truth-table for the compound proposition $p \rightarrow \sim q$.
   c. Show that $[(p \wedge q) \vee p] \rightarrow \sim q = p \rightarrow \sim q$.

2. Show that $(p \wedge q) \vee p = p$.

3. Is it true that $A = B$ whenever $A \rightarrow C = B \rightarrow C$?   (*Answer:* No)

4. Find propositions A, B, and C such that $A \rightarrow C$ and $B \rightarrow C$ are names of the same column, yet A and B are names of different columns.

5. Construct a truth-table for the compound proposition
$$[(p \rightarrow r) \wedge (q \rightarrow r)] \rightarrow (p \leftrightarrow q).$$

6. What property do the propositions $p \vee \sim p$ and $(p \rightarrow q) \vee (q \rightarrow p)$ have in common?

7. **a.** Simplify the proposition: "This course is easy, or the instructor is not kind and the course is not easy, if and only if the instructor is kind and the course is easy".
   b. Deduce from part **a** a disguised way of saying: "The instructor is not kind".

8. Simplify the proposition: "If I study or mathematics is easy, then it is not true that I study and mathematics is difficult".

9. Show that $\sim(p \wedge q) = \sim p \vee \sim q$.

10. Show that $\sim(p \vee q) = \sim p \wedge \sim q$.

11. Show that $p \rightarrow q = \sim p \vee q$.

12. Show that $p \leftrightarrow q = (p \rightarrow q) \wedge (q \rightarrow p)$.

13. Show that $p \leftrightarrow q = (p \wedge q) \vee (\sim p \wedge \sim q)$.

14. Show that $p \rightarrow q = \sim q \rightarrow \sim p$.

15. Show that $(\sim p \rightarrow q) \vee (p \wedge q) = p \vee q$.

16. Show that $(p \leftrightarrow q) \rightarrow (\sim p \wedge q) = (\sim p) \leftrightarrow q$.

17. Show that $(\sim p) \leftrightarrow q = \sim(p \leftrightarrow q)$.

1.3   Propositions Constructed from Independent Propositions

Our purpose in this section is to construct and name all the propositions that can be expressed in terms of two independent propositions. A more ambitious project is to construct and name all the propositions that can be expressed in terms of n independent propositions, where n is any natural number. This we shall not attempt; however, we shall compute the number of distinct propositions that can be expressed in terms of n independent propositions.

First, let us show that n independent propositions, where n is any natural number, can be assigned truth-values in 2^n distinct combinations. Observe that the number of combinations of truth-values among $k + 1$ independent propositions is exactly double the number of combinations of truth-values among k independent propositions, because each combination of truth-values of k independent propositions gives rise to two combinations of truth-values of $k + 1$ independent propositions—the one with the $k + 1$st proposition true, and the one with the $k + 1$st proposition false. Obviously, one independent proposition can be assigned a truth-value in exactly two ways; therefore, two independent propositions can be assigned truth-values in $2 \cdot 2 = 2^2$ ways; therefore, three independent propositions can be assigned truth-values in $2 \cdot 2^2 = 2^3$ ways; so, by mathematical induction, we see that n independent propositions can be assigned truth-values in 2^n ways —whenever n is a natural number.

It is now an easy matter to calculate the number of distinct propositions that can be expressed in terms of n independent propositions. Think of what is involved in constructing the truth-table of a proposition: first, we list all the truth-value cases; next, we compute the corresponding truth-values of the given proposition—which means that we adjoin a column of "T"'s and "F"'s to the table. We have previously observed that the given proposition *is* this column. The question we are faced with, then, is how many distinct columns can we construct? There are 2^n lines in the truth-table, so in forming a column we must make 2^n entries. Each entry is a "T" or is an "F". Since we have two choices for each of 2^n entries, we see there are $2^{(2^n)}$ distinct columns of "T"'s and "F"'s; hence, there are $2^{(2^n)}$ distinct propositions that can be expressed in terms of n independent propositions.

It is easier to understand the above argument if we consider a special case; for example, consider the case of two independent propositions. The truth-table that we are concerned with has four lines; therefore, we must determine the total number of distinct columns that we can construct, where each column has four entries. There are two choices, "T" or "F", for the first entry. Corresponding to each of these choices, we have two choices for the second entry, then two choices for the third entry, and finally two choices for the fourth entry. Therefore, we can form $2^4 = 16$ columns of "T"'s and "F"'s. Note that the sixteen propositions formed from p and q include the propositions p and q themselves.

Before actually constructing and naming the sixteen propositions that can be expressed in terms of two independent propositions, let us consider the much simpler problem of constructing the propositions that can be formed from a single proposition, say p. First, we note that there are exactly two truth-value cases — p may be true, or p may be false. So the body of our truth-table consists of two lines. We now ask how many distinct columns we can construct in this table. There are two choices for the first entry, and two choices for the second entry; therefore, there are $2^2 = 4$ columns. The four columns are exhibited in the Table 1.3.1; each line of the table represents a truth-value case. We must now decide on suitable names, in terms of p, for each of the three columns not named. Of course, we could invent a separate symbol to denote each column, but this turns out to be unnecessary since the logical connectives already available suffice. Clearly, "$p \vee \sim p$" is true whether p is true or false; also "$\sim p$" is false when p is true, and is true when p is false; "$p \wedge \sim p$" is false whether p is true or false. Hence, the completed truth-table is as shown in Table 1.3.2.

TABLE 1.3.1

p				p
T	T	F	F	T
F	T	T	F	F

TABLE 1.3.2

p	$p \vee \sim p$	$\sim p$	$p \wedge \sim p$	p
T	T	F	F	T
F	T	T	F	F

Let us now consider the task of listing the sixteen propositions that can be constructed in terms of two independent propositions, say p and q. Remember that when we enter "T", say, in a column, we are asserting that for that truth-value case the proposition concerned is true.

We exhibit in Table 1.3.3 the sixteen columns constructed by assigning truth-values to the four truth-value cases in all possible ways.

TABLE 1.3.3

p	q	1	2	3	4	5	6	7	8	9	10	11	12	13	14	15	16
T	T	F	F	F	F	T	F	F	T	F	T	T	F	T	T	T	T
T	F	F	F	F	T	F	F	T	F	T	F	T	T	F	T	T	T
F	T	F	F	T	F	F	T	F	F	T	T	F	T	T	F	T	T
F	F	F	T	F	F	F	T	T	T	F	F	F	T	T	T	F	T

Again, it is possible to introduce sixteen connectives, one for each column, but let us show instead that the three connectives $\sim$, $\vee$, $\wedge$ are sufficiently expressive, when combined together, to produce names for all sixteen propositions. We list suitable names of the sixteen columns:

1. $p \wedge \sim p$.
2. $\sim p \wedge \sim q$.
3. $\sim p \wedge q$.
4. $p \wedge \sim q$.
5. $p \wedge q$.
6. $\sim p$.
7. $\sim q$.
8. $(p \wedge q) \vee (\sim p \wedge \sim q)$.
9. $(p \wedge \sim q) \vee (\sim p \wedge q)$.
10. q.
11. p.
12. $\sim p \vee \sim q$.
13. $\sim p \vee q$.
14. $p \vee \sim q$.
15. $p \vee q$.
16. $p \vee \sim p$.

There are other names for these columns. For example, column 13 has the name "$p \rightarrow q$" and column 8 also has the name "$p \leftrightarrow q$".

In the following section, we shall develop a systematic method of naming a given proposition.

EXERCISES

1. Show that "$(\sim p \wedge q) \vee (\sim p \wedge \sim q)$" is a name of column 6 in Table 1.3.3.
2. For which columns are "$(\sim q) \rightarrow p$", "$q \leftrightarrow \sim p$", "$q \rightarrow (p \wedge q)$" suitable names?
3. **a.** Calculate the number of different combinations of truth-values that can be assigned to three independent propositions.
   b. Calculate the number of distinct propositions that can be expressed in terms of three independent propositions.
   c. Calculate the number of distinct propositions that can be expressed in terms of four independent propositions.   (*Answer:* 65,536)
4. Construct a truth-table for each of the following propositions:
$$[p \vee (q \wedge r)] \leftrightarrow [(p \vee q) \wedge (p \vee r)].$$
$$[p \wedge (q \vee r)] \leftrightarrow [(p \wedge q) \vee (p \wedge r)].$$
$$(p \rightarrow q) \rightarrow [(r \vee p) \rightarrow (r \vee q)].$$
What property do these propositions have in common?
5. Compute the truth-value of "$[(p \rightarrow q) \vee (\sim p \wedge q)] \wedge (r \rightarrow q)$", given the following:
   a. p is true, q is true, r is false.
   b. p is false, q is true, r is false.
   c. p is false, q is false, r is false.
   d. p is false, q is false, r is true.

6. Construct a truth-table for each of the following propositions:

    a. $[(p \to r) \wedge (q \to r)] \to (p \leftrightarrow q)$.

    b. $[(p \to q) \wedge (q \to r)] \to (p \to r)$.

7. Given that p, q, and r are any propositions, show the following:

    a. $p \vee (q \veebar r) = (p \veebar q) \veebar r$.

    b. $p \wedge (q \veebar r) = (p \wedge q) \veebar (p \wedge r)$.

    c. $(q \veebar r) \wedge p = (q \wedge p) \veebar (r \wedge p)$.

    d. $p \veebar (q \wedge r) \neq (p \veebar q) \wedge (p \veebar r)$.

8. Given that p and q are any propositions, show the following:

    a. $p \vee q = (p \veebar q) \veebar (p \wedge q)$.

    b. $p \wedge q = p \veebar (p \wedge \sim q)$.

1.4   The Disjunctive Normal Form

In the preceding section we saw that any proposition which involves only two independent propositions can be expressed in terms of the connectives $\sim$, $\vee$, $\wedge$. Let us establish now the even more surprising fact that any proposition at all can be expressed in terms of these connectives, no matter how many independent propositions are involved. Suppose that the independent propositions are $p_1, p_2, \cdots, p_n$—so there are 2^n truth-value cases. Furthermore, suppose we are faced with a given proposition, expressed in terms of our n independent propositions; this means that we know the column of truth-values involved, so that we can state the truth-value of the given proposition in each of the 2^n truth-value cases.

We shall now construct a name of this column. There are two cases: either each entry in the column is "F", or there is at least one "T". In the former case, $p_1 \wedge \sim p_1$ is a suitable name of the column. In the latter case, we construct a name of the column as follows. We begin by selecting a truth-value case such that the corresponding entry in the given column is "T"; let us now construct a proposition which is true only in this particular truth-value case. This is a simple matter since the proposition "$q_1 \wedge q_2 \wedge \cdots \wedge q_n$" is true just if each of the propositions $q_1, q_2, \cdots, q_n$ is true. Let q_1 be p_1 if p_1 is true in the particular truth-value case we are looking at, and let q_1 be $\sim p_1$ if p_1 is false in this particular truth-value case. Choose $q_2, \cdots, q_n$ according to the same prescription. Then the resulting proposition "$q_1 \wedge q_2 \wedge \cdots \wedge q_n$" is true in just this truth-value case. Now, do the same for each of the other truth-value cases such that the corresponding entry in the given column is "T". Finally, join all the resulting propositions with "$\vee$". The proposition we have constructed is true if one or more of its constituents is true, and it is false if none of its constituents is true.

This is precisely what we are after. We shall call any proposition obtained in this way the *disjunctive normal form* of the given proposition.

To illustrate the above construction, let $n = 3$, so that we have three independent propositions p_1, p_2, p_3. There are eight truth-value cases. Let us find the name, according to the above construction, of the column F, T, T, F, F, F, T, F (see Table 1.4.1). The entry in the main column is "T" in the

TABLE 1.4.1

	p_1	p_2	p_3	?
1.	T	T	T	F
2.	T	T	F	T
3.	T	F	T	T
4.	T	F	F	F
5.	F	T	T	F
6.	F	T	F	F
7.	F	F	T	T
8.	F	F	F	F

second truth-value case; a proposition true in just this truth-value case is "$p_1 \wedge p_2 \wedge \sim p_3$". The entry in the main column is "T" in the third truth-value case; a proposition true for just this truth-value case is "$p_1 \wedge \sim p_2 \wedge p_3$". Finally, the entry in the main column is "T" in the seventh truth-value case; a proposition true for just this case is "$\sim p_1 \wedge \sim p_2 \wedge p_3$". Forming the disjunction of the three propositions just constructed, we obtain

$$(p_1 \wedge p_2 \wedge \sim p_3) \vee (p_1 \wedge \sim p_2 \wedge p_3) \vee (\sim p_1 \wedge \sim p_2 \wedge p_3).$$

This proposition is true if any of its three constituents is true; hence, it is true in the second, third, and seventh truth-value cases; also, this proposition is false if each of its three constituents is false. But each of the three constituents is false in the remaining truth-value cases; therefore, the proposition we have constructed is false in the remaining five truth-value cases. This establishes that our proposition is a name of the given column; thus, we have expressed the given proposition in terms of the connectives $\sim$, $\vee$, $\wedge$.

In fact, we have achieved much more than our stated goal! More important than the fact that any proposition can be expressed by using only three connectives is the fact that we can now write down a name of a given proposition by following the simple and mechanical procedure outlined above. Later we shall put this ability to use (see Sec. 1.7).

E X E R C I S E S

1. Write down the disjunctive normal form of each of the following columns associated with the three independent propositions p_1, p_2, and p_3 of the example in the text:
   a. F, F, F, T, T, F, F, F.
   b. T, F, F, F, F, T, F, F.
   c. F, F, T, F, F, F, F, F.

2. By first computing the truth-table, obtain the disjunctive normal form of the following propositions; in each case use the minimum number of independent propositions:

   a. $p \to q$.
   b. $(\sim p) \to q$.
   c. $(p \lor q) \to r$.
   d. $(p \to q) \to r$.
   e. $p \to (q \to r)$.
   f. $[(p \lor q) \land (p \lor \sim r)] \leftrightarrow p$.
   g. $(p \to q) \leftrightarrow (q \to p)$.
   h. $[(p \land r) \to q] \land \sim r$.
   i. $[((\sim p) \leftrightarrow q) \lor r] \land ((\sim q) \land p)$.
   j. $(p \to q) \to (r \leftrightarrow \sim p)$.

3. Devise a procedure which, when applied to the disjunctive normal form of a given proposition, will produce the truth-value cases in which the proposition is true.

4. It is of theoretical interest to introduce a logical connective, namely "/", to denote column 12 in Table 1.3.3; this means that $p/q = \sim(p \land q)$. Show the following:

   a. $p/p = \sim p$.
   b. $(p/p)/(q/q) = p \lor q$.
   c. $(p/q)/(p/q) = p \land q$.
   d. $p/(q/q) = p \to q$.
   e. $[(p/q)/(p/q)]/(r/r) = (p \land q) \to r$.

5. Now show that any proposition can be expressed in terms of /, no matter how many independent propositions are involved. (This connective is called *Sheffer's stroke*, after the logician who first realized its importance.)

6. By the *conjunctive normal form* of a proposition, we mean the proposition constructed as follows. Select a truth-value case in which "F" appears in the main column. Write down the proposition "$q_1 \lor q_2 \lor \cdots \lor q_n$", where, for each k, $q_k = \sim p_k$ if p_k is true in this truth-value case; otherwise, $q_k = p_k$. Do the same for each truth-value case in which "F" appears in the main column. Finally, form the conjunction of all these propositions. The resulting proposition is a suitable name of the given column. If there are no "F"'s in the main column, then we take "$p_1 \lor \sim p_1$" as the conjunctive form of the given proposition.

   Question: Devise a procedure which, when applied to the conjunctive normal form of a given proposition, will produce the truth-value cases in which the proposition is false.

7. Let $p_1 \textcircled{V} p_2 \textcircled{V} \cdots \textcircled{V} p_n$ be the proposition which is true iff exactly one of p_1, p_2, $\cdots$, p_n is true, where n is any natural number greater than 1.
   a. Write down the disjunctive normal form of $p \textcircled{V} q \textcircled{V} r$.
   b. Write down the disjunctive normal form of $p \textcircled{V} q \textcircled{V} r \textcircled{V} s$.
   c. Simplify $p \textcircled{V} q \textcircled{V} q$.
   d. Simplify $p \textcircled{V} p$.
   e. Show that $p \textcircled{V} q = p \underline{\vee} q$.
   f. Simplify $p \textcircled{V} q \textcircled{V} \sim q$.
   g. Simplify $p \textcircled{V} \sim p$.
   h. Simplify $p \textcircled{V} (p \vee q) \textcircled{V} (p \vee \sim q)$.
   i. Simplify $p \textcircled{V} (p \wedge q) \textcircled{V} (p \wedge \sim q)$.
   j. Prove that $p \textcircled{V} q \textcircled{V} r \neq p \underline{\vee} (q \underline{\vee} r)$.

1.5 Tautologies and Valid Arguments

We have said that a proposition is a sentence which is either true or false, but not both. The truth value of a proposition such as "It is 12 o'clock" depends upon the state of affairs at the moment; for example, if both hands of your watch point at 12, you would say the given proposition is true; otherwise, you would say the proposition is false. However, there are many propositions which are true without reference to the world about us. For example, the truth of the proposition "It is 12 o'clock or it is not 12 o'clock" is independent of the state of affairs at the moment. Any proposition possessing the property that it is true no matter what the truth-values of its component propositions are, is called a *tautology* or *logically* true. Let p and q be propositions; then $(p \vee q) \leftrightarrow (q \vee p)$ is a tautology and $\sim (p \wedge q) \leftrightarrow (\sim p \vee \sim q)$ is a tautology — as we can easily check by truth-table analysis. For example, let us carry out a truth-table analysis of $\sim (p \wedge q) \leftrightarrow (\sim p \vee \sim q)$. Since the main column of Table 1.5.1 consists of "T"'s, we conclude that "$\sim (p \wedge q) \leftrightarrow (\sim p \vee \sim q)$" is a tautology.

TABLE 1.5.1

p	q	$\sim (p \wedge q)$		$\leftrightarrow$	$(\sim p \vee \sim q)$
T	T	F	T	T	F
T	F	T	F	T	T
F	T	T	F	T	T
F	F	T	F	T	T

The concept of a tautology is important because it is involved in the idea of a valid argument, i.e., a logically correct argument. When a person wishes to convince someone that a proposition, q say, is true, he presents as evidence a list of propositions, called *assumptions,* which he claims everyone accepts as true, and then states that his conclusion, q, must also be true. The role played by logic in the above process is in demonstrating that the truth of the assumptions *entails* the truth of the conclusion. It is a separate problem to determine whether or not the assumptions are true; so, it is quite possible by means of a false assumption to reach a false conclusion even though the argument is valid.

By an *argument,* then, we mean a list of propositions, one of which is called the *conclusion* of the argument and the others the *assumptions* of the argument.

By a *valid* argument, we mean an argument which possesses the property that the conclusion is true in each truth-value case under which each assumption is true. For example, consider the argument in which the assumptions are "If it is cloudy tonight, it will rain tomorrow" and "If it rains tomorrow, I shall be home late tomorrow", and the conclusion is "If it is cloudy tonight, I shall be home late tomorrow". There are three independent propositions involved in the argument: "It rains tomorrow" — q, "It is cloudy tonight" — p, "I shall be home late tomorrow" — r. Then the assumptions are $p \rightarrow q$, $q \rightarrow r$, and the conclusion is $p \rightarrow r$. Let us show that any combination of truth-values of the independent propositions that makes both assumptions true also makes the conclusion true. This can most conveniently be seen by means of a truth-table, as shown in Table 1.5.2. Both assumptions are true in cases 1, 5, 7, 8, and the conclusion is true in

TABLE 1.5.2

	p	q	r	Assumptions		Conclusion
				$p \rightarrow q$	$q \rightarrow r$	$p \rightarrow r$
1.	T	T	T	T	T	T ✓
2.	T	T	F	T	F	F
3.	T	F	T	F	T	T
4.	T	F	F	F	T	F
5.	F	T	T	T	T	T ✓
6.	F	T	F	T	F	T
7.	F	F	T	T	T	T ✓
8.	F	F	F	T	T	T ✓

each of these cases. Thus, the argument is valid. It must be emphasized that the conclusion of a valid argument may *in fact* be false; but this can happen only if *in fact* one or more of the assumptions are false.

When analyzing an argument, it is not necessary to complete the entire truth-table; it is enough to consider a portion of the truth-table. Indeed, we may restrict ourselves to those truth-value cases under which each of the assumptions is true. It is pointless to work out the truth-value of the conclusion for a truth-value case under which one or more of the assumptions is false. Moreover, in the case of an invalid arugment we have only to work out one line of the truth-table; namely, a truth-value case under which each assumption is true and the conclusion is false.

As an example of an *invalid* argument, consider the following: "If it is good soap, then it is Whiz Soap! It is Whiz Soap; therefore, it is good soap". Let p denote "It is good soap", and q denote "It is Whiz Soap". Then the assumptions are $p \rightarrow q$, q, and the conclusion is p. The truth-table analysis is shown in Table 1.5.3. The assumptions are both true in case 3, yet the conclusion is false in this case. Thus, we must say that the argument is invalid.

TABLE 1.5.3

			Assumptions		Conclusion
	p	q	$p \rightarrow q$	q	p
1.	T	T	T	T	T
2.	T	F	F	F	T
3.	F	T	T	T	F
4.	F	F	T	F	F

We present one more example. Consider the following argument: "If a man is married, he has troubles. This man has no troubles. Therefore, this man is not married". To show that the argument is valid, we first express the argument symbolically. Let m denote "this man is married", and let

TABLE 1.5.4

	m	t	$m \rightarrow t$	$\sim t$	$\sim m$
1.	T	T	T	F	F
2.	T	F	F	T	F
3.	F	T	T	F	T
4.	F	F	T	T	T

t denote "this man has troubles". Then the assumptions of the argument are $m \rightarrow t$, $\sim t$, and the conclusion is $\sim m$. In Table 1.5.4 we construct a truth-table which displays the truth-values of the assumptions and the conclusion in each of the four truth-value cases. There is only one truth-value case in which both assumptions are true – the fourth case. Since the conclusion is also true in this case, we conclude that the argument is valid.

The connection between tautologies and arguments is displayed by the following theorem.

THEOREM 1.5.1.   The argument with assumptions $p_1, p_2, \cdots, p_n$ and conclusion q is valid iff the proposition "$(p_1 \wedge p_2 \wedge \cdots \wedge p_n) \rightarrow q$" is a tautology.

Proof: Since we are involved with an "if and only if" theorem, there are two parts to the proof.

1. We must show that if the argument is valid then the proposition "$(p_1 \wedge p_2 \wedge \cdots \wedge p_n) \rightarrow q$" is a tautology; i.e., we must show that the truth-value of "$(p_1 \wedge p_2 \wedge \cdots \wedge p_n) \rightarrow q$" is T for each possible truth-value combination of the independent propositions. Consider the truth-table for "$(p_1 \wedge p_2 \wedge \cdots \wedge p_n) \rightarrow q$"; we shall show that the main column consists of "T"'s only. Consider any line of the truth-table such that one or more of the $p_1, p_2, \cdots, p_n$ has the truth-value F. Then the proposition "$p_1 \wedge p_2 \wedge \cdots \wedge p_n$" has the truth-value F, and so the proposition "$(p_1 \wedge p_2 \wedge \cdots \wedge p_n) \rightarrow q$" has the truth-value T Now consider any line of the table such that each of $p_1, p_2, \cdots, p_n$ has the truth-value T. By assumption – since the given argument is valid – the truth-value of q is also T: thus, the truth-value of "$(p_1 \wedge p_2 \wedge \cdots \wedge p_n) \rightarrow q$" is T. Hence, "$(p_1 \wedge p_2 \wedge \cdots \wedge p_n) \rightarrow q$" is a tautology.

2. We must now show that if the proposition "$(p_1 \wedge p_2 \wedge \cdots \wedge p_n) \rightarrow q$" is a tautology, then the given argument is valid. But this is easy! Since "$(p_1 \wedge p_2 \wedge \cdots \wedge p_n) \rightarrow q$" is a tautology, the main column of its truth-table consists of "T"'s only. Consider any line of this truth-table such that the truth-value of each of $p_1, p_2, \cdots, p_n$ is T. It follows that the truth-value of "$p_1 \wedge p_2 \wedge \cdots \wedge p_n$" is T, and so the truth-value of q must also be T (if the truth-value of q is F, then the truth-value of "$(p_1 \wedge p_2 \wedge \cdots \wedge p_n) \rightarrow q$" would be F). Hence, the given argument is valid.

This establishes that the argument with assumptions $p_1, p_2, \cdots, p_n$ and conclusion q is valid precisely in the case that the proposition "$(p_1 \wedge p_2 \wedge \cdots \wedge p_n) \rightarrow q$" is a tautology.

The basic rules of logical inference are easily established when interpreted as an argument. For example, consider the following rule of inference.

MODUS PONENS.   From the assumptions p and $p \to q$, infer the conclusion q.

Constructing a truth-table, we easily see that this argument is valid.

One final point: any proposition whose truth-value is F in each possible truth-value case is said to be *logically false*. For example, "$p \wedge \sim p$" is logically false.

EXERCISES

Show that the following are tautologies:

1. $[\sim(\sim p)] \leftrightarrow p$.
2. $[\sim(p \vee q)] \leftrightarrow [(\sim p) \wedge \sim q]$.
3. $[\sim(p \wedge q)] \leftrightarrow [(\sim p) \vee \sim q]$.
4. $[(p \wedge q) \vee (p \wedge r)] \leftrightarrow [p \wedge (q \vee r)]$.
5. $(p \to q) \to [(r \vee p) \to (r \vee q)]$.
6. $(p \to q) \leftrightarrow [(\sim q) \to \sim p]$.
7. $[p \wedge (q \vee \sim q)] \leftrightarrow p$.
8. $[p \vee (q \wedge \sim q)] \leftrightarrow p$.
9. $p \to p$.
10. $[\sim(p \vee q)] \to \sim p$.
11. $(p \to q) \vee (p \to \sim q)$.
12. $(p \vee q) \vee (p \to q)$.
13. $(p \to q) \vee (q \to r)$.
14. $p \vee (p \to q)$.
15. $[(p \to q) \to p] \to p$.
16. $(p \wedge q) \vee (p \to \sim q)$.
17. $[(p \to q) \to q] \to (p \vee q)$.
18. $[\sim(p \to q)] \leftrightarrow (p \wedge \sim q)$.

Determine which of the following propositions are tautologies:

19. $p \to (p \wedge q)$.
20. $p \to (p \vee q)$.
21. $p \to [(\sim p) \vee q]$.
22. $(p \wedge q) \to p$.
23. $(p \wedge q) \to (p \wedge r)$.
24. $(p \wedge q) \to (p \vee r)$.
25. $[(p \vee q) \wedge (p \vee \sim q)] \leftrightarrow p$.
26. $[(p \vee q) \wedge (p \vee \sim q)] \leftrightarrow q$.
27. $(p \to q) \vee (q \to p)$.
28. $(p \wedge \sim q) \vee (q \wedge \sim p)$.
29. $(p \vee \sim q) \wedge (q \vee \sim p)$.
30. $[p \wedge (q \to p)] \to p$.
31. $[p \wedge (p \to q)] \to q$.
32. $[p \wedge (p \to q)] \leftrightarrow q$.
33. $(p \to q) \to [(\sim q) \to \sim p]$.
34. $(p \to q) \to (q \to p)$.

Which of the following arguments are valid?

35. If today is Friday, then yesterday was Thursday. Yesterday was Thursday; therefore, today is Friday.

36. Only if I save money will I finish college. I do not save money. Hence, I will not finish college.

37. If food is expensive, then health suffers. Canadians excel in athletics only if their health is excellent. Therefore, Canadians excel in athletics or food is expensive.

38. Music and art are not being encouraged. They must be encouraged if they are to flourish. Consequently, music and art will not flourish.

39. If Smith is a property owner, then he may vote in municipal elections. Smith votes in municipal elections. Therefore, Smith is a property owner.

40. The train is late if it snows. It is not snowing. Thus, the train is not late.

41. Today we had a war scare because the stock market dropped sharply, and the stock market drops sharply whenever there is a war scare.

42. If the movie is made in England, then it is worth seeing. The movie is expensive or it is not worth seeing. But the movie is not expensive. Therefore, it is not made in England.

43. If I do not study, I will sleep. If I am worried, I will not sleep. Therefore, if I am worried, I will study.

44. A democracy can survive only if the electorate is well informed or no candidate for public office is dishonest. The electorate is well-informed only if education is free. If all candidates for public office are honest, then God exists. Therefore, a democracy can survive only if education is free or God exists.

45. I have a headache if I study logic. I take an aspirin whenever I have a headache. If I take an aspirin, I drink water. Therefore, I drink water whenever I study logic.

46. Show that "$p \rightarrow q$; therefore, $(\sim q) \rightarrow \sim p$" is a valid argument.

47. Let p and q be any propositions, not necessarily independent. Show that $p = q$ iff "$p \leftrightarrow q$" is a tautology.

1.6 The Algebra of Propositions

It is clear that any component of a proposition can be replaced by an equivalent proposition—without affecting the truth-table of the given proposition. This remark is the basis of an extremely effective method of simplifying propositions. To simplify a proposition, one must find another proposition having a simpler form (i.e., involving fewer connectives), yet equal to the given proposition. For example, consider the propositions "$p \lor (q \land \sim p)$" and "$p \lor q$"; it is easy to see that $p \lor (q \land \sim p) = p \lor q$ by constructing a truth-table; furthermore, "$p \lor q$" is simpler than "$p \lor (q \land \sim p)$"—count the connectives in each proposition. The question is: given "$p \lor (q \land \sim p)$", how do we find a simpler proposition equal to it?

The object of this section is to build up a technique which will enable us to construct from a given proposition another proposition equal to it and having a simpler form—provided there is one. This is accomplished by replacing a proposition appearing in the given proposition by an equal proposition, doing the same to the resulting proposition, and continuing this process until a proposition of sufficiently simple form is obtained.

Clearly, to carry out this method, we must possess an adequate stock of pairs of equal propositions. It turns out that the following 19 pairs of equal propositions do the job. To emphasize the importance of these statements, we shall call them laws.

If p, q, and r are any propositions, then:

LAW 1. $\sim(\sim p) = p$.
LAW 2. $p \lor p = p$.
LAW 3. $p \land p = p$.
LAW 4. $p \lor q = q \lor p$.
LAW 5. $p \land q = q \land p$.
LAW 6. $p \lor (q \lor r) = (p \lor q) \lor r$.
LAW 7. $p \land (q \land r) = (p \land q) \land r$.
LAW 8. $p \lor (q \land r) = (p \lor q) \land (p \lor r)$.
LAW 9. $p \land (q \lor r) = (p \land q) \lor (p \land r)$.
LAW 10. $\sim(p \lor q) = (\sim p) \land (\sim q)$.
LAW 11. $\sim(p \land q) = (\sim p) \lor (\sim q)$.
LAW 12. $p \to q = (\sim p) \lor q$.
LAW 13. $p \leftrightarrow q = (p \land q) \lor [(\sim p) \land (\sim q)]$.
LAW 14. $\sim t = f$.
LAW 15. $\sim f = t$.
LAW 16. $p \lor t = t$.
LAW 17. $p \land t = p$.
LAW 18. $p \lor f = p$.
LAW 19. $p \land f = f$.

In these laws "t" denotes any logically true proposition, and "f" denotes any logically false proposition.

Laws 4 and 5 are called the *commutative* laws for $\lor$ and $\land$ respectively; Laws 6 and 7 are called the *associative* laws for $\lor$ and $\land$ respectively; Laws 8 and 9 are called the *distributive* laws; Laws 10 and 11 are known as the *De Morgan* laws. Laws 16, 17, 18, and 19 are rather more sophisticated statements than the other laws. For example, Law 17 states that for any propositions p and q, $p \land q = p$ provided that q is logically true; Law 18 states that for any propositions p and q, $p \lor q = p$ provided that q is logically false.

It is a routine matter to establish these 19 laws by constructing truth-tables; do so! Now we are entitled to use the laws. Let us simplify the proposition that appeared at the beginning of this section, namely, "$p \vee (q \wedge {\sim}p)$". Now,

$$
\begin{aligned}
p \vee (q \wedge {\sim}p) &= (p \vee q) \wedge (p \vee {\sim}p) && \text{by Law 8} \\
&= (p \vee q) \wedge t && \text{since ``}p \vee {\sim}p\text{'' is logically true} \\
&= p \vee q && \text{by Law 17.}
\end{aligned}
$$

As another example of this technique, we simplify "$p \wedge (p \vee q)$". Now,

$$
\begin{aligned}
p \wedge (p \vee q) &= (p \vee f) \wedge (p \vee q) && \text{by Law 18} \\
&= p \vee (f \wedge q) && \text{by Law 8} \\
&= p \vee (q \wedge f) && \text{by Law 5} \\
&= p \vee f && \text{by Law 19} \\
&= p && \text{by Law 18.}
\end{aligned}
$$

Of course, it is easy to show that $p \wedge (p \vee q) = p$ by carrying out a truth-table analysis; the point is that the algebraic manipulations lead us to p, from the given proposition.

With practice, we can speed up the process of simplifying a proposition by telescoping several steps into one. This is accomplished by performing steps mentally, where possible, and by operating on different components of a proposition in one step. A powerful weapon in this regard is the following *parentheses-omitting* convention. Law 6 asserts that for any propositions p, q, and r, $p \vee (q \vee r) = (p \vee q) \vee r$; therefore, there is no possible ambiguity in denoting either of these propositions by "$p \vee q \vee r$", the expression obtained from either proposition by omitting parentheses. In the same way, let us agree to drop the parentheses from the propositions "$p \wedge (q \wedge r)$" and "$(p \wedge q) \wedge r$", writing "$p \wedge q \wedge r$"; this is justified by Law 7. Similarly, let us agree to denote the propositions "$p \vee (q \vee r \vee s)$", "$(p \vee q \vee r) \vee s$", and "$(p \vee q) \vee (r \vee s)$" by writing "$p \vee q \vee r \vee s$". Again, the same convention applies to "$\wedge$". Another simple method of telescoping steps is to observe that, by Law 17, $p \wedge t = p$; therefore, there is no point in writing down "$p \wedge t$" at a step in a simplification — simply write down "p"! The same observation applies to "$p \vee f$".

These ideas are used in the following example, in which we show that $a = b$, where

$$
a = \{p \vee [(q \vee r) \wedge {\sim}(q \wedge r)]\} \wedge {\sim}\{p \wedge [(q \vee r) \wedge {\sim}(q \wedge r)]\}
$$

and $b = \{[(p \vee q) \wedge {\sim}(p \wedge q)] \vee r\} \wedge {\sim}\{[(p \vee q) \wedge {\sim}(p \wedge q)] \wedge r\}$.

Now,

$$a = \{p \lor [(q \lor r) \land (\sim q \lor \sim r)]\} \land \{\sim p \lor [(\sim q \land \sim r) \lor (q \land r)]\}$$
$$= (p \lor q \lor r) \land (p \lor \sim q \lor \sim r)$$
$$\land \{\sim p \lor [(\sim q \lor (q \land r)) \land (\sim r \lor (q \land r))]\}$$
$$= (p \lor q \lor r) \land (p \lor \sim q \lor \sim r) \land \{\sim p \lor [(\sim q \lor r) \land (\sim r \lor q)]\}$$
$$= (p \lor q \lor r) \land (p \lor \sim q \lor \sim r) \land (\sim p \lor \sim q \lor r) \land (\sim p \lor \sim r \lor q);$$

and

$$b = \{(p \lor q \lor r) \land (\sim p \lor \sim q \lor r)\} \land \{[(\sim p \land \sim q) \lor (p \land q)] \lor \sim r\}$$
$$= (p \lor q \lor r) \land (\sim p \lor \sim q \lor r)$$
$$\land \{[(\sim p \lor (p \land q)) \land (\sim q \lor (p \land q))] \lor \sim r\}$$
$$= (p \lor q \lor r) \land (\sim p \lor \sim q \lor r) \land \{[(\sim p \lor q) \land (p \lor \sim q)] \lor \sim r\}$$
$$= (p \lor q \lor r) \land (\sim p \lor \sim q \lor r) \land (\sim p \lor q \lor \sim r) \land (p \lor \sim q \lor \sim r).$$

Hence,

$$a = b.$$

We now introduce a useful parentheses-omitting convention. Parentheses are inserted in a proposition to indicate the main connective of the proposition and the main connective of each component of the proposition. Consider a proposition which involves some or all of the connectives $\leftrightarrow$, $\rightarrow$, $\land$, $\lor$, $\sim$; in case parentheses have been omitted, we shall assume that the main connective of the proposition is "$\leftrightarrow$"; if this connective does not appear in the proposition, then we shall assume that the main connective is "$\rightarrow$"; if this connective does not appear, we shall assume that the main connective is "$\land$"; if this connective does not appear, we shall assume that "$\lor$" is the main connective; if this connective does not appear, then "$\sim$" is the main connective of the proposition. In short, we assign a bracketing power to the connectives $\sim$, $\lor$, $\land$, $\rightarrow$, $\leftrightarrow$ (weakest connectives have been listed first).

For example, "$(p \land q) \rightarrow r$" is denoted by "$p \land q \rightarrow r$"; "$(p \lor \sim q) \rightarrow (q \land r)$" is denoted by "$p \lor \sim q \rightarrow q \land r$"; and "$(p \rightarrow q) \leftrightarrow ((\sim q) \rightarrow \sim p)$" is denoted by "$p \rightarrow q \leftrightarrow \sim q \rightarrow \sim p$".

EXERCISES

1. **a.** Prove that any two propositions obtained by inserting parentheses in "$p \lor q \lor r \lor s$" are equal.

b. State a parentheses-omitting convention for a proposition consisting of four propositions joined by three "∨"'s.

c. State and justify a parentheses-omitting convention for a proposition consisting of five propositions joined by four "∨"'s.

d. State and justify a parentheses-omitting convention for a proposition consisting of $n + 1$ propositions joined by n "∨"'s — whenever n is a natural number. *Note:* A proposition which has this form is said to be a *disjunction*.

2. State and justify a parentheses-omitting convention for a proposition consisting of $n + 1$ propositions joined by n "∧"'s — whenever n is a natural number. *Note:* A proposition which has this form is said to be a *conjunction*.

Simplify the following propositions:

3. $p \land (q \land {\sim}p)$.

4. $(p \land q) \lor p$.

5. $(p \to q) \lor {\sim}p$.

6. $(p \to q) \lor p$.

7. $(q \to p) \to p$.

8. $p \to (q \to p)$.

9. $(p \leftrightarrow {\sim}q) \lor q$.

10. $p \land {\sim}(q \to p)$.

11. $\{(p \land q) \lor [({\sim}p \land {\sim}q) \lor q]\} \land p$.

12. $[p \lor (q \land r)] \lor [(q \land {\sim}p) \lor p]$.

13. $({\sim}p \land {\sim}q \land r) \lor (p \land q \land r)$
$\qquad\qquad\qquad \lor (p \land {\sim}q \land r)$.

14. $[p \lor (q \leftrightarrow {\sim}p)] \to {\sim}q$.

1.7 Applications to Switching Networks

Before continuing our development of symbolic logic, we pause to consider a most unexpected and powerful application of the techniques presented in the preceding pages — the design of switching networks. Our main interest here, however, is not switching networks; rather, we want to use our symbolic logic to solve problems that arise in a simple situation. This will demonstrate the value of our work.

A switching network consists of a number of wires capable of carrying current, and a number of switches each capable of creating a gap in a wire. The simplest example of a switching network is

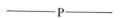

a single wire. If current is applied at one end, it is transmitted to the other end. Not quite so trivial is the switching network consisting of one wire and one switch:

————P————

When the switch P is closed, current can flow; opening the switch creates a gap in the wire so that current cannot flow. This simple network suggests two propositions: "Switch P is closed" and "Current flows". Denote the former by "p" and the latter by "c"; notice that the truth-value of c depends upon the truth-value of p. Table 1.7.1 makes this clear. Examining this truth-table, we see that $c = p$. Thus, in this example, the proposition "Current flows" is logically the same as the proposition "Switch P is closed"

TABLE 1.7.1

p	c
T	T
F	F

In a similar way, the switching network

which consists of one wire and two switches, suggests three propositions: "Switch P is closed", "Switch Q is closed", and "Current flows". Denoting these propositions by "p", "q", and "c" respectively, we readily establish that $c = p \land q$. In this case, the switches P and Q are said to be in series.

Next, consider a switching network with two switches in parallel (Fig. 1.7.1). Here, current flows iff P is closed or Q is closed. Thus, $c = p \lor q$.

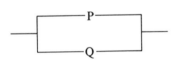

Figure 1.7.1

Complicated networks can be constructed by joining together two given networks in series or in parallel. Let M and N be given switching networks, and consider the switching networks I and II constructed as follows: M and N are in series (Fig. 1.7.2), and M and N are in parallel (Fig. 1.7.3). Let "m" denote current flows through M, and let "n" denote current flows through N. It is easily seen that the proposition "Current flows through I" is given by $m \land n$, and the proposition "Current flows through II" is given by $m \lor n$.

Figure 1.7.2   Figure 1.7.3

To illustrate this technique of breaking down a problem into several simpler problems, we compute "current flows" for the switching network shown in Fig. 1.7.4. This is an illustration of II, where M is

and N is

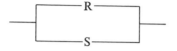

Thus, $m = p \wedge q$, and $n = r \vee s$; therefore, $c = (p \wedge q) \vee (r \vee s)$.

It is not always the case that the switches occurring in a network operate independently. For example, two switches may be so arranged that they close together and open together. In this case, we shall denote the switches by the same letter. We can also connect two switches so that when one is open the other is closed, and vice versa. In this case, should the first switch be P, we shall name the other P′. Notice that if "p" denotes "Switch P is closed", then "$\sim p$" denotes "Switch P′ is closed".

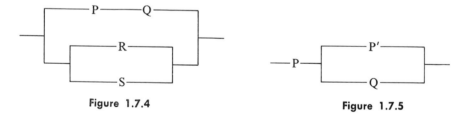

Figure 1.7.4   Figure 1.7.5

Consider the network shown in Fig. 1.7.5. Here, $c = p \wedge (\sim p \vee q)$; simplifying, $c = (p \wedge \sim p) \vee (p \wedge q) = p \wedge q$. Thus, "Current flows" is logically the same as "Switch P is closed and switch Q is closed". It follows that the given switching network can be replaced by the following simpler network:

Thus, the algebra of propositions has a direct bearing on the problem of simplifying a given switching network.

So far, we have been concerned with the problem of representing the proposition "Current flows" in terms of the state of the switches of a given switching network. Let us now turn to the preliminary question of designing a switching network so that it will possess certain stated properties. For

TABLE 1.7.2

p	q	c
T	T	
T	F	
F	T	
F	F	

TABLE 1.7.3

p	q	c
T	T	T
T	F	F
F	T	F
F	F	T

example, consider the switching network required for a room with two doors, one light, and at each door a switch which controls the light. The desired network, then, involves two independent switches such that changing the state of either switch changes the truth-value of "Current flows". The design of the network is effected by constructing a truth-table for c, as follows. We must insert "T"'s and "F"'s under c, so that changing the truth-value of either p or q changes the truth-value of c. We can accomplish this by entering a "T" under c iff an even number of "T"'s are assigned to p and q. Thus, we obtain the truth-table for c which is shown in Table 1.7.3. The proposition c is easily read off, in disjunctive normal form:

$$c = (p \wedge q) \vee (\sim p \wedge \sim q).$$

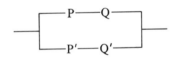

Figure 1.7.6

It is easy, now, to design the required switching network, displayed in Fig. 1.7.6.

The idea of analyzing switching networks in the manner of this section is attributed to Claude E. Shannon.[1]

EXERCISES

Represent the proposition "Current flows" for each of the following switching networks, simplifying in each case:

1.

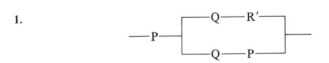

---

[1]"A Symbolic Analysis of Relay and Switching Circuits", *Trans. Am. Inst. Elec. Engrs.*, 57 (1939).

2.

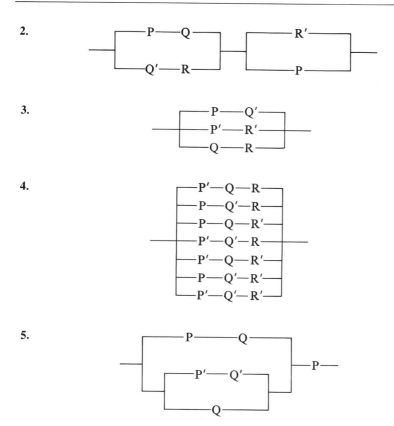

3.

4.

5.

6. Design an appropriate switching network for a room with three doors, a switch at each door, and one light.

7. Design an appropriate switching network for a room with four doors, a switch at each door, and one light.

8. Each member of a committee of three votes affirmatively for a proposal by closing a switch. If the majority has voted for the proposal, a light flashes on. Design an appropriate switching network.

9. As in Exercise 8, but for a committee of five members.

10. As in Exercise 8, but for a committee of four members. In case of a tie, the proposal is defeated if the chairman has voted against it, and is approved if the chairman has voted for it.

11. A committee has four members, A, B, C, and D. A has two votes, and each of the others has one vote. Each member votes. Design an appropriate switching network so that each member votes affirmatively by closing a switch and a light flashes on if the proposal has been approved.

1.8 The Universal Quantifier

Returning to the analysis of language, consider the following argument: "All students are clever; clever people are sure to succeed; hence, all students are sure to succeed". Examining this argument, we note that it involves three independent propositions: "All students are clever", "Clever people are sure to succeed", and "All students are sure to succeed". It is apparent that the conclusion does not involve, directly, the propositions appearing in the assumptions. Thus, even though the argument appeals strongly to our intuitive logical sense — in fact, we are sure the argument is valid — we must agree that, in terms of the symbolic logic so far developed, there is absolutely no logical connection between the assumptions and the conclusion. In other words, our logic does not succeed in breaking down the propositions involved in the argument to the point that the logical dependence of the conclusion upon the assumptions is made clear. We must conclude that our analysis of language, our search for the logical connectives and the basic components making up a given propositions, is not yet complete.

Studying the proposition "All students are clever", we observe that this statement can be rendered by "If a person is a student, then he is clever". Noting that "he" refers to "a person", let us replace both by a single letter, say "x". We obtain: "If x is a student, then x is clever". Notice that this is a *propositional form* rather than a proposition. Clearly, the expressions "x is a student" and "x is clever" do not possess truth-values; so these are not propositions. Similarly, the more complicated expression "If x is a student, then x is clever" does not possess a truth-value; hence, this expression is not a proposition. On the other hand, the expression "If x is a student, then x is clever" is capable of generating propositions — the propositions obtained by substituting a person's name for the "x" appearing in the propositional form. But the statement "All students are clever" is true provided that each proposition generated by the propositional form "If x is a student, then x is clever" is a *true* proposition. More directly, our proposition "All students are clever" is given by *"For each x, if x is a student, then x is clever"*. To facilitate matters, we introduce a symbol, called the *universal quantifier*, to stand for "for each", namely "$\forall$" — an upside-down "A". So we obtain: "$\forall x$ [if x is a student, then x is clever]". Notice that the *scope* (i.e., *extent* or *reach*) of the universal quantifier is indicated by brackets "[" and "]".

Next, we want to represent symbolically the phrases "x is a student" and "x is clever". Let "S" denote the collection of all students, let "C" denote the collection of all clever people, and let "$\in$" stand for the phrase "is a member of". Then "$x \in S$" stands for "x is a member of the collection of all students"; clearly, then, "$x \in S$" means "x is a student". Similarly, "$x \in C$" stands for "x is clever". Thus, the proposition "All students are clever" is represented symbolically by "$\forall x[x \in S \rightarrow x \in C]$". It must be emphasized that the proposition "$\forall x[x \in S \rightarrow x \in C]$" is true iff the propositional form "$x \in S \rightarrow x \in C$" generates only true propositions.

Through the introduction of the universal quantifier "$\forall$", we have succeeded in breaking down the proposition "All students are clever" into its basic components. It is worth stating, in general terms, the definition of this important connective. The following definition is a first attempt to pin down this logical connective.

DEFINITION 1.8.1.   Let $P(x)$ be any propositional form; then the proposition "$\forall x[P(x)]$" is said to be true iff each expression obtained from $P(x)$ by substituting the name of an object for "x" is a true proposition.

For example, consider "$\forall x[x < x + 1]$"; here, our propositional form is "$x < x + 1$". Substituting "3" for "x", we obtain "$3 < 4$", which is a true proposition. However, substituting "moon" for "x", we obtain "Moon $<$ moon $+ 1$", which is not a proposition; rather, it is a nonsensical expression. Clearly, we must restrict ourselves to objects that are numbers, say natural numbers. Let "N" denote the collection of all natural numbers; let us replace the propositional form given above by "$x \in N \rightarrow x < x + 1$", which appears to restrict us to natural numbers. Are we any better off than before? Well, let us substitute "moon" for "x", just as before, and see what results. We obtain "Moon $\in N \rightarrow$ moon $<$ moon $+ 1$", an expression of the form "$p \rightarrow q$". Here, p is false, so we might be tempted to assert that "$p \rightarrow q$" is true. Notice, however, that q is "Moon $<$ moon $+ 1$", which is not a proposition. Therefore, "Moon $\in N \rightarrow$ moon $<$ moon $+ 1$" is not a proposition. We conclude that this procedure has failed.

Let us try modifying Definition 1.8.1. We can easily phrase our definition so that we permit $P(x)$ to generate both propositions and expressions that are not propositions. We have only to insist that the propositions generated by $P(x)$ be true. For example:

DEFINITION 1.8.2.   Let $P(x)$ be any propositional form; then the proposition "$\forall x[P(x)]$" is said to be true iff each proposition generated by $P(x)$ is true.

The intent of this definition is that we shall ignore each expression generated by $P(x)$ which is not a proposition. We require only that the propositions generated by $P(x)$ be true.

There are some disadvantages here, too. For one thing, suppose $P(x)$

generates only expressions which are not propositions; then, according to Definition 1.8.2, "$\forall x[P(x)]$" is true. For example, "$\forall x[x$ is a round number]" is true, and "$\forall x[x < 5$ and x is a student]" is true. Another disadvantage is that when we assert that each object has some stated property, we usually restrict ourselves to the objects of a certain collection; i.e., we mean that each object in a certain collection possesses the stated property. The collection of objects involved in a given discussion is usually clear from the outset; this collection is called the *universe of discourse* or the *basic set*. In a mathematical investigation, the universe of discourse is clearly stated and is given in advance. It is this collection of objects that is involved in the process of generating propositions from a particular propositional form.

At last we are in a position to formulate our definition with some precision.

DEFINITION 1.8.3.   Let $P(x)$ be any propositional form; then the proposition "$\forall x[P(x)]$" is said to be true iff each expression obtained from $P(x)$ by substituting for "x" the *name* of an object in a given universe of discourse is a true proposition.

To illustrate, let the universe of discourse be N, the collection of all natural numbers; then the proposition "$\forall x[x \leq x^2]$" is true. On the other hand, this same proposition is false in case the universe of discourse is the collection of all real numbers; for then the propositional form "$x \leq x^2$" generates the proposition "$.1 \leq .01$", which is false. Our point is simply this: the truth-value of "$\forall x[P(x)]$" depends upon the universe of discourse. By the way, at this stage our references to natural numbers and to real numbers are informal and are intended merely as illustrations.

Now that we have worked out a satisfactory definition, please ignore Definition 1.8.1 and Definition 1.8.2.

So far in this discussion we have been talking about the proposition "$\forall x[P(x)]$"; let us now concentrate on the universal quantifier itself. Now, $\forall$ is certainly a logical connective; since each logical connective is a function, to define "$\forall$" we must state the truth-value of "$\forall x[P(x)]$" in each of the possible truth-value cases. What are the truth-value cases in this situation? First, we must determine the propositions that the connective $\forall$ connects. This is obvious: $\forall$ connects the propositions that are generated by the propositional form $P(x)$. We have our universe of discourse; replacing "x" throughout $P(x)$ by a particular member of the universe of discourse, we obtain one of the propositions connected by $\forall$. In short, $\forall$ connects the propositions generated by the propositional form $P(x)$. Assigning truth-values to the propositions generated by $P(x)$ we obtain one truth-value case; this truth-value case will appear in the truth-table for "$\forall x[P(x)]$". We shall enter "T" under "$\forall x[P(x)]$" if each of the propositions generated by $P(x)$ has been assigned "T" in this truth-value case; otherwise, we shall enter "F" under "$\forall x[P(x)]$". This is the truth-table definition of the logical connective $\forall$. Notice that the "x" which appears in "$\forall x[P(x)]$" is merely a place-holder; here, we could use other symbols in place of "x", say "y" or "z" or even "?".

We now return to our analysis of the argument which appears in the first paragraph of this section. Here, the universe of discourse is the collection of all persons. We have already symbolized the first proposition contained in the argument. In order to symbolize the remaining propositions appearing in the argument, let "R" denote the collection of all people who are sure to succeed. Then "Clever people are sure to succeed" is symbolized by "$\forall x[x \in C \rightarrow x \in R]$"; and "All students are sure to succeed" is represented by "$\forall x[x \in S \rightarrow x \in R]$". Thus, the argument is symbolized as follows:

> Assumptions: $\forall x[x \in S \rightarrow x \in C]$, $\forall x[x \in C \rightarrow x \in R]$.
> Conclusion: $\forall x[x \in S \rightarrow x \in R]$.

Before analyzing this argument, we note that the independent propositions involved in the argument are the propositions obtained from the propositional forms $x \in S$, $x \in C$, and $x \in R$ by replacing "x" with a person's name.

To show that this is a valid argument, we must demonstrate that the conclusion is true under each combination of truth-values of the independent propositions which makes both assumptions true. Of course, we cannot construct a truth-table to show that this is so, because there are too many independent propositions: for example, "Jones $\in S$", "Brown $\in R$", "Smith $\in C$" are each independent propositions, and in each truth-value case are assigned truth-values "T" or "F". Nor can we utilize an algebraic approach, since we have not yet discussed the properties of the universal quantifier. What are we to do? Well, although we cannot carry out a truth-table analysis in its entirety, we can construct a portion of the truth-table. In short, we shall use the *method* of truth-table analysis to reach a decision about the validity of the given argument. Imagine that we have assigned truth-values to the independent propositions so that both assumptions are true, yet the conclusion is false. But assuming that "$\forall x[x \in S \rightarrow x \in R]$" is false under our assignment of truth-values means that there is a person, say Mr. Brown, to whom truth-values have been assigned so that the proposition "Mr. Brown $\in S \rightarrow$ Mr. Brown $\in R$" is false. Therefore, the truth-value of "Mr. Brown $\in S$" is T, and the truth-value of "Mr. Brown $\in R$" is F. Since the proposition "$\forall x[x \in S \rightarrow x \in C]$" is true in this truth-value case, we know that the proposition obtained from the propositional form "$x \in S \rightarrow x \in C$" by substituting "Mr. Brown" for "x" is true. Thus, the proposition "Mr. Brown $\in S \rightarrow$ Mr. Brown $\in C$" is true; it follows that the truth-value of "Mr. Brown $\in C$" is T. Since the proposition "$\forall x[x \in C \rightarrow x \in R]$" is true in this truth-value case, we see that the proposition "Mr. Brown $\in C \rightarrow$ Mr. Brown $\in R$" is also true in this truth-value case; therefore, the truth-value of "Mr. Brown $\in R$" is T. But this is impossible, since we have already seen that the truth-value of "Mr. Brown $\in R$" is F. We conclude that it is impossible to construct a truth-value case under which both assumptions are true and the conclusion is false. Thus, the given argument is valid.

We now state the fundamental property of the universal quantifier.

THEOREM 1.8.1.   Let $P(x)$ be any propositional form, and let a be any member of the universe of discourse; then the proposition "$\forall x[P(x)] \rightarrow P(a)$" is a tautology.

Proof: The proposition "$\forall x[P(x)]$" is either true or false.

1. Suppose $\forall x[P(x)]$ is true. In view of Definition 1.8.3, it follows that the propositional form $P(x)$ generates only true propositions; in particular, $P(a)$ is true. Therefore, in this case, "$\forall x[P(x)] \rightarrow P(a)$" is true.

2. Suppose "$\forall x[P(x)]$" is false. Then "$\forall x[P(x)] \rightarrow P(a)$" is true, since this is a proposition of the form "$p \rightarrow q$" and we are given that p is false.

In this section we have investigated the meaning of the word "all"; our analysis has revealed the existence of three fundamental notions – the universal quantifier, the propositional form, and the universe of discourse. These concepts enable us to break down a proposition of the type handled here so as to reveal its basic components. In this way, we are able to use a truth-table analysis to investigate the validity of a given argument.

EXERCISES

Let "C" denote the class of all Canadians, and let "H" denote the class of all honest people. Express the following propositions in words, as briefly as possible, and state the truth-value of each (it is understood that the universe of discourse is the collection of all persons):

1. $\forall x[x \in C]$.

2. $\forall y[y \in H]$.

3. $\forall z[\sim(z \in H)]$.

4. $\sim(\forall z[\sim(z \in H)])$.

5. $\forall t[t \in C \rightarrow t \in H]$.

6. $\forall u[u \in H \rightarrow u \in C]$.

7. $\forall v[v \in C \rightarrow v \in H] \wedge \forall w[w \in H \rightarrow w \in C]$.

8. $\forall x[x \in C \leftrightarrow x \in H]$.

9. Show that the following arguments are valid:
   a. All men are mortal; Socrates in a man. Hence, Socrates is mortal.
   b. All students are scholars; all scholars are gentlemen. Therefore, all students are gentlemen.

10. Let $P(y)$ be any propositional form, and let a and b be members of the universe of discourse. Show that the proposition "$\forall y[P(y)] \rightarrow [P(a) \wedge P(b)]$" is a tautology.

11. Let $P(x)$ and $Q(x)$ be any propositional forms. Show that the proposition "$\forall x[P(x) \wedge Q(x)] \rightarrow (\forall x[P(x)] \wedge \forall x[Q(x)])$" is a tautology.

12. Let $P(x)$ and $Q(x)$ be any propositional forms. Show that the proposition "$(\forall x[P(x)] \wedge \forall x[Q(x)]) \rightarrow \forall y[P(y) \wedge Q(y)]$" is a tautology.

13. Let $P(y)$ and $Q(y)$ be any propositional forms. Show that the proposition "$\forall y[P(y) \rightarrow Q(y)] \rightarrow (\forall y[P(y)] \rightarrow \forall y[Q(y)])$" is a tautology.

14. Let $P(z)$ and $Q(z)$ be any propositional forms. Show that the proposition "$(\forall z[P(z)] \rightarrow \forall z[Q(z)]) \rightarrow \forall z[P(z) \rightarrow Q(z)]$" is *not* a tautology.

15. Distinguish, in your own words, between a proposition and a propositional form.

16. Show that a proposition can generate a propositional form.

17. Is there an essential difference between the propositional forms $P(x)$ and $P(y)$?

1.9   The Existential Quantifier

Consider the proposition: "Some students are clever". Unfortunately, the word "some" is vague; in mathematics, however, it is customary to interpret "some" as meaning "one or more". Let "S" denote the collection of all students, and let "C" denote the collection of all clever persons. Then the proposition "Some students are clever" is true, provided that the propositional form "$x \in S \wedge x \in C$" generates one or more true propositions. It is clear that we are involved with a quantifier. Let us introduce a symbol, called the *existential quantifier,* to stand for the phrase "There is at least one", namely "$\exists$" — a reverse "E". So we obtain "$\exists x[x \in S \wedge x \in C]$", which is read as "There is at least one x such that $x \in S \wedge x \in C$". Clearly, "$\exists x[x \in S \wedge x \in C]$" symbolizes the proposition "Some students are clever". Notice that we have succeeded in displaying the basic components of the proposition "Some students are clever".

DEFINITION 1.9.1.   Let $P(x)$ be any propositional form; then the proposition "$\exists x[P(x)]$" is said to be true iff each expression obtained from $P(x)$ by substituting for "x" the *name* of an object in a given universe of discourse is a proposition; moreover, at least one of these propositions is required to be true.

It is worthwhile to restate Definition 1.9.1 from the viewpoint of propositional functions. The logical connective ∃ is really a propositional function; to define this function we must state the truth-value of "$\exists x[P(x)]$" in each of the possible truth-value cases. To do this we must determine the propositions that the connective ∃ connects. We have our universe of discourse; replacing "x" throughout $P(x)$ by a particular member of the universe of discourse, we obtain one of the propositions connected by ∃. In short, ∃ connects the propositions generated by the propositional form $P(x)$. Assigning truth-values to each of these propositions we obtain one truth-value case; this truth-value case will appear in the truth-table for "$\exists x[P(x)]$". We shall enter "F" under "$\exists x[P(x)]$" if each of the propositions generated by $P(x)$ has been assigned "F" in this truth-value case; otherwise, we shall enter "T". This is the truth-table definition of the logical connective ∃. Notice that the "x" which appears in "$\exists x[P(x)]$" is merely a place-holder; here, we could use other symbols in place of "x", say "y" or "z" or even "$?$".

It turns out that the universal and existential quantifiers are closely related.

THEOREM 1.9.1.   Let $P(x)$ be any propositional form; then $\sim\forall x[P(x)] = \exists x[\sim P(x)]$.

Proof: We must show that the propositions "$\sim\forall x[P(x)]$" and "$\exists x[\sim P(x)]$" are logically the same, i.e., that they possess the same truth-values in each truth-value case. Suppose that "$\sim\forall x[P(x)]$" is true in a given truth-value case. Then "$\forall x[P(x)]$" is false in that truth-value case; hence, at least one of the propositions generated by $P(x)$ is false, and so at least one of the propositions generated by $\sim P(x)$ is true. Hence, "$\exists x[\sim P(x)]$" is true. Next, suppose that "$\sim\forall x[P(x)]$" is false in a given truth-value case. Then "$\forall x[P(x)]$" is true in that truth-value case; hence, each proposition generated by $P(x)$ is true, and so each proposition generated by $\sim P(x)$ is false. Therefore, "$\exists x[\sim P(x)]$" is false. This establishes our theorem.

The following corollaries are easily proven.

COROLLARY 1.9.1. $\sim\forall x[\sim P(x)] = \exists x[P(x)]$.

COROLLARY 1.9.2. $\sim\exists x[\sim P(x)] = \forall x[P(x)]$.

COROLLARY 1.9.3. $\sim\exists x[P(x)] = \forall x[\sim P(x)]$.

To illustrate the value of our quantifiers, let us consider the following argument: "Some professors are humorous; all humorous persons are well-liked; therefore, some professors are well-liked". Analyzing the argument, let "P" denote the collection of all professors, let "H" denote the collection of all humorous persons, and let "L" denote the collection of all well-liked persons. Then the argument takes the following symbolic form:

Assumptions: $\exists x[x \in P \wedge x \in H]$, $\forall y[y \in H \rightarrow y \in L]$.
Conclusion: $\exists z[z \in P \wedge z \in L]$.

We note that the independent propositions involved in this argument are the propositions generated by the propositional forms $x \in P$, $x \in H$, and $x \in L$.

To demonstrate that this argument is valid, we must show that the conclusion is true in each truth-value case under which both assumptions are true. Again, we shall prove this by applying the truth-table method, though we shall not actually construct a truth-table. Consider any truth-value case under which both assumptions are true. In particular, "$\exists x[x \in P \wedge x \in H]$" is true; therefore, there is a person, let us say Mr. Brown, such that the truth-value of "Mr. Brown $\in P \wedge$ Mr. Brown $\in H$" is T. This means that the truth-value of "Mr. Brown $\in P$" is T, and the truth-value of "Mr. Brown $\in H$" is T. Since "$\forall y[y \in H \rightarrow y \in L]$" is true, in this truth-value case, it follows that the truth-value of "Mr. Brown $\in H \rightarrow$ Mr. Brown $\in L$" is T; therefore, the truth-value of "Mr. Brown $\in L$" is T. We conclude that the truth-value of "Mr. Brown $\in P \wedge$ Mr. Brown $\in L$" is T. Thus, "$\exists z[z \in P \wedge z \in L]$" is true in the given truth-value case. This demonstrates that the argument is valid.

As an illustration of an invalid argument, consider the following argument: "All students are clever; some clever people are geniuses; therefore, some students are geniuses". This argument is symbolized by letting "G" denote the collection of all geniuses, and introducing "S" and "C" as before. We obtain:

Assumptions: $\forall x[x \in S \rightarrow x \in C]$, $\exists x[x \in C \wedge x \in G]$.
Conclusion: $\exists x[x \in S \wedge x \in G]$.

To show that the argument is invalid, we must construct a truth-value case under which both assumptions are true and the conclusion is false. This is easy. Let "Mr. Brown $\in C$" be true, and let "Mr. Brown $\in G$" be true. This makes the second assumption true. Also, let "Mr. Brown $\in S$" be false; in fact, assign truth-values so that each proposition generated by "$x \in S$" is false, and each proposition generated by "$x \in C$" and "$x \in G$" is true. We have now spelled out a truth-value case under which both assumptions are true, yet the conclusion is false. This means that the argument is invalid.

We now consider a theorem about the existential quantifier.

THEOREM 1.9.2. Let $P(x)$ and $Q(x)$ be any propositional forms; then the proposition "$\exists x[P(x) \wedge Q(x)] \rightarrow (\exists x[P(x)] \wedge \exists x[Q(x)])$" is a tautology.

Proof: Consider any truth-value case under which "$\exists x[P(x) \wedge Q(x)]$" is true; it follows that "$\exists x[P(x)]$" and "$\exists x[Q(x)]$" are both true in this truth-value case. This establishes Theorem 1.9.2.

The proofs of this section and the preceding section have deliberately stressed the truth-table method. There are easier ways of persuading oneself that a given argument of the sort considered here is either valid or invalid. For example, there is a pictorial technique involving Venn diagrams, which is quite easy to apply. However, methods of this type are limited to the very simple kind of argument, or theorem, considered here – involving only propositions with one quantifier. On the other hand, the truth-table method presented here will handle the more complicated arguments that occur in mathematics – arguments in which the assumptions and conclusion may involve several quantifiers, not just one. Since it is much easier to understand and master a method when it is applied to simple rather than to complicated examples, here is the proper place to study the technique of analyzing quantifier-type arguments.

Finally, we present an example which illustrates the necessity for care when handling quantifiers.

Example: Let $P(x)$ and $Q(x)$ be any propositional forms; show that the proposition "$\exists x[P(x) \rightarrow Q(x)] \rightarrow (\exists x[P(x)] \rightarrow \exists x[Q(x)])$" is *not* a tautology.

Solution: The given proposition is a tautology iff it is true under any assignment of truth values to its independent propositions. The independent propositions are the propositions generated by the propositional forms $P(x)$ and $Q(x)$. Consider a truth-value case under which just one proposition generated by $P(x)$ is true, and each proposition generated by $Q(x)$ is false. Assuming that our universe of discourse contains at least two members, we see that "$\exists x[P(x) \rightarrow Q(x)]$" is true (replace "$x$" by "$a$" where "$P(a)$" if false). Moreover, "$\exists x[P(x)]$" is true and "$\exists x[Q(x)]$" is false; so "$\exists x[P(x)] \rightarrow \exists x[Q(x)]$" is false. This demonstrates that "$\exists x[P(x) \rightarrow Q(x)] \rightarrow (\exists x[P(x)] \rightarrow \exists x[Q(x)])$" is not a tautology.

On the other hand, one can demonstrate that the proposition "$(\exists x[P(x)] \rightarrow \exists x[Q(x)]) \rightarrow \exists x[P(x) \rightarrow Q(x)]$" is a tautology. This is left to the student.

EXERCISES

Test the validity of the following arguments:

1. Television programs are designed for the masses; nothing designed for the masses can be of high quality; therefore, no television program is of high quality.
2. No teacher has a sense of humor; some clever people do not have a sense of humor; hence, some teachers are clever.
3. Some mammals live in the water. All things that live in the water are fish. Therefore, some mammals are fish.
4. Some cars are vehicles. Some buses are cars. No vehicles are buses. Therefore, some cars are not vehicles.
5. All professors are wealthy, pleasant, or handsome. All wealthy people are intelligent or handsome. All handsome people are intelligent and pleasant. Some pleasant people are intelligent. Therefore, some professors are intelligent.
6. Babies are illogical. Nobody is despised who can manage a crocodile. Illogical persons are despised. Therefore, some babies can manage crocodiles.
7. Everyone who is sane can do logic. No lunatics are fit to serve on a jury. None of your friends can do logic. Therefore, none of your friends is fit to serve on a jury.
8. Some professors are fools. No fools are learned. Hence, no professors are learned.
9. Let $P(y)$ and $Q(y)$ be any propositional forms; show that the proposition "$(\exists x[P(x)] \wedge \exists y[Q(y)]) \to \exists z[P(z) \wedge Q(z)]$" is *not* a tautology.
10. Let $P(x)$ and $Q(x)$ be any propositional forms; show that the proposition "$\exists x[P(x) \vee Q(x)] \to (\exists x[P(x)] \vee \exists x[Q(x)])$" is a tautology.
11. Suppose that, for a particular discussion, the quantifiers refer to objects a or b. Let $P(x)$ be any propositional form; show that $\forall x[P(x)] = P(a) \wedge P(b)$, and $\exists x[P(x)] = P(a) \vee P(b)$.
12. Suppose that, for a particular discussion, the quantifiers refer to objects a_1, $a_2, \cdots, a_n$. Let $P(x)$ be any propositional form; show that $\forall x[P(x)] = P(a_1) \wedge P(a_2) \wedge \cdots \wedge P(a_n)$, and $\exists x[P(x)] = P(a_1) \vee P(a_2) \vee \cdots \vee P(a_n)$.
13. Mathematics commonly makes use of quantifiers other than the universal and existential quantifier. For example, "$\exists!$" denotes "There is a unique", so that "$\exists!x[P(x)]$" is true iff exactly one of the propositions generated by $P(x)$ is true. Show that this quantifier, called the *unique existential quantifier*, can be expressed in terms of the universal and existential quantifiers.
14. Let $P(x)$ and $Q(x)$ be any propositional forms; show that "$\exists!x[P(x) \vee Q(x)] \to (\exists!x[P(x)] \vee \exists!x[Q(x)])$" is a tautology.
15. Let $P(x)$ and $Q(x)$ be any propositional forms; show that "$(\exists x[P(x)] \to \exists x[Q(x)]) \to \exists x[P(x) \to Q(x)]$" is a tautology.

1.10   Propositions Involving Several Quantifiers

In Chapter 3, where we come to grips with the axiomatic method, we shall work with propositions which involve more than one quantifier. Indeed, in mathematics this is the rule rather than the exception. Our purpose, here, is to develop a technique for working out the truth-value of such a proposition.

Consider, for example, the proposition: "Given any number, say x, there is a number, say y, such that $x + y = 0$". Expressed symbolically, this becomes "$\forall x [\exists y [x + y = 0]]$". Here, the main connective is "$\forall x$"; therefore, the given proposition is true iff the propositional form "$\exists y [x + y = 0]$" generates only true propositions. For example, substituting "3" for "x", we obtain the proposition "$\exists y [3 + y = 0]$". Is this proposition true? Well, "$\exists y [3 + y = 0]$" is true iff the propositional form "$3 + y = 0$" generates at least one true proposition. Substituting "-3" for "y", we obtain the proposition "$3 + -3 = 0$"—which is true. Similarly, each of the propositions generated by "$\exists y [x + y = 0]$" can be shown to be true. Thus, "$\forall x [\exists y [x + y = 0]]$" is true.

Consider the proposition: "There is a number, say x, such that $x \cdot y = 0$ whenever y is a number". This proposition is symbolized by "$\exists x [\forall y [x \cdot y = 0]]$". Here, the main connective is "$\exists x$"; therefore, the given proposition is true iff the propositional form "$\forall y [x \cdot y = 0]$" generates at least one true proposition. Substituting "0" for "x", we obtain the proposition "$\forall y [0 \cdot y = 0]$". But the propositional form "$0 \cdot y = 0$" generates only true propositions; therefore, "$\forall y [0 \cdot y = 0]$" is true; hence "$\exists x [\forall y [x \cdot y = 0]]$" is true.

As an example of a false proposition, consider the statement: "There is a number, say y, such that $x + y = 0$ whenever x is a number". This proposition is symbolized by "$\exists y [\forall x [x + y = 0]]$"; note that it can be obtained from the first example given above by merely reversing the order of the quantifiers. We wish to prove that the given proposition is false. Suppose it is true; then the propositional form "$\forall x [x + y = 0]$" generates at least one true proposition. Let a be a number such that the result of substituting "a" for "y" is a true proposition. Then "$\forall x [x + a = 0]$" is true. This means that the propositional form "$x + a = 0$" generates only true propositions. In particular, substituting "$1 + -a$" for "x", we obtain the proposition "$(1 + -a) + a = 0$", which clearly is false. We conclude that the given proposition is false.

In a given proposition whenever a symbol, say "x", is immediately preceded by a quantifier, we shall say that "x" is a *place-holder* or *variable*. The function of a quantified symbol is not only to indicate that the following proposition is true of *all* objects (in the case of the *universal* quantifier) or of *some* objects (in the case of the *existential* quantifier), but also to indicate that certain places throughout the proposition are to be filled with the *same* name, so that the symbol marks the places in which the name of a single object is to be inserted.

The preceding examples are intended to display the technique involved in computing the truth-value of a proposition containing several quantifiers. Summarizing this technique, the question of the truth-value of such a proposition is reduced to the question of the truth-values of a host of propositions, each obtained from the given proposition by deleting one quantifier and replacing the corresponding place-holder with the name of a definite object. By applying this process as many times as there are quantifiers in the given proposition, we see that the truth-value of the given proposition depends upon the truth-values of a large number of propositions which involve no quantifiers; hence, these truth-values are readily determined. The technique, then, is to strip away quantifiers one at a time.

Once again, we introduce a bracket-omitting convention. Since we read from left to right, we shall denote the proposition "$\forall x[\exists y[P(x,y)]]$" by writing "$\forall x \exists y[P(x,y)]$", and we shall denote the proposition "$\exists x[\forall y[P(x,y)]]$" by writing "$\exists x \forall y[P(x,y)]$". In general, we shall say that the quantifier at the left of a block of quantifiers is the main connective of the proposition. For example, "$\forall x \forall y \forall z[x + (y + z) = (x + y) + z]$" denotes "$\forall x[\forall y[\forall z[x + (y + z) = (x + y) + z]]]$". We shall make frequent use of this convention in Chapter 3.

We shall now establish one property of our quantifiers.

THEOREM 1.10.1. Let $P(x,y)$ be any propositional form involving two place-holders; then the proposition "$\exists x \forall y[P(x,y)] \rightarrow \forall y \exists x[P(x,y)]$" is a tautology.

Proof: Consider any truth-value case under which "$\exists x \forall y[P(x,y)]$" is true. It follows that there is an object, say a, such that the proposition "$\forall y[P(a,y)]$" is true. Hence, the propositional form $P(a,y)$ generates only true propositions. This means that the proposition "$P(a,b)$" is true whenever b is an object. But the proposition "$\forall y \exists x[P(x,y)]$" is true iff the propositional form $\exists x[P(x,y)]$ generates only true propositions. Let b be any object; we shall show that the proposition "$\exists x[P(x,b)]$" is true. Substituting "a" for "x" in the propositional form $P(x,b)$, we obtain "$P(a,b)$"—a true proposition. Therefore, the proposition "$\exists x(P(x,b)]$" is true—whenever b is an object. This establishes Theorem 1.10.1.

EXERCISES

Express the following propositions symbolically, and compute the truth-value of each proposition:

1. Any number equals itself.
2. If a number equals a second number, then the second number equals the first number.
3. If a number equals a second number, and that number equals a third number, then the first number equals the third number also.
4. We can find two numbers which are not equal.
5. Given any number, there is a number which equals it.
6. There is a number such that if multiplied by itself the result is itself.
7. There is a number which when added to itself results in the same number.
8. Any two numbers are equal or are different.
9. The sum of two numbers is independent of the order in which they are added.
10. a is a brother of b whenever b is a brother of a.
11. Brothers have the same parents.
12. a is a parent of b whenever b is a child of a.
13. a is the father of b whenever b is the child of a.
14. a is the father of b whenever b is the father of a.

Compute the truth-values of the following propositions where quantification is over the real numbers:

15. $\forall x \forall y [x \cdot y = y \cdot x]$.
16. $\forall x \forall y [x < y]$.
17. $\forall x \exists y [x < y]$.
18. $\forall x \forall y [x < y \rightarrow 5 + x < 5 + y]$.
19. $\exists x \forall y [x < y]$.
20. $\forall x \forall y \forall z [x \cdot (y \cdot z) = (x \cdot y) \cdot z]$.
21. $\forall x \forall y \forall z [x \cdot (y + z) = x \cdot y + x \cdot z]$.
22. $\forall x \forall y [x = y \lor x < y \lor y < x]$.
23. $\forall x [x \cdot x = 2]$.
24. $\exists x [x \cdot x = 2]$.
25. $\forall x [x \cdot x = 2] \rightarrow \exists x [x \cdot x = 2]$.
26. $\forall x [x \cdot x = 2] \rightarrow \exists y [y \cdot y = 2]$.

27. Let $P(x,y)$ be any propositional form involving two place-holders; prove that the proposition "$\forall x \forall y [P(x,y)] \leftrightarrow \forall y \forall x [P(x,y)]$" is a tautology.
28. Let $P(x,y)$ be any propositional form involving two place-holders; prove that the proposition "$\exists x \exists y [P(x,y)] \leftrightarrow \exists y \exists x [P(x,y)]$" is a tautology.
29. Let $P(x,y)$ be any propositional form involving two place-holders; prove that the proposition "$\forall x \exists y [P(x,y)] \rightarrow \exists y \forall x [P(x,y)]$" is *not* a tautology.

Chapter 2

Set Theory

2.1 Sets

The notion of a set, which has always been implicit in mathematics, was first explicitly introduced and developed by the brilliant mathematician G. Cantor (1845–1918) in the late nineteenth century. By a set, Cantor meant any collection of definite, well-distinguished objects — either of perception or thought. Thus, a member of a set is either a physical object (for example, a piece of chalk) or a mental object — an object that has no physical existence in the world about us, but rather exists in the mind of man (for example, the number 3). By a specific set, we mean a specific collection of objects; i.e., a set is determined once we know of each object whether or not it is a member of the set. In other words, a set is defined iff we can assert of each object either that the object is a member of the set or that the object is not a member of the set. In the intuitive approach to set theory presented here, just about anything is considered to be an object; in particular, sets themselves are objects, the objects constructed from given objects by gathering them together conceptually.

There are many synonyms for "set", for example, "aggregate", "bundle", "class", "collection", "ensemble", "family". Although we shall usually use the term "set", we shall feel free to use any of its synonyms. In particular, it is customary to avoid the term "set" in the case of a set whose members themselves are sets. So, we shall speak of the *class* whose members are certain sets.

Generally, sets are denoted by capital letters, and the members of sets by small letters. Thus "$x \in A$" expresses the statement "The object x is a member of the set A". Since a set is merely a collection of objects, it is clear that two sets are the same iff they possess precisely the same members. Thus, the set whose members are 5 and 6 *is* the set whose members are 6

45

and 5. Also, the set whose only member is the integer 2 *is* the set of all positive even primes.

For the purposes of a particular mathematical investigation, it is customary to designate in advance the objects under discussion. The set of all such objects is called the *universal* set or the *universe of discourse* and is denoted by "*I*". Needless to say, the universal set of one mathematical investigation may not be the universal set of a second mathematical investigation.

We turn now to the problem of *naming* sets; it is much easier to talk about a specific set if we have an efficient method of naming or denoting a set. There are two widely used methods of naming a set: one is to list the members of the set, the other is to state a property which is possessed by each member of the set and is not possessed by any other object. As an example of the first method, consider the set S such that $2 \in S$, $3 \in S$, and $5 \in S$, while no other object is a member of S. Listing the members of S, we obtain 2, 3, 5. As it stands, this will hardly do as a name of S; i.e., we do not want to write "$S = 2, 3, 5$". For this reason, we insert braces, "{" and "}", around the list, thereby obtaining the expression "$\{2, 3, 5\}$", which we take to be a name of S. Thus, we are entitled to write "$S = \{2, 3, 5\}$". A definite code is being used: the braces, "{" and "}", stand for "the set"; we then interpose "whose members are"; finally, we read off the objects listed. This code is displayed as follows:

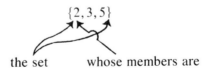

the set   whose members are

There is nothing mysterious here. When decoded, the mathematical expression "$\{2, 3, 5\}$" yields "the set whose members are 2, 3, and 5". Clearly, then, "$\{2, 3, 5\}$" is a name of S.

We turn now to the second method of naming a set. The idea is to present a property which characterizes the members of the set. For example, the collection of all positive primes is a set, since it is clear of any object whether it is a positive prime (we note that a prime is an integer t which has exactly four divisors: $1, -1, t$ and $-t$). We shall denote this set by writing:

$$\{x \mid x \text{ is a positive prime}\}.$$

Again, a definite code is being used here. The two braces stand for "the set"; we then interpose "of all objects, say"; the vertical line stands for "such that"; finally, we read off the stated condition. This code is displayed as follows:

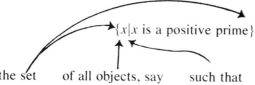

Thus, when decoded, the mathematical expression "$\{x|x$ is a positive prime$\}$" yields "the set of all objects, say x, such that x is a positive prime". Clearly, "$\{x|x$ is a positive prime$\}$" is a name of the set of all positive primes. To further illustrate this notation, let "P" denote the set of all positive primes; then $\{x|x \in P \wedge x < 6\}$ is the set of all positive primes less than 6. Hence, $\{x|x \in P \wedge x < 6\} = \{2, 3, 5\}$. In general, let $P(y)$ be any propositional form, and consider the set of all objects, say t, such that the proposition "$P(t)$" is true. This set is denoted by writing "$\{y|P(y)\}$".

We have said that the fundamental property of a set is that we can assert of each object whether or not it is a member of the set. Consider the set constructed by asserting of each object that it is *not* a member of the set; this set has no members and is therefore called the *empty* set. It is easy to construct names of the empty set by using the two methods given above. Listing the members of the empty set, we obtain "$\{\ \ \}$", which clearly denotes the set that has no members. Observing that each object has the property that it is equal to itself, we see that we can characterize the empty set as the set of all objects, say x, such that x differs from x; thus, we obtain the name "$\{x|x \neq x\}$". It is customary, also, to denote the empty set by writing "$\varnothing$"; thus

$$\varnothing = \{\ \ \} = \{x|x \neq x\}.$$

One more convention. Since nonmembership in a set is as important as membership in a set, we shall denote the phrase "is *not* a member of" by writing "$\overline{\in}$". Thus, "$a \overline{\in} A$" stands for "a is not a member of A."

EXERCISES

Let "P" denote the set of all positive primes, let "I" denote the set of all integers, and let "C" denote the set of all nonprime integers. Show the following:

1. $\{a|a \in P \wedge a \in I\} = P$.

2. $\{b|b \in P \vee b \in I\} = I$.

3. $\{c|c \in C \wedge 3 < c \wedge c < 10\} = \{4, 6, 8, 9\}$.

4. $\{d|d \in P \wedge 5 < d \wedge d < 10\} = \{7\}$.

5. $\{e|e \in P \wedge -10 < e \wedge e < -2\} = \varnothing$.

6. $\{f|f \in P \vee -f \in P \vee f \in C\} = I$.

7. $\{g|g \bar{\in} P \wedge -g \bar{\in} P\} = C$.

8. $\{h|h \in P \wedge h \bar{\in} C\} = P$.

9. $\{i|(i \in C \rightarrow i \in P) \wedge i \in I\} = \{j|j \in P \vee -j \in P\}$.

10. $\{k|(-k \in P \rightarrow k \in P) \wedge k \in I\} = \{l|l \in P \vee l \in C\}$.

11. $\{m|(m \in P \rightarrow m \in C) \wedge m \in I\} = \{n|-n \in P \vee n \in C\}$.

12. $\{o|o \in P \wedge \exists p[p \in I \wedge p + p = o]\} = \{2\}$.

13. Characterize $\{q|\exists r[r + r = q \wedge r \in I]\}$.

14. Characterize $\{s|\exists t[t + t = s + 1 \wedge t \in I]\}$.

15. Characterize $\{u|u \in P \wedge \exists v[v + v = u + 1 \wedge v \in I]\}$.

16. Characterize $\{w|(w \in P \vee -w \in P) \wedge \exists x[x \in I \wedge x + x = w + 1]\}$.

17. Characterize $\{y|(y \in P \vee -y \in P) \wedge \exists z[z \in I \wedge z + z = y]\}$.

18. Characterize $\{a|a \in I \wedge \forall b[b \in I \rightarrow a \cdot b = 0]\}$.

19. Characterize $\{c|c \in I \wedge \forall d[d \in I \rightarrow c \cdot d = d]\}$.

20. Characterize $\{e|e \in I \wedge \forall f[f \in I \rightarrow e + f = f]\}$.

Let "S" denote the set of all students at a university, "M" the set of all male students, "C" the set of all coeds, and "K" the set of all coeds who have never been kissed. Show the following:

21. $\{g|g \in M \vee g \in C\} = S$.

22. $\{h|h \in C \vee h \in K\} = C$.

23. $\{i|i \in C \wedge i \in K\} = K$.

24. $\{j|j \in S \wedge (j \in S \rightarrow j \in C)\} = C$.

25. $\{k|k \in M \wedge k \in C\} = \varnothing$.

26. Characterize $\{l|l \in C \wedge l \bar{\in} K\}$.

27. Discuss the truth or falsity of the statement: $x = \{x\}$.

28. Show that $\{2, 3, 5\} = \{z|z = 2 \vee z = 3 \vee z = 5\}$.

29. Show that $\{x|x \in \varnothing \rightarrow x = 2\} = \{y|y = y\}$.

30. a. Show that a set, say S, has *at least* two members iff $\exists x \exists y[x \neq y \wedge x \in S \wedge y \in S]$.

    b. Show that S has *at most* two members iff $\exists x \exists y \forall z[z \in S \rightarrow z = x \vee z = y]$.

31. Show that a set S has *exactly* two members iff $\exists x \exists y \forall z[z \in S \rightarrow z = x \veebar z = y]$.

32. Symbolize the proposition: "S has exactly three members".

33. Symbolize the proposition: "S has exactly four members".

2.2   Russell's Paradox

In the preceding section, we considered a method of naming a given set by presenting a property that characterizes the members of the set. The order here is important. First, we have a set; next, we construct a name of that set. We must be careful not to reverse the procedure; as we shall see, it can be dangerous first to construct a name, and then to consider the set named!

The situation has been clarified by the famous philosopher and logician Bertrand Russell. Let us consider his famous paradox. Russell observed that if S is a set, then either $S \in S$ or $S \overline{\in} S$ – since a given object either is a member of a given set or is not a member of that set. Generally, a set is not a member of itself; therefore, let us consider the set of all sets that are not members of themselves – $\{x | x$ is a set, and $x \overline{\in} x\}$, which we shall denote by "R". Since R is an object, either $R \in R$ or $R \overline{\in} R$. Consider both possibilities: (1) Assume $R \in R$. Then, R is a set and $R \overline{\in} R$, by the definition of R. But we cannot have both $R \in R$ and $R \overline{\in} R$. (2) Assume $R \overline{\in} R$. Then, $R \in R$, by the definition of R, since we are assuming that R is a set. But we cannot have both $R \overline{\in} R$ and $R \in R$. We conclude from (1) and (2) that we cannot assert $R \in R$ and we cannot assert $R \overline{\in} R$. This is Russell's Paradox.

Examining this argument in the light of our fundamental requirement that a set be a definite collection of objects (so that we can assert of any object whether or not it is a member of the set), we see that Russell's argument demonstrates that R is not a set. Russell has found an object – R itself – which eludes the defining property of R. We conclude that R is not a set.

To repeat, the reason that R is not a set is that the presented definition of R is unsatisfactory: there is one object, R itself, about which we can neither assert that it is a member of the collection nor assert that it is not a member of the collection.

The lesson contained in Russell's Paradox, then, is this: when defining a set by the *characteristic property* method, take care that there actually is a set behind the name. We must be alert to the possibility that a supposedly well-defined set is not a set at all.

To illustrate, consider "$\{x | x$ is a set$\}$" – in words, "the set of all sets". Is there such an animal? Applying Russell's result, we shall see that "$\{x | x$ is a set$\}$" is a meaningless name. Assume, for the moment, that "$\{x | x$ is a set$\}$" is a name of a set, say S. Now, consider an object A such that $A \in S$; we can examine A to see whether $A \overline{\in} A$. In other words, we can form $\{x | x \in S \wedge x \overline{\in} x\}$ – which we know does not exist. This contradiction forces us to conclude that the assumption of the argument is false. Thus, S does not exist. There is no such thing, then, as the set of *all* sets.

There are several popularizations of Russell's Paradox which illustrate the idea of the paradox. Consider the ambitious barber who sets himself the goal of shaving all persons in his village [for convenience, we assume that our barber lives in a sparsely populated region] who do not shave themselves, but no others. Can he achieve this goal? Let us suppose that our barber is so skilled at his profession that no other barber has a customer from this village; even so, he cannot achieve his goal. For who shaves the barber? If he shaves himself, then he has shaved someone who shaves himself. If he does not shave himself, then there is one person in his village who does not shave himself, and whom our barber does not shave. We conclude that our ambitious barber has set himself an impossible task.

Next, consider the learned librarian who observes that certain catalogues do not list themselves. In fairness to these modest catalogues our librarian decides to make a catalogue of all catalogues that do not list themselves. Let us show that this is an impossible task. For suppose that such a catalogue could be compiled; then call it "C". There are two possibilities: (1) C lists itself; (2) C does not list itself.

But if (1), then C does not belong in the catalogue of all catalogues that do not list themselves. Moreover, if (2) then C should be listed in the catalogue of all catalogues that do not list themselves. Thus, either C lists a catalogue which lists itself, or there is a catalogue, namely C itself, which does not list itself and does not appear in C. We conclude that there is no such catalogue. Our librarian has set himself an impossible task.

2.3   Operations on Sets

Let I be the universal set of a particular mathematical investigation, and let A and B be composed of certain members of I. It may happen that each member of A is also a member of B; we shall say, then, that A is a subset of B, and write "$A \subset B$". A is said to be a *proper* subset of B iff $A \subset B$ and $A \neq B$. For example, $\{2,4\} \subset \{2,3,4\}$; indeed, $\{2,4\}$ is a proper subset of $\{2,3,4\}$. The set of *all* subsets of I is called the *power* set of I and is denoted by "$\mathcal{P}I$".

DEFINITION 2.3.1.   Let A be any set; then $\mathcal{P}A$ is $\{S \mid S \subset A\}$.

For example, $\mathcal{P}\{1,2\} = \{\varnothing, \{1\}, \{2\}, \{1,2\}\}$.

Again, let A and B be subsets of I. It is natural to merge these two sets together to form a (possibly) larger set, called the *union* of A and B and denoted by writing "$A \cup B$" (read "A union B").

DEFINITION 2.3.2. $A \cup B$ is $\{x | x \in A \lor x \in B\}$.

For example, $\{1, 5, 2\} \cup \{3, 1, 4, 7\} = \{1, 2, 3, 4, 5, 7\}$.

Also, it is natural to inquire if A and B have any common members; we shall call the set of objects common to A and B the *intersection* of A and B, and shall denote this set by writing "$A \cap B$" (read "A intersect B").

DEFINITION 2.3.3 $A \cap B$ is $\{y | y \in A \land y \in B\}$.

For example, $\{1, 5, 2\} \cap \{3, 1, 4, 7\} = \{1\}$.

Suppose that two given sets are *disjoint*, i.e., have no member in common; in this case, it follows from the definition that their intersection is the empty set $\varnothing$.

Given a set A, let us consider the set of all objects in I, the universal set, which are not members of A. We call this set the *complement* of A, and denote it by writing "A'" or "$\mathcal{C}A$".

DEFINITION 2.3.4. A' is $\{z | z \in I \land z \overline{\in} A\}$.

For example, if $I = \{1, 2, 3, 4, 5, 6, 7, 8, 9\}$, then $\{1, 2, 3, 4, 5\}' = \{6, 7, 8, 9\}$.

We wish to establish some of the properties of the operations $\cup$, $\cap$, and $'$. But first we need a practical criterion for demonstrating that two given sets are in fact the same.

FUNDAMENTAL CRITERION. $A = B$ iff $A \subset B \land B \subset A$.

Proof: First, we note that two sets are the same iff they have exactly the same members. Since there is an "iff" in the theorem, there will be two parts to the proof.

1. Suppose that $A = B$. Then A and B have exactly the same members. Hence, $\forall x [x \in A \rightarrow x \in B]$ and $\forall y [y \in B \rightarrow y \in A]$; i.e., $A \subset B$ and $B \subset A$.

2. Suppose that $A \subset B$ and $B \subset A$. If $A \neq B$, then either $\exists x [x \in A \land x \overline{\in} B]$ or $\exists y [y \in B \land y \overline{\in} A]$, or both. If the former, then A is not a subset of B; if the latter, then B is not a subset of A. Hence, $A = B$. This establishes the Fundamental Criterion.

We now make use of the preceding result to establish certain fundamental properties of the operations $\cup$, $\cap$, and $'$.

THEOREM 2.3.1 $A \cup B = B \cup A$ whenever A and B are sets.

Proof: We shall show that $A \cup B \subset B \cup A$ and $B \cup A \subset A \cup B$. Suppose $x \in A \cup B$; then $x \in A \vee x \in B$; thus, $x \in B \vee x \in A$; hence, $x \in B \cup A$. This establishes that $A \cup B \subset B \cup A$. Now suppose $y \in B \cup A$; then $y \in B \vee y \in A$; thus, $y \in A \vee y \in B$; hence, $y \in A \cup B$. This establishes that $B \cup A \subset A \cup B$. Applying the Fundamental Criterion, we have our result.

THEOREM 2.3.2. $A \cup (B \cap C) = (A \cup B) \cap (A \cup C)$ whenever A, B, and C are sets.

Proof: Suppose $x \in A \cup (B \cap C)$; then $x \in A \vee x \in B \cap C$, and so $x \in A \vee (x \in B \wedge x \in C)$; hence, $(x \in A \vee x \in B) \wedge (x \in A \vee x \in C)$; thus, $x \in A \cup B \wedge x \in A \cup C$.   Therefore, $x \in (A \cup B) \cap (A \cup C)$.   Hence, $A \cup (B \cap C) \subset (A \cup B) \cap (A \cup C)$.   Now   suppose $y \in (A \cup B) \cap (A \cup C)$;   then $y \in A \cup B \wedge y \in A \cup C$,   and   so $(y \in A \vee y \in B) \wedge (y \in A \vee y \in C)$; thus, $y \in A \vee (y \in B \wedge y \in C)$, i.e., $y \in A \vee y \in B \cap C$; thus, $y \in A \cup (B \cap C)$. Hence, $(A \cup B) \cap (A \cup C) \subset A \cup (B \cap C)$. Finally we apply the Fundamental Criterion.

THEOREM 2.3.3. $(A \cup B)' = A' \cap B'$ whenever A and B are sets.

Proof: Suppose $x \in (A \cup B)'$; then $x \bar{\in} A \cup B$, i.e., $\sim(x \in A \vee x \in B)$; hence, $\sim(x \in A) \wedge \sim(x \in B)$; therefore, $x \in A' \wedge x \in B'$; thus, $x \in A' \cap B'$. Hence, $(A \cup B)' \subset A' \cap B'$. Now suppose $y \in A' \cap B'$; then $y \in A' \wedge y \in B'$,   i.e., $\sim(y \in A) \wedge \sim(y \in B)$;   hence, $\sim(y \in A \vee y \in B)$,   i.e., $y \bar{\in} A \cup B$; therefore, $y \in (A \cup B)'$. Thus, $A' \cap B' \subset (A \cup B)'$. Finally, we apply the Fundamental Criterion.

THEOREM 2.3.4. $A \cap I = A$ whenever A is a set.

Proof: Suppose $x \in A \cap I$; then $x \in A$. Therefore, $A \cap I \subset A$. Now suppose $y \in A$; then $y \in A \wedge y \in I$, since I is the universal set. Hence, $y \in A \cap I$. Therefore, $A \subset A \cap I$. In view of the Fundamental Criterion, we have established Theorem 2.3.4.

E X E R C I S E S

Assuming that the universal set, I, is the set of all integers, show the following:

1. $\{8, 6, 7\} \cup \{5, 1, 7, 8\} = \{8, 6, 7, 5, 1\}$.
2. $\{8, 6, 7\} \cap \{5, 1, 7, 8\} = \{7, 8\}$.
3. $\{8, 6, 7\} \cap \{5, 1, 7, 8\}' = \{6\}$.

4. $\{8,6,7\}' \cap \{5,1,7,8\} = \{5,1\}$.

5. $\{8,6,7\}' \cap \{5,1,7,8\}' = \{8,6,7,5,1\}'$.

6. $\{x|\exists y(y \in I \wedge y + y = x)\}$ is the set of all even integers.

7. $\{x|\exists y(y \in I \wedge y + y = x + 1)\}$ is the set of all odd integers.

8. $\{x|\exists y(y \in I \wedge y + y = x)\}' = \{x|\exists y(y \in I \wedge y + y = x + 1)\}$.

9. $\{x|\exists y(y \in I \wedge y + y = x)\} \cup \{x|\exists y(y \in I \wedge y + y = x + 1)\} = I$.

10. $\{y|\exists x(x \in I \wedge x + x = y)\} \cap \{y|\exists x(x \in I \wedge x + x = y + 1)\} = \emptyset$.

Let A, B, and C be any subsets of I; show the following:

11. $A \cap B = B \cap A$.

12. $A \cup (B \cup C) = (A \cup B) \cup C$.

13. $A \cap (B \cap C) = (A \cap B) \cap C$.

14. $A \cap (B \cup C) = (A \cap B) \cup (A \cap C)$.

15. $(A \cap B)' = A' \cup B'$.

16. $A \cup I = I$.

17. $A \cup \emptyset = A$.

18. $A \cap \emptyset = \emptyset$.

19. $(A')' = A$.

20. $A \subset B \wedge B \subset C \rightarrow A \subset C$.

21. $A \subset B \rightarrow C \cup A \subset C \cup B$.

22. Suppose that A is a proper subset of B; is it necessarily true that $C \cup A$ is a proper subset of $C \cup B$?

23. Show that $A \subset B \rightarrow B' \subset A'$ whenever A and B are subsets of I.

24. Let $P(x)$ and $Q(x)$ be any propositional forms; show the following:
    a. $\{x|P(x) \vee Q(x)\} = \{x|P(x)\} \cup \{x|Q(x)\}$.
    b. $\{x|P(x) \wedge Q(x)\} = \{x|P(x)\} \cap \{x|Q(x)\}$.
    c. $\{x|\sim P(x)\} = \{x|P(x)\}'$.

25. It is customary to denote the set $\{x|x \in A \wedge x \overline{\in} B\}$ by writing "$A - B$".
    a. Show that $(A - B) - C = (A - C) - B$.
    b. Show that $A - (B - C) = A \cap (B' \cup C)$.

26. Let A be a given nonempty set, and suppose that corresponding to each member of A, say a, there is a set B_a. It is customary to denote the set $\{x|\exists a[a \in A \wedge x \in B_a]\}$ by writing "$\underset{a \in A}{\bigcup} B_a$", or by writing "$\underset{a}{\bigcup} B_a$" in case the *indexing* set A is indicated by the context. Notice that $\underset{a \in A}{\bigcup} B_a$ is the *union* of all the sets B_a. Similarly, the set $\{x|\forall a[a \in A \rightarrow x \in B_a]\}$ is denoted by writing "$\underset{a \in A}{\bigcap} B_a$", or by writing "$\underset{a}{\bigcap} B_a$". Notice that $\underset{a \in A}{\bigcap} B_a$ is the *intersection* of all the sets B_a.
    a. Prove that $[\underset{a \in A}{\bigcup} B_a]' = \underset{a \in A}{\bigcap} B_a'$.
    b. Prove that $[\underset{a \in A}{\bigcap} B_a]' = \underset{a \in A}{\bigcup} B_a'$.
    c. Prove that $B = \underset{a \in A}{\bigcap} B_a \cup \underset{a \in A}{\bigcup} (B - B_a)$, given that $\forall a[a \in A \rightarrow B_a \subset B]$.

27. Given that $B_{n+1} \subset B_n$ whenever n is a natural number, show that
$$B_1 = \underset{n \in N}{\bigcap} B_{n+1} \cup \underset{n \in N}{\bigcup} (B_n - B_{n+1}),$$
where "N" denotes the set of all natural numbers.

28. Given that $B_n \subset B_1$ whenever $n \in N$, prove that
$$B_1 = \underset{n \in N}{\bigcap} B_n \cup \underset{n \in N}{\bigcup} (B_n - B_{n+1}).$$

29. Given that $A_{n+1} \subset A_n$ and $B_{n+1} \subset B_n$ whenever $n \in N$, prove that
$$\bigcap_{n \in N} (A_n \cup B_n) = \bigcap_{n \in N} A_n \cup \bigcap_{n \in N} B_n.$$

30. It is customary to denote the set $\{x | x \in A \vee x \in B\}$ by writing "$A \doteq B$"; this set is said to be the *symmetric difference* of A and B. Show the following:

    a. $A \doteq B = (A \cup B) - (A \cap B)$. 　d. $A \doteq B = B \doteq A$.

    b. $A \doteq B = (A - B) \cup (B - A)$. 　e. $A \cap (B \doteq C) = (A \cap B) \doteq (A \cap C)$.

    c. $A \doteq (B \doteq C) = (A \doteq B) \doteq C$.

31. a. Given that $A \cap B = \varnothing$, show that $A \doteq B = A \cup B$.

    b. Show that $A \cup B = (A \doteq B) \doteq (A \cap B)$.

2.4   The Algebra of Sets

In the preceding section we considered the problem of showing that two sets are the same, and we developed a basic technique to handle the problem. However, this technique becomes tedious should the expressions involved be at all complicated. What we propose is this: we shall develop an algebra of sets, differing somewhat from ordinary algebra, to assist us in simplifying a given expression. Thus, after establishing certain laws by means of the basic technique, we shall utilize these laws to simplify expressions. The following basic laws are easily established:

LAW 1. $(A')' = A$.

LAW 2. $A \cup B = B \cup A$.

LAW 3. $A \cap B = B \cap A$.

LAW 4. $A \cup (B \cup C) = (A \cup B) \cup C$.

LAW 5. $A \cap (B \cap C) = (A \cap B) \cap C$.

LAW 6. $A \cup (B \cap C) = (A \cup B) \cap (A \cup C)$.

LAW 7. $A \cap (B \cup C) = (A \cap B) \cup (A \cap C)$.

LAW 8. $(A \cup B)' = A' \cap B'$.

LAW 9. $(A \cap B)' = A' \cup B'$.

LAW 10. $I' = \varnothing$.

LAW 11. $\varnothing' = I$.

LAW 12. $A \cup \varnothing = A$.

LAW 13. $A \cup I = I$.

LAW 14. $A \cap I = A$.

LAW 15. $A \cap \varnothing = \varnothing$.

LAW 16. $A \cup A' = I$.

LAW 17. $A \cap A' = \varnothing$.

Let us show, by using the algebra of sets, that $A \cup (B \cap A') = A \cup B$. Now,

$$\begin{aligned} A \cup (B \cap A') &= (A \cup B) \cap (A \cup A') && \text{by Law 6} \\ &= (A \cup B) \cap I && \text{by Law 16} \\ &= A \cup B && \text{by Law 14.} \end{aligned}$$

As another example, we show that $[(B \cap C) \cup A] \cap [(B \cap C) \cup B] = B \cap (C \cup A)$. Now,

$$[(B \cap C) \cup A] \cap [(B \cap C) \cup B] = (B \cap C) \cup (A \cap B) \qquad \text{by Law 6}$$
$$= (B \cap C) \cup (B \cap A) \qquad \text{by Law 3}$$
$$= B \cap (C \cup A) \qquad \text{by Law 7.}$$

EXERCISES

Given that A, B, and C are subsets of I, use the algebra of sets to prove the following statements:

1. $(A \cup B')' = A' \cap B$.
2. $[A \cup (B \cap C)]' = A' \cap (B' \cup C')$.
3. $[(A \cup B)' \cup C]' = (A \cup B) \cap C'$.
4. $[(A \cup B)' \cup A]' = B \cap A'$.
5. $(A \cap B \cap C) \cup (A' \cup B' \cup C') = I$.
6. $A \cup B \cup (A' \cap B') = I$.
7. $A \cup A = A$.
8. $A \cap A = A$.
9. $A \cup (B \cap A) = A$.
10. $A \cap (B \cup A) = A$.

2.5   Ordered n-Tuples

We have said that a set is a collection such that for any object it can be determined whether it is a member of the collection. Of course, the concept of set carries with it absolutely no notion of order among its members. An object either is a member of the set, or it is not a member of the set — nothing more is said. In short, a set is completely democratic; no member is considered superior to another member. In particular, the order in which the members of a set are listed is completely immaterial. Certainly, when listing the members of a set we must, of necessity, first denote one member of the set, then another, and so on. However, the resulting order is entirely accidental and is not intended to be meaningful. For example, all that we can say about $\{1, 5, 7, 8\}$ is that the members of this set are 1, 5, 7 and 8; but the set denoted by "$\{5, 8, 7, 1\}$" has the same members. Therefore, "$\{1, 5, 7, 8\}$" and "$\{5, 8, 7, 1\}$" are names of the same set.

But still, in the world about us, the notion of order is of paramount importance. For example, it is customary first to insert paper into a typewriter and then to type, rather than to type first and then to insert paper into a typewriter. Also, it is preferable first to repair your brakes and then to find yourself in an emergency requiring a sudden stop; rather than first to find yourself in such an emergency, and then to repair your brakes. As a mathematical example of the importance of order, recall that analytic plane geometry is based upon the fact that with each point in a plane, one can associate, following a prescribed rule, an *ordered* pair of real numbers. A dictionary is another example of the use of order since the words defined herein are listed in a certain well-known order for the convenience of the reader. Imagine a dictionary produced by a berserk printer, who listed the words according to his mood and inclination!

It is clear that the raw notion of a set does not meet the demands of life and mathematics. We need the more sophisticated concept of a set whose members have been arranged in a certain order. Such objects, which are constructed from a set by *ordering* the members of the set, are of fundamental importance in mathematics and deserve a name; we shall call them *ordered n-tuples* where *n* is suitably chosen. For example, consider the set of letters occuring in the word "ordered". This set is denoted by "$\{'o','r','d','e'\}$". Let us rearrange the members of this set so that they are listed in alphabetical order – so: "$\{'d','e','o','r'\}$". To show that the order in which the members of this set are listed is deliberate, we replace the braces by parentheses – obtaining "$('d','e','o','r')$", an ordered 4-tuple. Notice our code: braces indicate a set, and parentheses indicate an ordered *n*-tuple. To repeat, the set whose members are the letters occuring in "ordered", is denoted by "$\{'d','e','o','r'\}$" – here the order in which the letters are listed is meaningless. On the other hand, the ordered 4-tuple obtained by listing the members of $\{'o','r','d','e'\}$ in alphabetical order is denoted by "$('d','e','o','r')$" – here the order in which the letters are listed is deliberate, and indicates that "d" is the first member of the ordered 4-tuple, "e" is the second member of the ordered 4-tuple, "o" is the third member of the ordered 4-tuple, and "r" is the fourth member of the ordered 4-tuple. Clearly two ordered *n*-tuples are the same iff they have the same first member, the same second member, the same third member, and so on. Now we begin to see what we mean by an ordered *n*-tuple: an ordered *n*-tuple is an object which possesses "terms"; the various terms of an ordered *n*-tuple are distinguished amongst themselves by being called the "first" term, the "second" term, the "third" term, and so on. It is possible that several terms of an ordered set will in fact be the same object. Consider, for example, the ordered *n*-tuple obtained by writing down the letters occuring in the word "ordered", in the order in which they appear in this word – namely, the ordered 7-tuple $('o','r','d','e','r','e','d')$. Note that the second term and the fifth term of this ordered set are the same – namely "r"; again, the third term and the seventh term are the same; indeed, the fourth term and the sixth term are the same. This example illustrates one further instance of the use of an ordered *n*-tuple in daily life: namely, in answering the question "How is this word spelled?".

Recalling the simplified treatment of geometry resulting from the introduction of coordinates, we see that ordered 2-tuples are of great value in mathematics. An ordered 2-tuple is also called an *ordered pair*. Similarly, an ordered 3-tuple is called an *ordered triple*. Our discussion is summarized by the following definition.

DEFINITION 2.5.1. Let n be any natural number, and let a_1, a_2, $\cdots$, a_n be any objects. Then "$(a_1, a_2, \cdots, a_n)$" denotes the ordered n-tuple with first term a_1, second term a_2, $\cdots$, and nth term a_n.

For example, "$(5,7)$" denotes the ordered pair whose first term is 5, and whose second term is 7. Note that $(5,7,2)$ is an ordered triple, and $(5,7,2,5)$ is an ordered 4-tuple. Observe that the ordered pair whose first term is a, and whose second term is a, is denoted by "(a,a)"; while the ordered triple whose first term is a, whose second term is a, and whose third term is a, is denoted by "(a,a,a)". It follows that $(a,a) \neq (a,a,a)$. On the other hand, "$\{a,a\}$" denotes the set whose only member is a, and "$\{a,a,a\}$" denotes the set whose only member is a. Therefore, $\{a,a\} = \{a,a,a\}$.

With regard to the distinction between sets and ordered n-tuples, note that we speak of the *members* of a set and the *kth term* of an ordered n-tuple. The fundamental statement we can make about a set is that a given object is a member of the set; the fundamental statement we can make about an ordered n-tuple, is that a given object is the kth term of the ordered n-tuple.

We are now in a position to introduce a vitally important operation on two sets. Let A and B be any nonempty sets (not necessarily distinct); the set of all ordered pairs with first term in A and second term in B is of enormous value in constructing mathematical objects, as we shall presently see. This set is called the Cartesian product of A and B, and is denoted by writing "$A \times B$".

DEFINITION 2.5.2. Let A and B be any nonempty sets; then $A \times B$ is $\{x | \exists a \exists b [x = (a,b) \wedge a \in A \wedge b \in B]\}$.

Notice that two quantifiers are involved in this characterization of $A \times B$. It is possible to eliminate these quantifiers (and so simplify our definition) by using a slightly more elaborate code in naming sets. We shall indicate the fact that members of our set are ordered pairs by inserting an ordered pair to the left of "$|$", in place of the "x" that appears in the definition; this means that the propositional form to the right of "$|$" will involve two place-holders. Thus, "$\{(a,b) | a \in A \wedge b \in B\}$" denotes the set of all ordered pairs, say (a,b), such that $a \in A \wedge b \in B$. Hence, $A \times B = \{(a,b) | a \in A \wedge b \in B\}$.

If A and B are both finite sets, it is easy to see that the number of mem-

bers of $A \times B$ is precisely the product of the number of members of A and the number of members of B. For example,
$$\{1,2,3\} \times \{2,5\} = \{(1,2),(1,5),(2,2),(2,5),(3,2),(3,5)\}.$$
Generalizing the idea of the product of two sets, we define the product of nonempty sets A, B, and C as follows:

DEFINITION 2.5.3. $A \times B \times C$ is $\{(a,b,c)|a \in A \wedge b \in B \wedge c \in C\}$.

In general, given that $A_1, A_2, \cdots, A_n$ are nonempty sets, their product is defined as follows:

DEFINITION 2.5.4. $A_1 \times A_2 \times \cdots \times A_n$ is $\{(a_1,a_2,\cdots,a_n)|a_1 \in A_1 \wedge a_2 \in A_2 \wedge \cdots \wedge a_n \in A_n\}$.

The primary purpose of this section has been the introduction of the notion of an ordered pair. The idea is to link together objects a and b in such a manner that we recognize one of the given objects as being *first* and the other as being *second*. Since we read from left to right, we have agreed to denote the ordered pair with first term a and second term b by writing "(a,b)". Thus, the object whose name is to the left of the comma is regarded as being first, and to the right of the comma, second. It is possible to achieve this same goal by using only sets! Since we wish to link objects a and b, why not consider the set with members a and b, namely $\{a,b\}$? We observe that $\{a,b\} = \{b,a\}$, so we cannot distinguish which object is first and which object is second. Right! How about $\{a,\{b\}\}$? The members of this set are a and $\{b\}$; we can regard a as first and b as second. Unfortunately, this code is ambiguous — consider $\{\{1\},\{2\}\}$; this set denotes either the ordered pair $(\{1\},2)$ or the ordered pair $(\{2\},1)$. Finally, we try $\{\{a\},\{a,b\}\}$ — the set whose members are $\{a\}$ and $\{a,b\}$. Clearly, the objects a and b have been linked; furthermore, one of the members of our set $\{\{a\},\{a,b\}\}$ is a subset of the other (clearly, $\{a\} \subset \{a,b\}$). We shall say, then, that a is the first term of our ordered pair, and the remaining object, b, is the second term of our ordered pair. Thus, by the ordered pair with first term a and second term b, we mean the set $\{\{a\},\{a,b\}\}$. Notice that $\{\{a\},\{a,b\}\} = \{\{c\},\{c,d\}\}$ iff $a = c$ and $b = d$.

This means that "(a,b)" is a name of the set $\{\{a\},\{a,b\}\}$. Thus, the notion of an ordered pair has been expressed in terms of sets. Furthermore, it is easily seen that the concept of an ordered n-tuple can be reduced to the notion of an ordered pair. First, we show that an ordered $k + 1$-tuple, where $k > 1$, can be expressed in terms of an ordered k-tuple and an ordered pair; this is so because $((a_1,a_2,\cdots,a_k),a_{k+1}) = ((b_1,b_2,\cdots,b_k),b_{k+1})$

iff $(a_1, a_2, \cdots, a_k) = (b_1, b_2, \cdots, b_k)$ and $a_{k+1} = b_{k+1}$; but $(a_1, a_1, \cdots, a_k) = (b_1, b_2, \cdots, b_k)$ iff $a_1 = b_1 \wedge a_2 = b_2 \wedge \cdots \wedge a_k = b_k$. Hence the ordered pair with first term $(a_1, a_2, \cdots, a_k)$ and second term a_{k+1} represents the ordered $k+1$-tuple $(a_1, a_2, \cdots, a_{k+1})$—whenever $k > 1$.

It is an easy exercise in mathematical induction to demonstrate that the preceding observation leads to the result: the concept of an ordered n-tuple can be expressed in terms of an ordered pair—whenever $n > 1$.

E X E R C I S E S

1. In your own words, distinguish between a set with n members and an ordered n-tuple.
2. Compute $\{2, 5\} \times \{1, 2, 3\}$.
3. Compute $\{a\} \times \{b\}$.
4. Compute $\{a\} \times \{a\}$.
5. Compute $\{a, b, c\} \times \{d\}$.
6. Compute $\{a, b, c\} \times \{a\}$.
7. Are $A \times B$ and $B \times A$ necessarily the same?
8. Suppose that $A \neq \varnothing$ and $B \neq \varnothing$; show that $A = B$ if $A \times B = B \times A$.
9. Suppose that $A \neq \varnothing$ and $B \neq \varnothing$; show that $A = B$ iff $A \times B = B \times A$.
10. Describe $A \times B \cup B \times A$ in words.
11. Describe $A \times B \cup B \times A \cup A \times A \cup B \times B$ in words.
12. Write down the set whose name is "$(5, 7)$".
13. Write down the set whose name is "(a, a)".
14. Write down the set whose name is "$(2, 2)$".
15. Show that $(a, b, c) = \{\{(a, b)\}, \{(a, b), c\}\}$.
16. Show that $(2, 2, 3) = \{\{\{\{2\}\}\}, \{\{\{2\}\}, 3\}\}$.
17. Show that $A \times B \times C = [A \times B] \times C$.
18. By definition, "(a)" denotes the ordered 1-tuple whose first term is a; show that $(a) = \{a\}$.

2.6 Mappings

One reason for the great vitality of mathematics, as we have seen, is that it draws its inspiration and motivation from the language of man, from the mental habits of man, indeed from the thought processes of man. The ease with which mathematics can be applied to the world about us is partially explained by the fact that the basic concepts of mathematics are rooted in man's experience as a living and thinking being. Of course, it takes sheer genius to discover which ingredients of the commonplace are important. For example, the appreciation of the connection between man's classifying instinct and mathematics, though implicit in the work of many of the great mathematicians, was recognized explicitly less than a century ago.

In this section, we shall explore another of the important concepts of mathematics—the notion of a mapping. But first, let's try an experiment designed to yield some information about our mental habits: visualize your best friend! Of course, the image of a certain individual forms in your mind. Good! But did you notice that accompanying the image, is a name —the name of your friend. Not only did you "see" your friend, you also thought of his name. In fact, is it possible for you to visualize *any* individual without his name forcing its way to the surface of your consciousness? Try! Furthermore, is it possible for you to think of the *name* of an individual without, at the same time, visualizing that individual? For example, regard the name "Napoleon". Do you automatically picture a rather oddly attired man wearing a three-cornered hat, whose right hand is thrust under the left side of his jacket? The point of the preceding experiment is to demonstrate that we habitually link together a person and his name; we seldom think of one without the other.

Let us see what there is of mathematical value in the above observation. But first, let us state the essentials of the situation. On the one hand, we have a set of persons; on the other hand, the set of names of these persons. With each member of the first set we associate a member of the second set in a natural way. It is in the process of associating members of one set with members of another set, that something new and exciting has been created. Let us analyze the situation mathematically. Denote the set of persons by "P", and the set of names by "N"; we want to associate with each member of P, an appropriately chosen member of N; in fact, we want to create a mathematical object which will characterize this association of members of N with members of P. We rely on one simple observation: there is no better way of indicating that two objects are linked together, than by actually writing down the names of the objects, one after the other; i.e., we indicate that two objects are associated, by pairing the objects. Now we see the importance of ordered pairs! The ordered pair (a, b) can be used to indicate that a and b are linked together. Now we see how to characterize associating members of N with members of P: construct the subset of $P \times N$ obtained by pairing with each person, his name. The resulting set of ordered pairs expresses mathematically the associating process described above, since the person and the name that belong together appear in the same ordered pair.

Now a definition. Let A and B be any nonempty sets; a subset of $A \times B$, say M, is said to be a *mapping of A into B* iff each member of A is a first term of exactly one ordered pair in M. Moreover, we shall say that the mapping M *associates* with a given member of A, say a, the member of B paired with a. To be precise, if $(a, b) \in M$, we shall say that b is associated with a under the mapping M; b is also called the *image* of a under the mapping.

Notice that our notion of a mapping of A into B expresses mathematically the intuitive idea of associating a member of B with each member of A.

Figure 2.6.1 may clarify the situation. Under the intuitive idea, b is associated with a; this is represented by the mathematical assertion $(a, b) \in M$. In short, the set M characterizes the intuitive idea of associating a member of B with each member of A.

This important idea deserves some illustration. Suppose that "S" denotes the set of all university students, and "C" denotes the set of all universities. Then the subset of $S \times C$ obtained by pairing with each student the university he attends is a mapping of S into C. Let "H" denote the set of all husbands, and let "W" denote the set of all wives. Then the subset of $H \times W$ obtained by pairing husband and wife is a mapping of H into W.

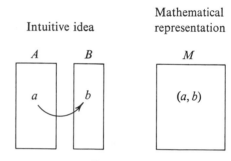

Figure 2.6.1

As an example of a type differing from the above, let "C" denote the set of all cities in the United States, and let "P" denote the set of all persons resident in these cities. Then the subset of $C \times P$ formed by pairing with each city its mayor is a mapping of C into P. The point brought out in this example is this: a mapping of a set A into a set B does not necessarily have the property that *each* member of B occurs as a second term of some ordered pair in the mapping. However, if M is a mapping of A into B such that each member of B is a second term of at least one member of M, then we shall say that M is a mapping of A *onto* B. Furthermore, if a mapping of A *into* B is such that no member of B is a second term of two ordered pairs in the mapping, then we shall say that this subset of $A \times B$ is a *one–one mapping of A into B*. For example, $\{(1, 3), (2, 4), (3, 5), (4, 6)\}$ is a one–one mapping of $\{1, 2, 3, 4\}$ into $\{1, 2, 3, 4, 5, 6, 7\}$. If M is both a one–one mapping of A into B and a mapping of A onto B, then M is said to be a *one–one mapping of A onto B*. For example, assuming monogamy, the mapping of H into W described above is a mapping of H *onto* W, and in fact is a *one–one* mapping of H *onto* W. On the other hand, the mapping of C into P is not a mapping of C onto P. Again, $\{(1,2),(2,4),(3,6)\}$ is a one–one mapping of $\{1,2,3\}$ onto $\{2,4,6\}$, as is $\{(1,4),(2,6),(3,2)\}$.

Note that a one–one mapping of A onto B pairs each member of A with a member of B in such a manner that no member of B is left out and no member of B is used twice. This expresses the idea that A and B are equinumerous; i.e., they have the same number of members. At the turn of the century, Russell showed that this idea of *same number of members* is fundamental to the notion of number itself.

A word about notation. Suppose that M is a mapping of A into B and that $a \in A$; let us agree to denote the image of a under M by writing "$M(a)$". In other words, "$M(a)$" denotes the member of B paired with a by the mapping M. Thus, if $(a,b) \in M$, then "$M(a)$" and "b" are names of the same object; hence, we write "$M(a) = b$". For example, let $M = \{(1,2),(2,4),(3,6)\}$; then $M(1) = 2, M(2) = 4$, and $M(3) = 6$. It is worth observing that a natural language possesses a corresponding naming device; we shall look into this in the next section.

E X E R C I S E S

1. a. State a method of associating a point with a circle which produces a mapping of the set of all circles of the plane *onto* the set of all points of the plane.

   b. Construct a mapping of the set of all points of the plane *into* the set of all circles of the plane.

2. If $A = \{2,3,4\}$ and $B = \{4,5,6\}$, which of the following sets are mappings of A into B, which are mappings of A onto B, which are one–one mappings of A onto B, and which are mappings of B into A?

   a. $\{(2,6),(3,6),(4,6)\}$.   e. $\{(4,5),(2,6),(3,4)\}$.
   b. $\{(2,6),(3,6)\}$.   f. $\{(4,4),(2,6),(2,5)\}$.
   c. $\{(2,6),(3,4),(4,4)\}$.   g. $\{(3,6),(4,4),(2,2)\}$.
   d. $\{(4,4),(6,2),(5,3)\}$.   h. $\{(2,5),(3,4),(4,2)\}$.

3. Suppose that a certain mapping of A into B is also a mapping of B into A.

   a. Show that $A = B$. (*Hint:* Consider the definition of a mapping.)

   b. Show that the mapping is not necessarily one–one. (*Hint:* Construct a set A and a mapping of A into A which is not one–one.)

4. Show that each mapping of A *onto* B is also a mapping of A *into* B.

5. Given that B is a subset of C, show that each mapping of A into B is also a mapping of A into C. Show that each mapping of A onto B is also a mapping of A into C.

6. Let M_1 and M_2 be mappings of A into B; prove that $M_1 = M_2$ iff
$$\forall x[x \in A \rightarrow M_1(x) = M_2(x)].$$

7. Let M be a mapping of A into B.
   a. Show that M is a one–one mapping of A into B iff
   $$\forall x \forall y [x \in A \land y \in A \land x \neq y \rightarrow M(x) \neq M(y)].$$
   b. Show that M is a one–one mapping of A into B iff
   $$\forall x \forall y [x \in A \land y \in A \land M(x) = M(y) \rightarrow x = y].$$
   c. Show that M is a one–one mapping of A onto B iff
   $$\forall x [x \in B \rightarrow \exists! y [y \in A \land M(y) = x]].$$

8. Let M be any mapping of A into B and let C be any subset of A. It is customary to denote $\{y | \exists x [x \in C \land y = M(x)]\}$ by "$M(C)$".
   a. Exhibit $M(\{1,4,5\})$, where $M = \{(1,2),(2,4),(3,6),(4,8),(5,10)\}$.
   b. Simplify $M(\varnothing)$.

9. Let M be a mapping of A into B; given that $A_1 \subset A$ and $A_2 \subset A$, prove the following:
   a. $M(A_1 \cup A_2) = M(A_1) \cup M(A_2)$.
   b. $M(A_1 \cap A_2) \subset M(A_1) \cap M(A_2)$.
   c. $M(A_1) - M(A_2) \subset M(A_1 - A_2)$.
   d. $M(A_1) \doteq M(A_2) \subset M(A_1 \doteq A_2)$.

10. Let M be a mapping of A into B such that $M(A_1 \cap A_2) = M(A_1) \cap M(A_2)$ whenever $A_1 \subset A$ and $A_2 \subset A$. Prove that M is a one–one mapping of A into B.

11. Let M be a mapping of A into B such that $M(A - A_1) = B - M(A_1)$ whenever $A_1 \subset A$. Prove that M is a one–one mapping of A onto B.

12. Let M be any mapping of A into B and let E be any subset of A; then $\{(x, M(x)) | x \in E\}$ is denoted by "$M|E$" (read "M *restricted to* E").
    a. Simplify $\{(1,2),(2,4),(3,6),(4,8),(5,10)\}|\{1,2,3\}$.
    b. Prove that $M|A = M$.
    c. Prove that $M|\varnothing = \varnothing$.
    d. Prove that $M|(E_1 \cup E_2) = M|E_1 \cup M|E_2$.
    e. Prove that $M|(E_1 \cap E_2) = M|E_1 \cap M|E_2$.
    f. Prove that $M|E \cup M|(A - E) = M$.

13. Let M_1 be any mapping of A into B, and let M_2 be any mapping of B into C; then "$M_2 \circ M_1$" denotes the mapping of A into C which associates $M_2(M_1(x))$ with x whenever $x \in A$. Let M_3 be any mapping of C into D; prove that $M_3 \circ (M_2 \circ M_1) = (M_3 \circ M_2) \circ M_1$.

2.7 Operations

Another basic concept of mathematics is the idea of an operation on a set. This is the mathematical version of a device found in any developed language, a device which permits the naming of a person without stating the person's name. For example, in a monogamous country, a person is named by the phrase "the wife of . . .", an appropriate name being inserted in place of the ellipsis. "The wife of Mr. Brown", for instance, denotes a definite person, namely Mrs. Brown. Of course, a name has been used, but not the name of the person being named. Another example of this device of language is the phrase "the author of". Again, this phrase has the function of transforming the following name into a person's name. Thus, "the author of" transforms the name "*The Republic*" into the name "Plato". So, when you read "the author of *The Republic*", you think "Plato".

Let us inquire into the mathematical version of this device of language. First, an example. Consider the phrase "the square of"; if a is an integer, then "the square of a" denotes an integer, usually different from a. In particular, "the square of 3" is a name of the integer 9. Here, the phrase "the square of" plays a role analogous to that played by "the wife of" or "the author of" in the above examples. Clearly, we are concerned with associating a member of a set with a member of a set. But this is nothing more than a mapping of the first set into the second set. In the case of the mathematical example, the two sets involved are the same—the integers. This special kind of mapping, in which the two sets are the same, is of extreme importance in mathematics; it is called a *unary operation*. Thus, if A is any nonempty set, then by a *unary operation on A* we shall mean any mapping of A into A. For example, let "I" denote the set of integers; then $\{(a,b)|a \in I \wedge b = a^2\}$ is a unary operation on I.

A somewhat more complicated type of operation is illustrated by the process of addition. Consider two integers, say 5 and 7, and the word "add"; immediately, a certain integer pops into mind—the integer 12. Again, we are involved with a mapping—a mapping of $I \times I$ into I; for the given integers constitute an ordered pair, and the instruction "add" associates an integer with that ordered pair. To be specific, we are involved with the mapping $\{((a,b),c)|a \in I \wedge b \in I \wedge c = a + b\}$. Now a definition: we shall call any mapping of $A \times A$ into A a *binary operation on A*. In the same way, we shall call any mapping of $A \times A \times A$ into A a *ternary operation on A*. In general, we shall call any mapping of $A \times A \times \cdots \times A$ (n "A"'s) into A an *n-ary operation on A*. Unary and binary operations are widespread throughout mathematics.

Let us see some more examples of operations. Clearly, $\{(n,b)|n \in N \wedge b = n!\}$ is a unary operation on N, the set of all natural numbers. Also, $\{(a,b)|a \in I \wedge b = -a\}$ is a unary operation on I. Multiplication is an important example of a binary operation; clearly, $\{((a,b),c)|a \in N \wedge b \in N \wedge c = a \cdot b\}$ is a binary operation on N.

A binary operation on A is a mapping of $A \times A$ into A, and so is a set of ordered pairs. However, the first terms are themselves ordered pairs; therefore, each member of a given binary operation is an ordered triple – for example, note that $((5,7),12) = (5,7,12)$. Thus, our analysis of ordered n-tuples (see Sec. 2.5) has resulted in an automatic *parentheses-omitting* convention. In this way, a binary operation on A is denoted by a set of ordered triples of members of A. For example, $\{(1,1,2),(1,2,2),(1,3,3),$ $(2,1,3),(2,2,2),(2,3,3),(3,1,1),(3,2,2),(3,3,3)\}$ is a binary operation on $\{1,2,3\}$.

Let "U" be the name of a unary operation on A; then "$U(a)$" denotes b whenever $(a,b) \in U$, since U is a mapping of A into A. It is customary to drop out the parentheses, writing "Ua" in place of "$U(a)$". Since "b" and "Ua" are names of the same object, we see that $b = Ua$. Furthermore, if "B" is the name of a binary operation on A, then we shall denote the third term of any ordered triple in B by writing down the first two terms of the ordered triple with "B" inserted in between. Thus, if $(a,b,c) \in B$, then c is denoted by writing "aBb"; hence, $c = aBb$.

Binary operations deserve special attention. It is convenient to represent a binary operation by a table; the first and second terms of a member of the operation are indicated by the *headings* of the table (i.e., the first column of the table and the first row of the table), and the third term of this member of the operation is given by the corresponding entry in the main body of the table. For example, the binary operation $\{(1,1,2),(1,2,2),(1,3,3),$ $(2,1,3),(2,2,2),(2,3,3),(3,1,1),(3,2,2),(3,3,3)\}$ is represented by table 2.7.1, where we have denoted this operation by "$\circ$". We emphasize

TABLE 2.7.1

$\circ$	1	2	3
1	2	2	3
2	3	2	3
3	1	2	3

that $a \circ b$ is found by looking up a in the first column and b in the first row, and selecting the entry in the main body of the table in the row and column indicated. For example, $3 \circ 2$ is found as follows:

$\circ$	1	②	3
1	2	2	3
2	3	2	3
③	1	②	3

Thus, $3 \circ 2 = 2$.

This method of representing a binary operation is particularly valuable because it displays the third terms of the members of the operation, thereby enabling the eye to observe at a glance properties of the binary operation that are otherwise obscured. For example, consider the following binary operation on $\{1,2,3\}$, which we shall call $+$: $\{(1,1,2),(1,2,3),(1,3,1),$ $(2,1,3),(2,2,1),(2,3,2),(3,1,1),(3,2,2),(3,3,3)\}$. Representing $+$ by a table, we obtain Table 2.7.2. Examining this table, we see at once that the first row is the same as the third row of the main body of the table;

TABLE 2.7.2

+	1	2	3
1	2	3	1
2	3	1	2
3	1	2	3

this means that "$\forall x[3 + x = x]$" is true here. Similarly, the first column is the same as the third column of the main body of the table; therefore, "$\forall x[x + 3 = x]$" is true here. Next, let us examine the main body of the table:

$$\begin{array}{ccc} 2 & 3 & 1 \\ 3 & 1 & 2 \\ 1 & 2 & 3 \end{array}$$

We see that the first column and the first row are the same, the second column and the second row are the same, and the third column and the third row are the same. In other words, the main body of the table is symmetric about the main diagonal 2, 1, 3. This means that $a + b = b + a$ for each a and b; thus, "$\forall x \forall y[x + y = y + x]$" is true.

E X E R C I S E S

1. **a.** Is *division* a binary operation on the real numbers?
   b. Find the largest subset of the real numbers on which *division* is a binary operation.
2. If $A = \{2,3,4\}$, which of the following sets are unary operations on A, and which are binary operations on A?
   a. $\{(2,2),(3,3),(4,4)\}$.   **b.** $\{(2,4),(4,2),(3,2)\}$.

c. $\{(3,5),(3,4),(4,4)\}$.

d. $\{(2,4),(3,4)\}$.

e. $\{(2,4),(3,4),(4,5)\}$.

f. $\{(2,3),(3,4),(4,5)\}$.

g. $\{(2,2,4),(3,2,4),(4,2,4)\}$.

h. $\{(2,3),(3,4),(4,2)\}$.

i. $\{(2,2,2),(2,3,3),(2,4,4),(3,2,2),(3,3,3),(3,4,4),(4,2,2),(4,3,3),$
$(4,4,4)\}$.

j. $\{(2,2,4),(2,3,5),(2,4,6),(3,2,5),(3,3,6),(3,4,7),(4,2,6),(4,3,7),$
$(4,4,8)\}$.

3. A binary operation on A, say $\circ$, is said to be *commutative* iff $\forall x\forall y[x\circ y = y\circ x]$, where quantification is over A. Show that $\{(a,b,c)\,|\,a \in I \wedge b \in I \wedge c = a - b\}$ is *not* commutative (where I is the set of all integers).

4. A binary operation on A, say $\circ$, is said to be *associative* iff $\forall x\forall y\forall z[x\circ(y\circ z) = (x\circ y)\circ z]$, where quantification is over A; show that the binary operation of Exercise 3 is *not* associative.

5. **a.** Suppose that "I" denotes the universal set and that "A" denotes the set of all subsets of I. Show that $\cup$ and $\cap$ are binary operations on A and that $'$ is a unary operation on A.

   b. Show that $\cup$ is commutative and associative.

   c. Show that $\cap$ is commutative and associative.

6. Suppose $\circ = \{(a,a,b),(a,b,a),(b,a,b),(b,b,b)\}$. Demonstrate the following propositions:

   a. $\circ$ is a binary operation on $\{a,b\}$.

   b. $a\circ b = a$.

   c. $b\circ a = b$.

   d. $a\circ (a\circ b) = b$.

   e. $(b\circ a)\circ (b\circ b) = b$.

   f. $b\circ [(a\circ a)\circ b] = b$.

   g. $a\circ [(a\circ a)\circ b] = a$.

   h. $[(a\circ a)\circ b]\circ a = b$.

   i. $\forall x[x\circ x = b]$.

   j. $\forall x\exists y[x\circ y = b]$.

   k. $\forall x\exists y[x\circ y = x]$.

7. Let $+ = \{(1,1,2),(1,2,3),(1,3,4),(1,4,1),(2,1,3),(2,2,4),(2,3,1),(2,4,2),$
$(3,1,4),(3,2,1),(3,3,2),(3,4,3),(4,1,1),(4,2,2),(4,3,3),(4,4,4)\}$.

   a. Show that $+$ is a binary operation on $\{1,2,3,4\}$.

   b. Represent $+$ by a table.

   c. Prove that $+$ is commutative by (i) eliminating quantifiers, (ii) inspecting the table for $+$.

   d. Prove that $\forall x\forall y[2 + (x + y) = (2 + x) + y]$ by eliminating quantifiers.

   e. Indicate how to prove that $+$ is associative.

   f. Prove that $\forall x[4 + x = x]$ by (i) eliminating the quantifier, (ii) inspecting the table for $+$.

   g. Prove that $\forall x\exists y[x + y = 4]$ by (i) eliminating quantifiers, (ii) inspecting the table for $+$.

   h. Prove that $\exists x\forall y[x + y = y]$ by (i) eliminating quantifiers, (ii) inspecting the table for $+$.

   i. Prove that $\exists x\exists y[x \neq y \wedge x + x = y + y]$ by (i) eliminating quantifiers, (ii) inspecting the table for $+$.

2.8   Relations

Some of the number systems of mathematics involve the symbol "<" (read "less than"). Given that a and b are numbers, we write "$a < b$" – this is either true or false, and hence is a proposition. Intuitively, if "$a < b$" is true, then "$b < a$" is false; thus, order is essential. This means that, when discussing "<", we are concerned with ordered pairs. The question remains: precisely what does the symbol "<" denote?

In a particular number system, it is easy to characterize the ordered pairs (a,b) such that $a < b$. For example, in the system of natural numbers, we write "$a < b$" iff "$\exists k[a + k = b]$" is true in the same number system. It is possible to dismiss the symbol "<" by regarding it as an abbreviation: i.e., we say that "$a < b$" denotes the proposition "$\exists k[a + k = b]$". However, it is far more useful to regard "<" as an object in itself, namely a set of ordered pairs, as follows: $< = \{(a,b)\,|\,\exists k[a + k = b]\}$.

We wish to assign a generic name to the object we have just constructed. Consider the following definitions.

DEFINITION 2.8.1. R is called a *binary relation on A* iff $R \subset A \times A$.

DEFINITION 2.8.2. R is called a *ternary relation on A* iff $R \subset A \times A \times A$.

DEFINITION 2.8.3.   In general, for any natural number n, R is called an *n-ary relation on A* iff $R \subset A \times A \times \cdots \times A$ (n "A"'s).

In words, any subset of $A \times A$ is called a binary relation on A; any subset of $A \times A \times A$ is called a ternary relation on A; and in general, whenever n is a natural number, any subset of $A \times A \times \cdots \times A$ (n "A"'s) is called an n-ary relation on A.

To illustrate, consider the following 4-ary relation on the set of real numbers: $\{(a,b,c,x)\,|\,ax^2 + bx + c = 0\}$. For example, the ordered 4-tuple $(2, -5, -3, 3)$ is a member of this relation. The notion of a *greatest common divisor* of integers a and b is familiar from elementary mathematics; this leads to the following ternary relation on the integers: $\{(g,a,b)\,|\,a$ and b are integers, and g is a greatest common divisor of a and $b\}$. For example, $(5, 10, 15)$ is a member of this relation. Later, we shall formalize this concept (see Def. 4.3.12).

A remark about notation. Suppose that R is any n-ary relation; then we shall denote the proposition "$(a_1, a_2, \cdots, a_n) \in R$" by writing "$R(a_1, a_2, \cdots, a_n)$". This is an $\in$-*omitting* convention. Furthermore, if R is a binary relation, we shall denote the proposition "$(a,b) \in R$" by writing "aRb". This is an $\in$-*omitting* and a *parentheses-omitting* convention.

Of course, there are many different binary relations on a set A. Let us see how to generalize our notion of the *less than* relation. We select two fundamental properties of *less than*; these are the Transitive Law and the Trichotomy Law.

TRANSITIVE LAW. $\forall x \forall y \forall z[x < y \wedge y < z \rightarrow x < z]$.
TRICHOTOMY LAW. $\forall x \forall y[x = y \textcircled{V} x < y \textcircled{V} y < x]$.

(Recall that "$p \textcircled{V} q \textcircled{V} r$" is true iff exactly one of p, q, r is true.)

Any binary relation on a set A which satisfies the Transitive Law and the Trichotomy Law, with quantification restricted to A, is called an *order relation on A*.

DEFINITION 2.8.4. R is said to be an *order relation on A* iff
(i) $\forall x \forall y \forall z[xRy \wedge yRz \rightarrow xRz]$,
(ii) $\forall x \forall y[x = y \textcircled{V} xRy \textcircled{V} yRx]$,
where quantification is restricted to A.

For example, $\{(0,1),(1,2),(0,2)\}$ is an order relation on $\{0,1,2\}$, whereas $\{(0,1),(1,2),(2,0)\}$ is *not* an order relation on $\{0,1,2\}$.

It may be useful to contrast binary relations and binary operations. A binary relation on a set A is a set of ordered pairs of members of A; a binary operation on A is a rule which associates a member of A with each ordered pair of members of A. To clarify this observation, consider the operation of addition on the natural numbers, and the relation *less than* on the natural numbers. In particular, consider the expressions "$2 + 3$" and "$2 < 3$". Since $+$ is a binary operation, "$2 + 3$" is a name of the natural number that $+$ associates with the ordered pair $(2,3)$; thus "$2 + 3$" denotes 5. On the other hand, $<$ is a binary relation on the natural numbers; therefore, "$2 < 3$" asserts that the ordered pair $(2,3)$ is a member of the relation $<$; that is, the expression "$2 < 3$" stands for the proposition "$(2,3) \in <$". In short, the expression "$2 + 3$" stands for a natural number, whereas the expression "$2 < 3$" stands for a proposition.

EXERCISES

1. $\{(a,b,x) \mid ax^2 + bx = 0\}$ is a ternary relation on the set of real numbers; determine one member of this relation.

2. $\{(b,x)|x^2 + bx = 0\}$ is a binary relation on the set of real numbers; determine one member of this relation.

3. $\{(a,b,x)|x^2 + bx = a\}$ is a ternary relation on the set of real numbers; determine one member of this relation.

4. $\{(a,b,c)|c^3 + 5c^2 + ac = b\}$ is a ternary relation on the set of real numbers; determine one member of this relation.

5. $\{(a,b,c)|c^2 - 3c = b\}$ is a ternary relation on the set of real numbers; determine one member of this relation.

6. $\{(a,b,c)|c^3 + 7c = a\}$ is a ternary relation on the set of real numbers; determine one member of this relation.

7. Show that $\{(2,7),(5,7),(2,5)\}$ is an order relation on $\{2,5,7\}$.

8. Show that $\{(5,2),(7,2),(5,7)\}$ is an order relation on $\{2,5,7\}$.

9. Show that $\{(7,5),(7,2),(2,5)\}$ is an order relation on $\{2,5,7\}$.

10. Show that $\{(5,7),(7,2),(2,5)\}$ is *not* an order relation on $\{2,5,7\}$.

11. Show that $\{(5,7),(2,7)\}$ is *not* an order relation on $\{2,5,7\}$.

12. Show that $\{(2,2),(5,5),(7,7)\}$ is *not* an order relation on $\{2,5,7\}$.

13. A 1-ary relation on A is also called a *unary relation on A*; characterize unary relations.

14. Let R be an $n+1$-ary relation on A; what properties must R possess in order to be also an n-ary operation on A?

15. A binary relation on A, say R, is said to be a *linear order relation on A* iff
$$\text{(i)} \quad \forall x[\sim xRx],$$
$$\text{(ii)} \quad \forall x\forall y[x \neq y \rightarrow xRy \lor yRx],$$
$$\text{(iii)} \quad \forall x\forall y\forall z[xRy \land yRz \rightarrow xRz],$$
where quantification is restricted to A. Given that R is a linear order relation on A, prove that:

a. $\forall x\forall y[\sim xRy \lor \sim yRx]$.

b. $\forall x\forall y[x = y \oslash xRy \oslash yRx]$.

c. R is an order relation on A.

16. A binary relation on A, say R, is said to be a *partial order relation on A* iff
$$\text{(i)} \quad \forall x[xRx],$$
$$\text{(ii)} \quad \forall x\forall y[xRy \land yRx \rightarrow x = y],$$
$$\text{(iii)} \quad \forall x\forall y\forall z[xRy \land yRz \rightarrow xRz],$$
where quantification is restricted to A.

a. Show, intuitively, that the relation $\leq$ is a partial order relation on the natural numbers.

b. Show that the relation *is a subset of* is a partial order relation on $\mathcal{P}\{1,2,3\}$.

c. Show that the relation *is a multiple of* is a partial order relation on $\{x|x$ is a natural number which divides $60\}$.

17. Let R be any binary relation on A; then the relation $\{(x,y)|yRx\}$ is called the *converse* of R and is denoted by "$\breve{R}$".

   a. Prove that $\check{R}$ is an order relation on A iff R is an order relation on A.
   b. Prove that $\check{R}$ is a linear order relation on A iff R is a linear order relation on A.
   c. Prove that $\check{R}$ is a partial order relation on A iff R is a partial order relation on A.

2.9 Equivalence Relations and Partitions

By using the language of relations, it is easy to characterize the meaning of the fundamental mathematical symbol "=". As we have suggested earlier, by "=" we mean "is"; thus, when we write "a = b", we mean "a is b". In fact, your instructor will sometimes say "is" when writing "=" on the blackboard. To be more precise, by the relation of equality on a set A, we mean the binary relation $\{(a, a) | a \in A\}$; this relation is denoted by "=". Thus, $a = b$, where $a \in A$ and $b \in A$, iff a and b are the same object. It is easily seen that this binary relation on A possesses the following properties, where quantification is restricted to the set A:

REFLEXIVE LAW. $\forall x[x = x]$.
SYMMETRIC LAW. $\forall x \forall y[x = y \rightarrow y = x]$.
TRANSITIVE LAW. $\forall x \forall y \forall z[x = y \wedge y = z \rightarrow x = z]$.

Of course, there are binary relations other than the identity relation which possess these properties. It turns out, however, that a binary relation which is reflexive, symmetric, and transitive is closely connected to the notion of equality; for this reason, it is customary to call any binary relation on a set A which possesses the above three properties an *equivalence relation on A*. In fact, it is possible to use an equivalence relation to do the work of "equals". To be precise, a binary relation on A, say R, is said to be an *equivalence relation on A* iff R possesses the following properties, where quantification is restricted to A:

REFLEXIVE LAW. $\forall x[xRx]$.
SYMMETRIC LAW. $\forall x \forall y[xRy \rightarrow yRx]$.
TRANSITIVE LAW. $\forall x \forall y \forall z[xRy \wedge yRz \rightarrow xRz]$.

(As an aid in associating the name of a law with the law, observe that the properties are listed in order of increasing complexity, whereas the names are listed alphabetically.)

To illustrate the idea, consider W the set of all words. Ordinarily, the important thing about a word is its meaning; however, to a typesetter, the *meaning* of a word is immaterial — it is the *length* of a word that interests him. Therefore, a typesetter regards two words as equal iff they possess the same length. In this way, a typesetter is involved with the following equivalence relation on $W: \{(a,b) | a \in W \wedge b \in W \wedge a$ and b have the same length$\}$.

To understand how an equivalence relation can be used in the place of *equals*, we need the method of creating mathematical objects which is called *partitioning*. Consider, for example, how the student body at a university is divided into first-year students, second-year students, third-year students, fourth-year students, graduate students, and special students. Each student fits into exactly one classification. Thus, the set of students is broken down into six subsets; moreover, the collection of subsets has the property that each student is a member of exactly one of the subsets. We say that the set of all students at the university has been partitioned into six subsets, and we call the collection of six subsets a *partition* of the set of all students. Of course, the same set of students can be partitioned in a different manner. For example, we can partition according to sex, thereby obtaining two subsets; or we can partition according to age, placing together all students of the same age. Again, we can partition the student body according to faculty — Arts, Science, Engineering, Medicine, and so on.

In general, any collection of subsets of a set A is called a *partition of A* iff each member of A is a member of exactly one of the subsets. For example, $\{\{a,b\},\{c\},\{d\}\}$ is a partition of $\{a,b,c,d\}$. Again, let "I" denote the set of all integers, let "E" denote the set of all even integers, and let "O" denote the set of all odd integers; then $\{E, O\}$ is a partition of I.

Observe that a partition of a set is a classification of the members of the set under which each member of the set is placed in precisely one category. Thus, we obtain a partition of the set of all students at the university by classifying according to residence groups; this means that two students are placed in the same category if they live in the same fraternity house, or the same sorority house, or the same dormitory, or the same private home.

There is an intimate connection between the concept of an equivalence relation on A and the concept of a partition of A. Let us demonstrate the very important fact that an equivalence relation on A induces, in a natural way, a partition of A; i.e., we can associate with a set A and an equivalence relation on A, say R, a unique partition of A. The idea is to gather together in the same subset all members of A paired in R, so that a and b are in the same subset iff $(a,b) \in R$. Thus, let $S_a = \{x | aRx\}$ whenever $a \in A$. We shall prove the following theorem.

THEOREM 2.9.1. $\{S_a | a \in A\}$ is a partition of A.

Proof: First, note that $\{S_a | a \in A\}$ is a collection of subsets of A. Secondly, note that $a \in S_a$ whenever $a \in A$, since R is reflexive. Thus, each member of A is in at least one subset. We shall show that no member of A is in two subsets. Suppose that $x \in S_a$ and $x \in S_b$; then aRx and bRx. But R is symmetric, therefore xRb; furthermore, R is transitive, therefore aRb. We shall now show that S_b is a subset of S_a. Suppose $y \in S_b$; then bRy. But aRb and R is transitive, therefore aRy; hence $y \in S_a$. This demonstrates that $S_b \subset S_a$. Similarly, it is easy to prove $S_a \subset S_b$. And so $S_a = S_b$. In short, the assumption that two subsets possess a common member forces us to conclude that the two subsets are in fact one. This proves Theorem 2.9.1.

To illustrate, suppose $A = \{1, 2, 3, 4, 5\}$ and $R = \{(1,1), (2,2), (3,3), (4,4), (5,5), (1,2), (2,1), (3,4), (4,3)\}$. It is easily checked that R is an equivalence relation on A. We now partition A by applying the technique described above; then $S_1 = \{1,2\}$, $S_2 = \{1,2\}$, $S_3 = \{3,4\}$, $S_4 = \{3,4\}$, and $S_5 = \{5\}$. Hence, the partition of A induced by the equivalence relation R is $\{\{1,2\}, \{3,4\}, \{5\}\}$. It should be observed that 5 and $\{5\}$ are quite different objects; the first is a number, and the second is a set with a single member. In the same way, the set A and the partition of A induced by the equivalence relation are quite different objects. Note also that the new mathematical object, the partition, has been constructed from the material present in A.

Finally, let us demonstrate that a partition on A induces, in a natural way, an equivalence relation on A; i.e., we can associate with A and a given partition of A a unique equivalence relation on A. Consider the following binary relation on A: $\{(a,b) | a \text{ and } b \text{ are members of the same subset in the given partition}\}$, which we shall denote by "R". Let us prove the following theorem.

THEOREM 2.9.2. R is an equivalence relation on A.

Proof: We must show that R is reflexive, symmetric, and transitive. Clearly, R is reflexive, since a and a are members of the same subset in the given partition. Furthermore, R is symmetric, since if a and b are members of the same subset, then b and a are members of the same subset. Finally, we must show that R is transitive. Suppose aRb and bRc; then a and b are members of the same subset, and b and c are members of the same subset. Therefore, a, b, and c are members of the same subset; in particular, *a* and *c* are members of the same subset. Hence, *aRc*. This proves Theorem 2.9.2.

We are now in a position to understand how an equivalence relation can be used in place of *equals*. Suppose that *A* is any nonempty set, and *R* is any equivalence relation on *A*. We wish to justify writing *a* = *b* when all that we know about *a* and *b* is that (*a*, *b*) ∈ *R*. Form the partition of *A* induced by *R*. This creates new mathematical objects, the members of the partition. Let us create names for these subsets. What do you suggest? How about taking each member of a subset as a name of that subset? This means that if *a* and *b* are in the same subset, then *a* is a name of that subset and so is *b*. Therefore, we can write *a* = *b*. But *a* and *b* are in the same subset iff (*a*, *b*) ∈ *R*; and so we are justified in writing *a* = *b* iff *aRb*. Notice that the "*a*" and "*b*" to the right of the "iff" denote members of *A*. To avoid ambiguilty, it is customary to denote the member of the partition containing *t* by "[*t*]" or "*t̄*" (read "the equivalence class of *t*"). Thus, we obtain [*a*] = [*b*] iff *aRb*.

EXERCISES

1. Show that {(4,4), (6,6), (8,8} is an equivalence relation on {4, 6, 8}.
2. Show that {(4,4), (6,6), (8,8), (4,6)} is *not* an equivalence relation on {4, 6, 8}.
3. Show that {(4,4), (6,6), (8,8), (4,8), (8,4)} is an equivalence relation on {4, 6, 8}.
4. Show that {(4,4), (6,6), (8,8), (4,8), (8,4)} is *not* an equivalence relation on {4, 6}.
5. Show that {(4,4), (6,6), (8,8), (4,8), (8,4)} is *not* an equivalence relation on {4, 6, 8, 9}.
6. Given that *R* is an order relation on *A*, prove that *R* is *not* an equivalence relation on *A*.
7. Given that *R* is an equivalence relation on *A*, prove that *R* is *not* an order relation on *A*.
8. Demonstrate that a binary relation on *A*, say *R*, is an equivalence relation on *A* iff $\forall x[xRx] \wedge \forall x \forall y \forall z[xRy \wedge yRz \rightarrow zRx]$.
9. Construct the partition of {*a*, *b*, *c*, *d*} induced by the equivalence relation {(*a*, *a*), (*b*, *b*), (*c*, *c*), (*d*, *d*), (*a*, *c*), (*c*, *a*), (*a*, *d*), (*d*, *a*), (*c*, *d*), (*d*, *c*)}.
10. Construct the partition of {*a*, *b*, *c*, *d*, *e*} induced by the equivalence relation {(*a*, *a*), (*b*, *b*), (*c*, *c*), (*d*, *d*), (*e*, *e*), (*a*, *e*), (*e*, *a*), (*c*, *d*), (*d*, *c*)}.
11. Construct the equivalence relation on {*a*, *b*, *c*, *d*, *e*} induced by the partition {{*a*, *b*, *c*}, {*d*, *e*}}.
12. Define a partition of the set of students.

13. Show that $\{\{a,b\},\{c\},\{d,a\}\}$ is not a partition of $\{a,b,c,d\}$.

14. Show that $\{\{a,b,c\},\{d\},\{e\}\}$ is not a partition of $\{a,b,c,d\}$.

15. Suppose that R is an equivalence relation on A, and that P is the partition of A induced by R. Prove that the equivalence relation on A induced by P is R.

16. Suppose that P is a partition of A, and that R is the equivalence relation on A induced by P. Prove that the partition of A induced by R is P.

17. Let $\{A_1, A_2, \cdots, A_s\}$ and $\{B_1, B_2, \cdots, B_t\}$ be partitions of S; the set $\{A_i \cap B_j | 1 \le i \le s$ and $1 \le j \le t\}$ is called the *cross-partition* of the given partitions. Show that $\{A_i \cap B_j | 1 \le i \le s$ and $1 \le j \le t\}$ is a partition of S.

18. Let P_1 and P_2 be partitions of S; then P_1 is said to be a *refinement* of P_2, provided that each member of P_1 is a subset of some member of P_2. Prove that the cross-partition of two partitions of S is a refinement of each of the partitions.

19. Let P_1 be a refinement of P_2 and let $B \in P_2$; show that $\{A | A \in P_1$ and $A \subset B\}$ is a partition of B.

20. Let P_1 be a refinement of P_2; show that P_1 can be constructed from P_2 by partitioning each member of P_2.

21. A partition of S amounts to a classification of the members of S; given two methods of classifying the members of S (i.e., two partitions of S), show that a more detailed classification is obtained by constructing the cross-partition of the given partitions.

22. Classify the students at a university in two ways, and construct the resulting cross-partition.

23. Let R be the binary relation on N defined as follows: let x and y be any natural numbers; then xRy iff x and y have the same remainder on division by 10. Prove that R is an equivalence relation on N. Construct the resulting partition of N.

2.10   Measure

In this section we shall develop a generalization of the ordinary notion of length. Our generalization possesses a surprising range of application, as we shall see.

We begin by stating two fundamental properties of length as applied to line segments:

1. The length of a line segment is a nonnegative real number.
2. The length of the line segment formed by placing two line segments end to end is the sum of the lengths of the given line segments.

Of course, much more can be said about length; here we are after the *essential* properties of length. Notice that *mass* possesses the same two properties:

1. The mass of an object is a nonnegative real number.
2. The mass of the object formed by combining two objects is the sum of the masses of the given objects.

Returning to our example of length, recall that a line segment is considered to be a set of points; thus, *length* associates a nonnegative real number with a given set. In particular, *length* is a mapping of a set of objects (line segments, say) into the real numbers.

As another example, consider a collection of finite sets. We can associate a real number with each set in the collection by counting up the members of the particular set: The resulting mapping has the same two properties (here, in applying property 2, we must be careful to consider only *disjoint* sets).

We now formulate our concept.

DEFINITION 2.10.1.   Let S be a collection of subsets of a given set such that $A \cup B \in S$ whenever $A \in S$ and $B \in S$. We shall say that μ is a *measure on* S iff μ is a mapping of S into the nonnegative real numbers such that $\mu(A \cup B) = \mu(A) + \mu(B)$ whenever $A \in S$, $B \in S$, and $A \cap B = \emptyset$.

Note: Any mapping which possesses the stated property is said to be *additive*.

For example, suppose S consists of sets of people; let $A \in S$, and suppose $\mu(A)$ is the total income of all members of A. Then μ is an additive mapping of S into the nonnegative real numbers; hence, μ is a measure on S.

Clearly, a measure on a collection actually measures a particular attribute of the sets in the collection. As another illustration, suppose each member of S is a finite set of natural numbers, and let $\mu(A)$ be the sum of the members of A. Then μ is a mapping of S into the nonnegative real numbers such that $\mu(A \cup B) = \mu(A) + \mu(B)$ whenever A and B are disjoint. Thus, here, μ is a measure on S.

Having illustrated the notion of a measure on a collection, let us prove some theorems about this concept. In the following theorems, we shall assume that S is nonempty collection of sets such that $A \cup B \in S$ and $A - B \in S$ whenever $A \in S$ and $B \in S$ (recall that $A - B = A \cap B'$). Also, we shall assume that μ is a measure on S.

THEOREM 2.10.1. $A \cap B \in S$ whenever $A \in S$ and $B \in S$.

Proof: Suppose $A \in S$ and $B \in S$; then $A - B \in S$; thus $A - (A - B) \in S$. But

$$A - (A - B) = A \cap (A - B)' = A \cap (A \cap B')' = A \cap (A' \cup B)$$
$$= (A \cap A') \cup (A \cap B) = \varnothing \cup (A \cap B) = A \cap B.$$

THEOREM 2.10.2. $\varnothing \in S$.

Proof: Let $A \in S$; then $A - A \in S$. But $A - A = A \cap A' = \varnothing$. Thus, $\varnothing \in S$.

THEOREM 2.10.3. $\mu(\varnothing) = 0$.

Proof: Let $A \in S$. But A and $\varnothing$ are disjoint; therefore, $\mu(A) = \mu(A \cup \varnothing) = \mu(A) + \mu(\varnothing)$. Thus, $\mu(\varnothing) = 0$.

THEOREM 2.10.4. $\mu(A \cup B) = \mu(A) + \mu(B) - \mu(A \cap B)$ whenever $A \in S$ and $B \in S$.

Proof: $A \cup B = (A \cup B) \cap I = (A \cup B) \cap (B \cup B') = B \cup (A \cap B')$. But B and $A \cap B'$ are disjoint; therefore, $\mu(A \cup B) = \mu(B) + \mu(A \cap B')$. Furthermore, $A = A \cap I = A \cap (B \cup B') = (A \cap B) \cup (A \cap B')$;   since $A \cap B$ and $A \cap B'$ are disjoint, it follows that $\mu(A) = \mu(A \cap B) + \mu(A \cap B')$,   i.e., $\mu(A \cap B') = \mu(A) - \mu(A \cap B)$. Hence, $\mu(A \cup B) = \mu(A) + \mu(B) - \mu(A \cap B)$.

We now consider some applications of Theorem 2.10.4. First, we extend this important theorem.

THEOREM 2.10.5. $\mu(A \cup B \cup C) = \mu(A) + \mu(B) + \mu(C) - \mu(A \cap B) - \mu(A \cap C) - \mu(B \cap C) + \mu(A \cap B \cap C)$ whenever $A \in S$, $B \in S$, and $C \in S$.

Proof: The proof requires two applications of Theorem 2.10.4 and is left as an exercise.

EXAMPLE 1.   At a certain college, there are 500 girls of whom 300 are brainy and 250 are beautiful. Assuming that each girl is brainy or beautiful, how many girls are both brainy and beautiful?
Solution: Here, S is the set of all subsets of the collection of girls at the college, and "$\mu(A)$" denotes the number of members of A whenever $A \in S$. Denote the set of all brainy girls at the college by "C" and the set of all beautiful girls at the college by "B"; then $\mu(C) = 300$, $\mu(B) = 250$, and $\mu(B \cup C) = 500$. By Theorem 2.10.4, $\mu(B \cup C) = \mu(B) + \mu(C) - \mu(B \cap C)$; hence, $\mu(B \cap C) = 250 + 300 - 500 = 50$. We conclude that 50 girls at the college are both brainy and beautiful.

EXAMPLE 2.   In a small town, a survey discloses that 200 persons smoke heavily, 800 smoke occasionally, and 900 pay income tax; furthermore, 100 persons smoke heavily and pay income tax, and 700 smoke occasionally and pay income tax. Assuming that each person in the survey smokes or pays income tax, how many persons participated in the survey?

Solution: Let S be the set of all persons in the survey, and let "$\mu(A)$" denote the number of persons in A. Denote the set of all persons surveyed who smoke heavily by "H", the set of all who smoke occasionally by "O", and the set of all who pay income tax by "T". Then $\mu(H) = 200$, $\mu(O) = 800$, $\mu(T) = 900$, $\mu(H \cap T) = 100$, $\mu(O \cap T) = 700$, $\mu(H \cap O) = 0$, and $\mu(H \cap O \cap T) = 0$. Therefore, by Theorem 2.10.5,

$$\mu(H \cup O \cup T) = \mu(H) + \mu(O) + \mu(T) - \mu(H \cap O) - \mu(H \cap T) - \mu(O \cap T)$$
$$+ \mu(H \cap O \cap T)$$
$$= 200 + 800 + 900 - 100 - 700$$
$$= 1100.$$

We conclude that 1100 persons were surveyed.

It is convenient to represent by intersecting circles the sets involved in a problem of the preceding type; the union and intersection of the sets involved can be easily picked off the diagram. Furthermore, the data regarding the given sets can be entered in the diagram, and conclusions can be read off directly. The diagram involved is said to be a *Venn diagram.* Consider the following illustration.

EXAMPLE 3.   Of a group of 20 persons, 10 are interested in music, 7 are interested in photography, and 4 like skiing; furthermore, 4 are interested in both music and photography, 3 are interested in both music and skiing, 2 are interested in both photography and skiing, and one is interested in music, photography, and skiing. How many are interested in photography but not in music or skiing?

Solution: We insert the given data in the diagram shown in Fig. 2.10.1, starting

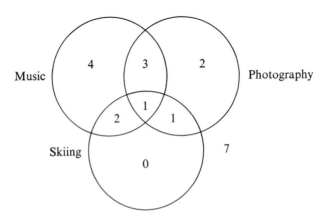

Figure 2.10.1

with the intersection of the three sets, and then work out the number of persons in each of the sets indicated in the diagram. For example, since one person is interested in music, photography, and skiing, and 3 are interested in music and skiing, it follows that there are 2 persons who are interested in music and skiing but not in photography. The remaining entries in the diagram are easily obtained by the same kind of argument. Examining the diagram, we see at once that 2 persons are interested in photography but not in music or skiing.

EXERCISES

1. Show that *area* is a measure.

2. Show that *volume* is a measure.

3. Let I be the collection of all income-tax payers, let S be the set of all subsets of I, and let $\mu(A)$ be the total income tax of all members of A. Show that μ is a measure on S.

4. Let S be the collection of all subsets of a decision-making body, and let $\mu(A)$ be the total number of votes possessed by the members of A. Show that μ is a measure on S.

5. At a certain college, each coed is brainy or beautiful or has buckteeth. A survey of the college discloses that 300 coeds are brainy, 400 are beautiful, and 50 have buckteeth; furthermore, 100 coeds are both brainy and beautiful, and 20 are brainy and have buckteeth. For the purpose of this survey, no girl with buckteeth is considered beautiful. How many girls attend this college?

(*Answer:* 630)

6. Prove that $\mu(A) \leq \mu(B)$ whenever $A \subset B$, given that μ is a measure.

7. Suppose that $A \cup B \in S$ and $A - B \in S$ whenever $A \in S$ and $B \in S$.
   a. Is it necessarily true that $A' \in S$ whenever $A \in S$?
   b. Is it necessarily true that $A \cap B \in S$ whenever $A \in S$ and $B \in S$?
   c. Is it necessarily true that $A \doteq B \in S$ whenever $A \in S$ and $B \in S$?

8. Prove Theorem 2.10.5 by applying Theorem 2.10.4.

9. Given that A, B, and C are pairwise disjoint, prove that
$$\mu(A \cup B \cup C) = \mu(A) + \mu(B) + \mu(C)$$
whenever μ is a measure.

10. a. Prove that $\mu(A \cap B) = \mu(A \cap B \cap C') + \mu(A \cap B \cap C)$
    and $\mu(A \cap C) = \mu(A \cap B' \cap C) + \mu(A \cap B \cap C)$
    whenever μ is a measure.
    b. Prove that $\mu(A \cap B) + \mu(A \cap C) - \mu(A \cap B \cap C) \leq \mu(A)$ whenever μ is a measure.

11. A survey discloses that of a group of 23 persons 20 are interested in music, 15 are interested in photography, and 8 like skiing; furthermore, 15 are interested in music and photography, 5 are interested in music and skiing, 3 are interested in photography and skiing, and 2 are interested in music, photography, and skiing. Show that the survey is in error.

Chapter 3

The Axiomatic Method and Abstract Algebra

3.1 Algebraic Systems

The axiomatic method in mathematics goes back to the days of the Greek geometers, who regarded mathematics as the supreme achievement of the human mind. Since Euclid's *Elements* is still in vogue we can only marvel at this triumph of Greek Civilization. In recent years, however, there has been a tremendous explosion in mathematical activity which has led to an unprecedented increase in mathematical knowledge. In particular, work at the foundations of mathematics has resulted in the emergence of *sets* as basic mathematical objects. This has led to a refinement of Euclid's method itself, which centers around the concept of an *algebraic system*. Essentially this is a matter of setting out the kinds of objects that are involved in a particular mathematical investigation. For example, in the study of geometry we are concerned with a set of objects called *points,* and with certain relations on this set. In the study of a number system we deal with a set of objects called *numbers,* two binary operations on this set, called *addition* and *multiplication,* the binary relation *less than,* and possibly the special numbers 0 and 1.

Generally speaking, a mathematical investigation involves a nonempty set, say A, possibly certain operations on A, possibly certain relations on A, and possibly certain special members of A. In any event there is at least one operation or relation on A. Thus, the ingredients of a mathematical investigation are found in the following list: a set, operations or relations on the set, specified members of the set. It is convenient to use an ordered n-tuple to display the particular ingredients required for a specific mathematical investigation. The first term of this ordered n-tuple is the set A referred to above, and the remaining terms are the operations on A, the relations on A, and the special members of A that are involved. Let us give a name to this very special type of ordered n-tuple; we shall call it an *algebraic system.* Furthermore, we shall call the first term of an algebraic system the *basic set* of the algebraic system. The basic set of an algebraic system is important because it fulfills the function of a universal set, or universe of discourse, for the algebraic system.

For example, the ordered pair $(S,\circ)$, where $S = \{a,b\}$ and $\circ = \{(a,a,b),$ $(a,b,a),(b,a,a),(b,b,b)\}$, is an algebraic system; the basic set of this algebraic system is $\{a,b\}$, and its second term, $\circ$, is a binary operation on $\{a,b\}$. Notice that b possesses the following properties: $\forall x[x \circ b = x]$ and $\forall x \exists y[x \circ y = b]$, where quantification is restricted to S, the basic set of this algebraic system. If we wish to draw attention to the algebraic properties of b, we do so by constructing the algebraic system $(S,\circ,b)$; in this way, b is displayed as a component part of the algebraic system.

As another example of an algebraic system, which we present informally, consider the natural number system $(N, +, \cdot, <, 1)$; here, N is the set of all natural numbers, $+$ and $\cdot$ are binary operations on N (namely, addition and multiplication), "$<$" denotes the relation *less than* on N, and $1 \in N$.

The preceding discussion is made precise in the following definition.

DEFINITION 3.1.1. Any ordered n-tuple whose first term is a nonempty set, say A, and whose remaining terms are operations on A, or relations on A, or specific members of A is called an *algebraic system* — provided that it involves at least one operation or relation on A.

In the following sections, we shall be concerned with statements of the form: "This proposition is true in this algebraic system", where the proposition mentioned involves quantifiers. We must be clear about what this means. The main consideration is that quantification is restricted to the basic set of the algebraic system mentioned. This is only natural, since the basic set plays the role of a universe of discourse. Consider, for example, the assertion that "$\forall x[x \circ b = x]$" is true in the algebraic system $(S,\circ,b)$. Recalling the technique for handling quantifiers (discussed in Sec. 1.10), we must show that the propositions $a \circ b = a$ and $b \circ b = b$ are true. But $(a,b,a) \in \circ$; hence, "$a \circ b$" denotes a; thus, the first proposition is true. Similarly, $(b,b,b) \in \circ$; therefore, "$b \circ b$" denotes b; thus, the second proposition is true. It follows from this that "$\forall x[x \circ b = x]$" is true in $(S,\circ,b)$.

We shall now prove that the proposition "$\forall x \exists y[x \circ y = b]$" is true in the algebraic system $(S,\circ,b)$. Stripping away the first quantifier, we obtain the propositions "$\exists y[a \circ y = b]$" and "$\exists y[b \circ y = b]$". We must show that both propositions are true in $(S,\circ,b)$. But "$a \circ a = b$" is true in this algebraic system, therefore "$\exists y[a \circ y = b]$" is true in $(S,\circ,b)$. Again, "$b \circ b = b$" is true in this algebraic system; therefore, "$\exists y[b \circ y = b]$" is true in $(S,\circ,b)$. This demonstrates that "$\forall x \exists y[x \circ y = b]$" is true in $(S,\circ,b)$.

Here is another example of an algebraic system. Consider the ordered

4-tuple $(B, ?, !, 0)$, where $B = \{0, 1\}$, $? = \{(0,0,0), (0,1,1), (1,0,1), (1,1,0)\}$, and $! = \{(0,0,0), (0,1,0), (1,0,0), (1,1,0)\}$. The first term of this ordered 4-tuple is a set, the second term, $?$, is a binary operation on B, the third term is also a binary operation on B, and the fourth term is a member of B. Therefore, our ordered 4-tuple is an algebraic system; furthermore, the basic set of this algebraic system is $\{0, 1\}$. Now consider the proposition "$\forall x[x ? 0 = x]$"; we shall show that this proposition is true in the algebraic system $(B, ?, !, 0)$. Stripping away the quantifier, we obtain the propositions "$0 ? 0 = 0$" and "$1 ? 0 = 1$". But $(0,0,0) \in ?$ and $(1,0,1) \in ?$; therefore, both propositions are true, and it follows that "$\forall x[x ? 0 = x]$" is true in $(B, ?, !, 0)$.

Note that the proposition "$(1 ! 1) ? 1 = 1 ? 1$" is false in $(B, ?, !, 0)$, since $(1 ! 1) ? 1 = 0 ? 1 = 1$, whereas $1 ? 1 = 0$. It follows from this observation that the proposition "$\forall x[(x ! x) ? x = x ? x]$" is false in $(B, ?, !, 0)$. However, let us show that the proposition "$\exists x[(x ! x) ? x = x ? x]$" is true in this algebraic system. Deleting "$\exists x$" and replacing "x" by "0", we obtain the proposition "$(0 ! 0) ? 0 = 0 ? 0$", which is true since $0 ! 0$ is 0. Therefore, "$\exists x[(x ! x) ? x = x ? x]$" is true in $(B, ?, !, 0)$.

Now consider, as another example, the ordered pair (S, R), where $S = \{a, b, c, d\}$ and $R = \{(a,b), (a,c), (a,d), (b,c), (b,d), (c,d)\}$. Since R is a binary relation on S, we see that (S, R) is an algebraic system. Let us show that the proposition "$\forall x \exists y[xRy \lor yRx]$" is true in (S, R). Stripping away the first quantifier, we obtain the following propositions: "$\exists y[aRy \lor yRa]$", "$\exists y[bRy \lor yRb]$", "$\exists y[cRy \lor yRc]$", "$\exists y[dRy \lor yRd]$". But "aRb" is true; hence, "$aRb \lor bRa$" is true; thus, "$\exists y[aRy \lor yRa]$" is true in (S, R); and "bRd" is true; hence, "$bRd \lor dRb$" is true; thus, "$\exists y[bRy \lor yRb]$" is true in (S, R); and "aRc" is true; hence, "$cRa \lor aRc$" is true; thus, "$\exists y[cRy \lor yRc]$" is true in (S, R); and "bRd" is true; hence, "$dRb \lor bRd$" is true; thus, "$\exists y[dRy \lor yRd]$" is true in (S, R). Therefore, "$\forall x \exists y[xRy \lor yRx]$" is true in (S, R).

Problem: Show that the propositions "$\forall x \forall y \forall z[xRy \land yRz \rightarrow xRz]$" and "$\forall x \forall y[x = y \lor xRy \lor yRx]$" are both true in (S, R).

The concept of the algebraic system is based on the elementary concepts of set theory. In the remaining sections of this chapter, we shall see how the notion of the algebraic system is itself used as a building-block in constructing mathematical concepts.

EXERCISES

1. Show that the following propositions are true in the algebraic system $(S, \circ)$ of the text:

a. $\forall x \forall y [x \circ y = y \circ x]$.

b. $\forall x \forall y [(x = y \rightarrow x \circ y = b) \wedge (x \neq y \rightarrow x \circ y = a)]$.

c. $\forall y \forall z [a \circ (y \circ z) = (a \circ y) \circ z]$.

d. $\forall y \forall z [b \circ (y \circ z) = (b \circ y) \circ z]$.

e. $\forall x \forall y \forall z [x \circ (y \circ z) = (x \circ y) \circ z]$.

2. In the algebraic system $(B, ?, !, 0)$ of the text, show the following:

    a. $1 ? (1 ! 0) = 1$.
               c. $[(1 ? 0) ? 1] ? 1 = (0 ! 0) ? (0 ? 1)$.

    b. $(0 ! 1) ? (1 ? 1) = (0 ? 1) ! (1 ! 1)$.
    d. $(0 ! 1) ! (0 ! 0) \neq (1 ? 0) ? (1 ? 1)$.

3. Show that the following propositions are true in the algebraic system $(B, ?, !, 0)$ of the text:

    a. $\forall x \forall y [x ? y = y ? x]$.
               e. $\forall y \forall z [0 ? (y ? z) = (0 ? y) ? z]$.

    b. $\forall x \forall y [x ! y = 0]$.
                f. $\forall y \forall z [1 ? (y ? z) = (1 ? y) ? z]$.

    c. $\forall x \forall y \forall z [x ? (y ! z) = x]$.
       g. $\forall x \forall y \forall z [x ? (y ? z) = (x ? y) ? z]$.

    d. $\forall x \exists y [x ? y = 0]$.
               h. $\forall x \forall y \exists z [x ? z = y]$.

    (*Hint:* Apply propositions **d** and **g** above.)

4. Consider the algebraic system $(\{a, b, c\}, +, \circ)$, where

$$+ = \{(a,a,b), (a,b,c), (a,c,a), (b,a,a), (b,b,c), (b,c,b),$$
$$(c,a,a), (c,b,b), (c,c,c)\},$$

and $\circ = \{(a,a,a), (a,b,b), (a,c,c), (b,a,a), (b,b,b), (b,c,c),$
$$(c,a,a), (c,b,b), (c,c,c)\}.$$

Calculate the following:

    $a + b$.
                    $(a \circ c) + b$.

    $a + (b + a)$.
                $a + (b \circ c)$.

    $(b + c) + (a + b)$.
          $[a + (b \circ c)] \circ b$.

    $(a + b) \circ c$.
                 $b \circ (c \circ b)$.

$$[(a + b) \circ (b + c)] + [(a + b) \circ (a + (b \circ c))]$$.

5. In the algebraic system of Exercise 4, which of the following propositions are true?

    a. $\forall x \forall y [x \circ y = y]$.
          g. $\forall x \forall y \forall z [x \circ (y + z) = (x \circ y) + (x \circ z)]$.

    b. $\forall x \forall y [x + y = y + x]$.
       h. $\forall x \forall y [x \circ y = y \circ x]$.

    c. $\forall x \exists y [x \circ y = y \circ x]$.
       i. $\forall x \exists y [x + y = y + x]$.

    d. $\exists x \forall y [x + y = y + x]$.
       j. $\forall x \forall y \forall z [x + (y + z) = (x + y) + z]$.

    e. $\forall x \forall y \forall z [x \circ (y \circ z) = (x \circ y) \circ z]$.
   k. $\forall x \forall y \forall z [x + (y \circ z) = (x + y) \circ z]$.

    f. $\forall x \forall y \forall z [x \circ (y + z) = (x \circ y) + z]$.
   l. $\forall x \forall y \forall z [x + (y \circ z) = (x + y) \circ (x + z)]$.

6. Which is more important, the nature of the members of the basic set of an algebraic system, or the operations and relations of the algebraic system?

3.2 The Axiomatic Method

Let's play a game! The game is called "Find the Algebraic System", and the object of the game is to construct an algebraic system—given certain hints about the desired algebraic system. For example, let us construct an algebraic system which consists of a basic set, say S, and a binary relation on S, say R. As additional hints, we are informed that the following propositions are true in this algebraic system:

$$\exists x \exists y[x \neq y],$$
$$\exists x \exists y \forall z[z = x \lor z = y],$$
$$\forall x \forall y[xRy \leftrightarrow x \neq y].$$

Examining the hints, we see that there are at least two members in S, since that is the meaning of the proposition $\exists x \exists y[x \neq y]$. Furthermore, we see there are at most two members in S, since that is what $\exists x \exists y \forall z[z = x \lor z = y]$ asserts. We conclude that S has exactly two members. Suppose the members of S are a and b; so $S = \{a,b\}$. Then, the remaining proposition, $\forall x \forall y[xRy \leftrightarrow x \neq y]$, tells us that $R = \{(a,b),(b,a)\}$. We have determined the desired algebraic system, namely $(\{a,b\},\{(a,b),(b,a)\})$. Of course, if c and d are any two objects, then the algebraic system $(\{c,d\}, \{(c,d),(d,c)\})$ also meets the given conditions.

Now suppose that we construct an algebraic system of the form (S,R), where R is a binary relation on S, in which the following propositions are true:

$$\exists x \exists y[x \neq y],$$
$$\exists x \exists y \forall z[z = x \lor z = y],$$
$$\forall x \forall y[x \neq y \rightarrow xRy];$$

note that the third proposition given above has been altered. Again, S has exactly two members, say a and b. However, we cannot be as definite about R as we were in the preceding case. There are four possibilities: $R = \{(a,b),(b,a)\}$ as before, or $R = \{(a,b),(b,a),(a,a)\}$, or $R = \{(a,b), (b,a),(b,b)\}$, or $R = \{(a,b),(b,a),(a,a),(b,b)\}$. Thus, the given hints lead us to four algebraic systems:

I $\quad (\{a,b\},\{(a,b),(b,a)\}),\quad (\{a,b\},\{(a,b),(b,a),(a,a)\}),$
$(\{a,b\},\{(a,b),(b,a),(b,b)\}),\quad (\{a,b\},\{(a,b),(b,a),(a,a),(b,b)\}).$

(In a sense which we shall make clear later, two of these algebraic systems are essentially the same.) Actually, there are many algebraic systems which meet the given conditions. For example, let c and d be distinct objects; then, the algebraic systems

II $\quad (\{c,d\},\{(c,d),(d,c)\}),\quad (\{c,d\},\{(c,d),(d,c),(c,c)\}),$
$(\{c,d\},\{(c,d),(d,c),(d,d)\}),\quad (\{c,d\},\{(c,d),(d,c),(c,c),(d,d)\}).$

also meet the given conditions. However, each of these algebraic systems can be constructed from the corresponding algebraic system listed in I by merely replacing "*a*" by "*c*", and replacing "*b*" by "*d*" throughout the algebraic system. In this sense, the algebraic systems of I characterize all the algebraic systems that meet the given conditions.

The two illustrations given above show that it is sometimes possible to characterize a given collection of algebraic systems *of the same type* by first specifying the type, and then listing certain propositions which are true in each of the algebraic systems. By the *type* of an algebraic system, we mean the general shape of the algebraic system, i.e., the kinds of things that are terms of the algebraic system.

The famous philosopher and logician Bertrand Russell has said that "mathematics may be defined as the subject in which we never know what we are talking about, nor whether what we are saying is true". Of course, this is a tongue-in-cheek statement and was intended to be amusing; nevertheless, Russell has pointed out most clearly the essentials of the axiomatic method. Since the power of mathematics lies in the generality of its results, one deliberately avoids spelling out precisely the objects and operations or relations being investigated. Rather, one describes the *type* of algebraic system being studied—by first stating that it involves a unary operation, or two binary operations, or a binary relation, or one special member of the basic set, as the case may be, and then listing certain propositions which are true in the algebraic system. The propositions are called *axioms* or *postulates*. On the basis of the given information, it is sometimes possible to establish that certain propositions are true in each of the algebraic systems so characterized. Such propositions are called *theorems*. Thus, we do not really know what we are talking about, nor do we know if our theorems are really true. However, should we encounter an algebraic system of the specified type in which each of the given postulates is true, then we can assert that each of our theorems is true in this algebraic system. In this way, the sum total of knowledge has been increased.

Notice there are two aspects to the axiomatic method. First, a class of algebraic systems is described by stating the type of algebraic system in the class, and then listing certain propositions which are true in each algebraic system of the class. Next, it is demonstrated that certain propositions are true in each algebraic system of the class; these propositions are called theorems. In general, a theorem is established by considering any algebraic system in the class (without specifying which one), and showing (usually by stripping away quantifiers) that the given proposition is true in that algebraic system.

To illustrate the axiomatic method, let us investigate the class of algebraic systems of the type $(S, \circ)$, where $\circ$ is a binary operation on S, in which the following propositions are true:

POSTULATES.   1. $\forall x[x \circ x = x]$.
2. $\forall x \forall y \forall z[x \circ (y \circ z) = (x \circ y) \circ z]$.

For example, the algebraic systems $(\{1\}, \{(1,1,1)\})$, $(\{0,1\}, \{(0,0,0), (0,1,0), (1,0,1), (1,1,1)\})$,   and $(\{0,1\}, \{(0,0,0), (0,1,1), (1,0,0), (1,1,1)\})$ are members of this class.

Having illustrated one aspect of the axiomatic method, we now demonstrate the manner in which a theorem is established.

THEOREM 3.2.1. $\forall x \forall y[x \circ (x \circ y) = x \circ y]$.

Proof: We must show that the given proposition "$\forall x \forall y[x \circ (x \circ y) = x \circ y]$" is true in each algebraic system of our class. Let $(S, \circ)$ be any algebraic system of our class; we wish to show that "$\forall x \forall y[x \circ (x \circ y) = x \circ y]$" is true in $(S, \circ)$. Stripping away quantifiers, we see that the given proposition is true in $(S, \circ)$ iff $a \circ (a \circ b) = a \circ b$ whenever $a \in S$ and $b \in S$. But

$$a \circ (a \circ b) = (a \circ a) \circ b \qquad \text{by Postulate 2}$$
$$= a \circ b \qquad \text{by Postulate 1.}$$

This establishes that "$\forall x \forall y[x \circ (x \circ y) = x \circ y]$" is true in each algebraic system of our class.

Note: In the proof of Theorem 3.2.1 we have used an efficient method of stripping away quantifiers. Any proposition which begins with a block of universal quantifiers can be handled in this way. For example, consider "$\forall x \forall y \forall z[P(x, y, z)]$". Stripping away quantifiers involves three steps, one for each quantifier; however, we can achieve the same result in one step by establishing the truth of "$P(a, b, c)$" whenever a, b, and c are members of the universe of discourse.

It should now be clear that although we do not know the precise objects we are talking about, we do know the type of algebraic system being discussed; and although we do not know if the theorems are true, we do know that they are true in any algebraic system of the specified type in which the postulates are true.

It is worth noting that the postulates characterizing a particular class of algebraic systems need not be propositions of the kind considered in Chapter 1 (which are called propositions of the *lower predicate calculus*). For example, consider the famous Peano Postulates, which are involved in characterizing the natural number system. An algebraic system of the type $(N, ', 1)$, where $'$ is a unary operation on N and $1 \in N$, is said to be a Peano system iff

(1) $\forall x[x' \neq 1]$,
(2) $\forall x \forall y[x' = y' \rightarrow x = y]$,
(3) $\forall S[(S \subset N \wedge 1 \in S \wedge \forall x[x \in S \rightarrow x' \in S]) \rightarrow S = N]$.

Here, (1) and (2) are propositions of the lower predicate calculus, but (3) is not. The point is that the quantifiers of (1) and (2) refer to the basic set of the algebraic system, whereas the universal quantifier of (3), "$\forall S$", refers to subsets of the basic set. In words, (3) asserts that no *proper* subset, S, of N has the property that $1 \in S \wedge \forall x[x \in S \rightarrow x' \in S]$.

In the subsequent pages of this chapter, we shall consider the axiomatic method against the background of modern algebra, since this important branch of mathematics serves well to illustrate the axiomatic approach. Here, briefly, we consider the axiomatic method as applied to geometry. The concept of a *projective plane*, for example, can be characterized as follows. By a projective plane, we mean any ordered triple, say (Σ, Λ, I) — where Σ is a nonempty set whose members are called *points* and are denoted by capital letters, Λ is a nonempty set whose members are called *lines* and are denoted by small letters, and I is a binary relation on $\Sigma \cup \Lambda$ called the *incidence* relation — such that

1. $\forall P \forall l[PIl \leftrightarrow lIP]$.
2. $\forall P \forall Q \exists ! l[P \neq Q \rightarrow PIl \wedge QIl]$.
3. $\forall p \forall q \exists ! L[p \neq q \rightarrow pIL \wedge qIL]$.
4. There are four points such that each line is incident with at most two of the four points.

Note that quantification is either over Σ (indicated by a capital letter) or over Λ (indicated by a small letter).

Though the ordered triple (Σ, Λ, I) is not an algebraic system, it is possible to represent (Σ, Λ, I) by an algebraic system, namely $(\Sigma \cup \Lambda, P, L, I)$ — where $\Sigma \cup \Lambda$ is the basic set of the algebraic system, P and L are unary relations on the basic set (in fact, $P = \Sigma$ and $L = \Lambda$), and I is a binary relation on the basic set. It is easy to translate the above postulates into this language; for example, Postulate 1 becomes

$$\forall x \forall y[P(x) \wedge L(y) \rightarrow (xIy \leftrightarrow yIx)],$$

where quantification is over the basic set of the algebraic system.

Thus, our analysis of the axiomatic method in terms of algebraic systems applies also to the study of geometry.

EXERCISES

1. Consider the class of all algebraic systems of the type $(S,')$, where $'$ is a unary operation on S, satisfying the postulates $\forall x[x' \neq x]$, $\forall x[(x')' = x]$.
   a. Show that S cannot have an odd number of members.
   b. Present an algebraic system in the class.
2. Consider the class of all algebraic systems of the type $(S, \circ)$, where $\circ$ is a binary operation on S, satisfying the postulate $\forall x \forall y[x \circ y = x]$.
   a. Prove that the following propositions are true in each algebraic system of the class: $\forall x[x \circ x = x]$, $\forall x \forall y \forall z[x \circ (y \circ z) = (x \circ y) \circ z]$, $\forall x \forall y \exists z[x \circ y = z]$.
   b. Present an algebraic system in the class.
3. Consider the class of all algebraic systems of the type (S, R), where R is a binary relation on S, satisfying the postulates
$$\forall x \forall y[xRy \rightarrow x \neq y], \qquad \forall x \forall y \forall z[xRy \wedge yRz \rightarrow xRz].$$
   a. Prove that the following propositions are true in each algebraic system of the class: $\forall x[\sim xRx]$, $\forall x \forall y[\sim xRy \vee \sim yRx]$.
   b. Present an algebraic system in the class.
4. Consider the class of all algebraic systems of the type $(S, \circ, R)$, where $\circ$ is a binary operation on S, and R is a binary relation on S, satisfying the postulates
$$\forall x \forall y[x \circ y = y \circ x], \qquad \forall x[x \circ x = x], \qquad \forall x \forall y[xRx \circ y].$$
   a. Prove that the following propositions are true in each algebraic system of the class: $\forall x \forall y[yRx \circ y]$, $\forall x[xRx]$.
   b. Present an algebraic system in the class.
5. By an *affine plane*, we mean an ordered triple (Σ, Λ, I) – where Σ is a nonempty set whose members are called *points* and are denoted by capital letters, Λ is a nonempty set whose members are called *lines* and are denoted by small letters, and I is a binary relation on $\Sigma \cup \Lambda$ called the *incidence relation* – such that (1) any two points are incident with exactly one line; (2) given a line and a point which are not incident, there is exactly one line incident with the given point and parallel to the given line (*note: p* and *q* are said to be *parallel* iff no point is incident with both *p* and *q*); (3) there are four points such that each line is incident with at most two of the four points. Show that the concept of an affine plane can be expressed in terms of algebraic systems, and that the postulates are propositions of the lower predicate calculus.
6. The mathematical system (M, d), where M is a nonempty set and d is a mapping of $M \times M$ into R, the set of all real numbers, is said to be a *metric space* iff
   (i) $\forall x \forall y[d(x, y) = 0 \leftrightarrow x = y]$,
   (ii) $\forall x \forall y[d(x, y) = d(y, x)]$,
   (iii) $\forall x \forall y \forall z[d(x, z) \leq d(x, y) + d(y, z)]$.

a. Prove that (R, d) is a metric space, where
$$d(x, y) = \begin{cases} 0 \text{ if } x = y, \\ 1 \text{ if } x \neq y. \end{cases}$$
b. Prove that $(R \times R, d)$ is a metric space, where
$$d(x, y) = [(x_1 - y_1)^2 + (x_2 - y_2)^2]^{1/2}$$
whenever $x = (x_1, x_2)$ and $y = (y_1, y_2)$.
c. Given that (M, d) is a metric space, prove that $\forall x \forall y [d(x, y) \geq 0]$.
d. Prove that (M, d) is a metric space iff
$$\text{(i) } \forall x \forall y [d(x, y) = 0 \leftrightarrow x = y],$$
$$\text{(ii) } \forall x \forall y \forall z [d(x, z) \leq d(x, y) + d(z, y)].$$

3.3   Semigroups

We now introduce the notion of a *semigroup*.

DEFINITION 3.3.1.   Any algebraic system of the type $(S, \circ)$ — where $\circ$ is a binary operation on S which is associative — is said to be a *semigroup*.

Thus, the one postulate for a semigroup is: $\forall x \forall y \forall z [x \circ (y \circ z) = (x \circ y) \circ z]$.

The simplest example of a semigroup is the algebraic system $(\{a\}, \{(a, a, a)\})$; this example is said to be *simple* because the basic set of the algebraic system has exactly one member.

Of course, there are many examples of semigroups. Speaking informally, the algebraic system $(N, +)$, whose first term is the set of all natural numbers, and whose second term is the usual operation of addition on the natural numbers, is a semigroup; taking multiplication in place of addition, we obtain another semigroup. Similarly, $(I, +)$ and $(I, \cdot)$ are semigroups, where "I" denotes the set of all integers.

It is desirable to develop an intuition about algebraic systems, and in particular to regard algebraic systems as mathematical objects. In order to build up a feeling of this kind, let us now characterize all semigroups in which the basic set has exactly two members. To this end, we first consider all distinct algebraic systems $(\{a, b\}, \circ)$, where $\circ$ is a binary operation on $\{a, b\}$. It is helpful to develop an efficient method for denoting a binary operation on $\{a, b\}$: let us agree to represent the binary operation $\{(a, a, c),$ $(a, b, d), (b, a, e), (b, b, f)\}$ by the array $\begin{pmatrix} c & d \\ e & f \end{pmatrix}$, which is the main body of the table for this binary operation (see Sec. 2.7). For example, $\{(a, a, b),$ $(a, b, a), (b, a, a), (b, b, b)\}$ is represented by $\begin{pmatrix} b & a \\ a & b \end{pmatrix}$. This agreement will enable us to avoid considerable writing.

It turns out that there are only ten distinct algebraic systems of the form $(\{a,b\},\circ)$, where $\circ$ is a binary operation on $\{a,b\}$. The binary operations of these ten algebraic systems are as follows:

1. $\begin{pmatrix} a & a \\ a & a \end{pmatrix}$ 2. $\begin{pmatrix} a & a \\ a & b \end{pmatrix}$ 3. $\begin{pmatrix} a & a \\ b & a \end{pmatrix}$ 4. $\begin{pmatrix} a & b \\ a & a \end{pmatrix}$ 5. $\begin{pmatrix} b & a \\ a & a \end{pmatrix}$

6. $\begin{pmatrix} b & a \\ a & b \end{pmatrix}$ 7. $\begin{pmatrix} a & a \\ b & b \end{pmatrix}$ 8. $\begin{pmatrix} a & b \\ a & b \end{pmatrix}$ 9. $\begin{pmatrix} b & a \\ b & a \end{pmatrix}$ 10. $\begin{pmatrix} b & b \\ a & a \end{pmatrix}$

Having named ten binary operations on $\{a,b\}$, we have in effect named ten algebraic systems. For example, using the second binary operation listed above, we obtain the algebraic system $(\{a,b\},\{(a,a,a),(a,b,a),(b,a,a),(b,b,b)\})$. Let us show that this algebraic system is a semigroup. Denoting the binary operation of this algebraic system by "$\circ$", we see by inspection that "$\forall x[a \circ x = a]$" is true here; also, "$\forall x[b \circ x = x]$" is true in the given algebraic system. Now consider the associative law: "$\forall x \forall y \forall z [x \circ (y \circ z) = (x \circ y) \circ z]$". Stripping away the first quantifier, we obtain propositions   "$\forall y \forall z[a \circ (y \circ z) = (a \circ y) \circ z]$"   and   "$\forall y \forall z[b \circ (y \circ z) = (b \circ y) \circ z]$". But $\forall x[a \circ x = a]$; therefore, $a \circ (y \circ z) = a$ and $(a \circ y) \circ z = a \circ z = a$, no matter what we put in place of "y" and "z". Also, $\forall x[b \circ x = x]$; therefore, $b \circ (y \circ z) = y \circ z$ and $(b \circ y) \circ z = y \circ z$, no matter what we put in place of "y" and "z". It follows that the associative law is true in this algebraic system.

Five of the algebraic systems listed above are, in fact, semigroups; the remaining five algebraic systems are not semigroups. The results are listed as follows:

1. Semigroup   2. Semigroup   3. No   4. No   5. No
6. Semigroup   7. Semigroup   8. Semigroup   9. No   10. No

For example, let us demonstrate that the third algebraic system listed here, namely $(\{a,b\},\{(a,a,a),(a,b,a),(b,a,b),(b,b,a)\})$, is not a semigroup: denoting the binary operation of this algebraic system by "?", we note that $b?(b?b) = b?a = b$ and $(b?b)?b = a?b = a$. It follows that the associative law is not true in this algebraic system; hence, this is not a semigroup.

We turn now to the observation that there are really only ten essentially different algebraic systems consisting of a basic set with exactly two members and a binary operation. At first sight, it appears that there are sixteen distinct algebraic systems possessing the stated form. For example, the algebraic system with binary operation $\begin{pmatrix} a & b \\ b & a \end{pmatrix}$ seems to have been left out. But this algebraic system is essentially the same as $(\{c,d\},\{(c,c,c),$ $(c,d,d),(d,c,d),(d,d,c)\})$. Now, consider the sixth algebraic system in the above list, namely $(\{a,b\},\{(a,a,b),(a,b,a),(b,a,a),(b,b,b)\})$, and consider the one–one mapping of $\{a,b\}$ onto $\{c,d\}$ which associates d with a and associates c with b. Under this mapping, the sixth algebraic system of our list becomes $(\{d,c\},\{(d,d,c),(d,c,d),(c,d,d),(c,c,c)\})$, the algebraic system which apparently had been omitted from the list. Following a similar procedure, it is easy to show that all of the remaining five algebraic systems which appear to have been omitted are in fact represented in the above list.

In this section we have discussed the important notion of two algebraic systems that are essentially the same, i.e., have the property that one of the algebraic systems can be constructed from the other by applying a suitably chosen one–one mapping to the given algebraic system. The technical term used in this connection is the word *isomorphic*. Before formalizing this important concept, we must clarify what we mean by applying a mapping to an algebraic system.

Let S be the basic set of $\mathcal{S}$ and let μ be any mapping of S into some set; then "$\mu\mathcal{S}$" denotes the algebraic system obtained from $\mathcal{S}$ by replacing each instance in $\mathcal{S}$ of a member of S, say x, by μx. For example, let $\mu 0 = a$ and $\mu 1 = b$; then

$$\mu(\{0,1\},\{(0,0,0),(0,1,1),(1,0,1),(1,1,0)\},0)$$
$$= (\{a,b\},\{(a,a,a),(a,b,b),(b,a,b),(b,b,a)\},a).$$

DEFINITION 3.3.2. $\mathcal{S}$ is said to be isomorphic to $\mathcal{J}$ (in symbols, $\mathcal{S} \cong \mathcal{J}$) iff there exists a one–one mapping of the basic set of $\mathcal{S}$ onto the basic set of $\mathcal{J}$, say μ, such that $\mu\mathcal{S} = \mathcal{J}$.

For example,

$$(\{0,1\},\{(0,0,0),(0,1,1),(1,0,1),(1,1,0)\},0)$$
$$\cong (\{a,b\},\{(a,a,a),(a,b,b),(b,a,b),(b,b,a)\},a).$$

Clearly, $\cong$ is a binary relation on algebraic systems. It is easy to prove that $\cong$ is an equivalence relation on the class of all algebraic systems. For this reason, we regard isomorphic algebraic systems as equal—from the algebraic viewpoint.

E X E R C I S E S

1. Construct a semigroup whose basic set has exactly three members.
2. **a.** Prove that the algebraic systems numbered 1, 6, 7, and 8 (on page 90 of the text) are semigroups.
   b. Prove that the algebraic systems numbered 4, 5, 9, and 10 are not semigroups.
3. **a.** List the operations of the six algebraic systems that apparently are not included in the list on page 90 of the text.
   b. Demonstrate that each of these algebraic systems is in fact represented in the list.
4. Show that $(I, \circ)$, where "I" denotes the set of all integers, and $\circ = \{(a, b, c) \mid a \in I \wedge b \in I \wedge c = a - b\}$, is not a semigroup.
5. Show that $(I, ?)$, where "I" denotes the set of all integers, and $? = \{(a, b, c) \mid a \in I \wedge b \in I \wedge c = a \cdot (a + b)\}$, is not a semigroup.
6. Consider the algebraic system $(\{a, b\}, \{(a, a, b), (a, b, a), (b, a, a), (b, b, a)\})$.
   a. Prove that $\forall x[a \circ x \neq x]$, where "$\circ$" denotes the binary operation of the given algebraic system.
   b. Prove that $\forall x[b \circ x = a]$.
7. Consider the algebraic system $(\{a, b\}, ?)$, where $? = \{(a, a, b), (a, b, a), (b, a, a), (b, b, b)\}$.
   a. Prove that $\forall x[a ? x \neq x]$.
   b. Prove that $\forall x[b ? x = x]$.
   c. Prove that $\exists y \forall x[y ? x \neq x]$.
   d. Prove that $\exists y \forall x[y ? x = x]$.
   e. Prove that $\exists x \forall y[y ? y = x]$.
   f. Prove that $\exists x \forall y[y ? y \neq x]$.
   g. Prove that $\forall x \exists y[x ? y = y]$.
   h. Prove that $\forall x \forall y[x ? y = y ? x]$.
8. Given that the algebraic system $(S, \circ)$ is a semigroup, show that it is not necessarily the case that $\circ$ is a mapping of $S \times S$ onto S.
9. Show that $(\mathcal{P}S, \cup)$, where S is a set, is a semigroup.
10. Show that $(\mathcal{P}S, \cap)$, where S is a set, is a semigroup.

3.4   Groups

In this section we shall apply the axiomatic method to the study of a significant mathematical concept – the notion of a *group*.

First, we present some terminology. Let $(S, \circ)$ by any algebraic system such that $\circ$ is a binary operation on S. A member of S, say e, is said to be a *right identity* iff $x \circ e = x$ whenever $x \in S$; e is said to be a *left identity* iff $e \circ x = x$ whenever $x \in S$. A member of S, say e, is said to be an *identity* iff e is both a right identity and a left identity. Moreover, in case e is a right or left identity, y is said to be a *right inverse* of x, and x is said to be a *left inverse* of y iff $x \circ y = e$.

Let us now define the term *group*.

DEFINITION 3.4.1.   An algebraic system, say $(S, \circ, e)$, where $\circ$ is a binary operation on S and $e \in S$, is said to be a *group* iff

(i) $\forall x \forall y \forall z [x \circ (y \circ z) = (x \circ y) \circ z]$,
(ii) $\forall x [x \circ e = x]$,
(iii) $\forall x \exists y [x \circ y = e]$.

In other words, $(S, \circ, e)$ is a group iff $\circ$ is associative, e is a right identity, and each member of S possesses a right inverse with respect to e.

For example, $(I, +, 0)$, where I is the set of all integers, is a group; $(S, \cdot, 1)$, where S is the set of all nonzero rational numbers, is a group; $(\mathscr{P}S, \div, \varnothing)$, where S is a set, is a group. The first two of these examples are offered at an intuitive level only; in Chapter 4 we shall be in a position to prove these statements. On the other hand, it is easy to verify that the third example is a group, since we have already established the properties of the symmetric difference.

The three propositions, (i), (ii), and (iii), are called the *group postulates*. Let us apply the axiomatic method to establish the truth in any group of certain other propositions. Let $(S, \circ, e)$ be any group; the following theorems refer to this group.

THEOREM 3.4.1. $e \circ e = e$.

Proof: We are given that "$\forall x [x \circ e = x]$" is true where the universe of discourse is S. But $e \in S$; therefore, $e \circ e = e$. This establishes our result.

We now prove that if y is a right inverse of x with respect to e, then y is a left inverse of x with respect to e.

THEOREM 3.4.2. $\forall x \forall y [x \circ y = e \rightarrow y \circ x = e]$.

Proof: Suppose that $x \circ y = e$. By (iii), there is a member of S, say c, such that $y \circ c = e$. Therefore,

$$
\begin{aligned}
y \circ x &= (y \circ x) \circ e & &\text{by (ii)} \\
&= (y \circ x) \circ (y \circ c) & &\text{since } y \circ c = e \\
&= [(y \circ x) \circ y] \circ c & &\text{by (i)} \\
&= [y \circ (x \circ y)] \circ c & &\text{by (i)} \\
&= (y \circ e) \circ c & &\text{since } x \circ y = e \\
&= y \circ c & &\text{by (ii)} \\
&= e.
\end{aligned}
$$

This establishes Theorem 3.4.2.

Next, we show that each member of S possesses a *left* inverse with respect to e.

COROLLARY 3.4.1. $\forall x \exists y [y \circ x = e]$.

Proof: Consider Theorem 3.4.2 and (iii).

We now establish a *cancellation* law.

THEOREM 3.4.3. $\forall x \forall y \forall z [x \circ z = y \circ z \rightarrow x = y]$.

Proof: Let $x \in S$, let $y \in S$, let $z \in S$, and suppose that $x \circ z = y \circ z$. By (iii), there is a member of S, say a, such that $z \circ a = e$. Therefore,

$$(x \circ z) \circ a = (y \circ z) \circ a \qquad \text{since } x \circ z = y \circ z.$$

Now,
$$(x \circ z) \circ a = x \circ (z \circ a) \qquad \text{by (i)}$$
$$= x \circ e \qquad \text{since } z \circ a = e$$
$$= x \qquad \text{by (ii).}$$

Moreover,
$$(y \circ z) \circ a = y \circ (z \circ a) \qquad \text{by (i)}$$
$$= y \circ e \qquad \text{since } z \circ a = e$$
$$= y \qquad \text{by (ii).}$$

Hence, $x = y$. This completes the proof.

Next, we prove that e is a *left* identity.

THEOREM 3.4.4. $\forall x [e \circ x = x]$.

Proof: Let $x \in S$; by (iii), there is a member of S, say a, such that $x \circ a = e$. Therefore,

$$e \circ x = (x \circ a) \circ x = x \circ (a \circ x) \qquad \text{by (i)}$$
$$= x \circ e \qquad \text{by Th. 3.4.2}$$
$$= x \qquad \text{by (ii).}$$

We have established our result.

We now consider another *cancellation* law.

THEOREM 3.4.5. $\forall x \forall y \forall z [z \circ x = z \circ y \rightarrow x = y]$.

Proof: The proof is similar to the proof of Theorem 3.4.3; use Corollary 3.4.1 in place of (iii), and use Theorem 3.4.4 in place of (ii).

We now establish that each member of the basic set of a group possesses a *unique* right inverse.

THEOREM 3.4.6. $\forall x \exists! y [x \circ y = e]$.

Proof: Let $a \in S$. We know that a possesses a right inverse; suppose that a possesses two right inverses, say b and c. Then $a \circ b = e$ and $a \circ c = e$. Therefore,

$$
\begin{array}{ll}
c \circ (a \circ b) = c \circ e = c & \text{by (ii)} \\
(c \circ a) \circ b = c & \text{by (i)} \\
e \circ b = c & \text{by Th. 3.4.2} \\
b = c & \text{by Th. 3.4.4.}
\end{array}
$$

This contradiction establishes Theorem 3.4.6.

COROLLARY 3.4.2. $\forall x \exists! y [x \circ y = e \wedge y \circ x = e]$.

Proof: Apply Theorem 3.4.2.

Since each member of S has a unique inverse, we may speak of *the* inverse of a member of S. It is useful to introduce a unary operation on S which associates the inverse of x with x whenever $x \in S$. In case the group operation is denoted by "$\circ$" or "$\cdot$", the inverse of x is denoted by "x^{-1}"; in case the group operation is denoted by "$+$", the inverse of x is denoted by "$-x$".

It turns out that a group possesses just one right identity and just one left identity. Indeed, it is easy to prove the following theorem.

THEOREM 3.4.7. $\exists! y \forall x [x \circ y = x]$ and $\exists! y \forall x [y \circ x = x]$.

Moreover, we can establish another theorem.

THEOREM 3.4.8. $\exists! y \forall x [x \circ y = x \wedge y \circ x = x]$.

(These theorems are easy to prove; the proofs are left as exercises.)
In view of Theorem 3.4.8, we may speak of *the* identity of a group. In case the binary operation of a group is denoted by "$+$", it is convenient to denote the identity of the group by "0". Accordingly, let $(S, +, 0)$ be any group. The following theorems are easily established; remember that "$-x$" denotes the unique inverse of x, so $x + -x = 0$ whenever $x \in S$.

THEOREM 3.4.9. $\forall x[-(-x) = x]$.

THEOREM 3.4.10. $\forall x \forall y[-(x+y) = -y + -x]$.

The operations + and − give rise to a binary operation on S which associates $x + -y$ with the ordered pair (x,y); this binary operation is usually denoted by "−". Of course, it is possible to confuse the binary operation − with the unary operation −; however, it is generally clear from the context whether a unary or a binary operation is under discussion.

DEFINITION 3.4.2. $x - y = x + -y$ whenever $x \in S$ and $y \in S$.

To illustrate, consider the group $(\{0,1,2\}, +, 0)$, where + is given by

TABLE 3.4.1

+	0	1	2
0	0	1	2
1	1	2	0
2	2	0	1

Table 3.4.1. Here, the unary operation − is as follows:

$$- = \{(0,0), (1,2), (2,1)\}.$$

Moreover, the binary operation − is given by Table 3.4.2.

TABLE 3.4.2

−	0	1	2
0	0	2	1
1	1	0	2
2	2	1	0

The following theorems are easy to establish and are left as exercises.

THEOREM 3.4.11. $\forall x[x - x = 0]$.

THEOREM 3.4.12. $\forall x[x - 0 = x]$.

THEOREM 3.4.13. $\forall x \forall y[(x+y) - y = x]$.

THEOREM 3.4.14. $\forall x \forall y[-(x-y) = y - x]$.

THEOREM 3.4.15. $\forall x \forall y \forall z[x - (y - z) = (x+z) - y]$.

THEOREM 3.4.16. $\forall x \forall y \forall z[x + (y - z) = (x+y) - z]$.

THEOREM 3.4.17. $\forall x \forall y \forall z[x - (y+z) = (x-z) - y]$.

EXERCISES

1. Show, intuitively, that $(I, +, 0)$ is a group, where "I" denotes the set of all integers.

2. Show that $(\{0, 1, 2\}, *, 0)$ is a group, where
$* = \{(0,0,0), (0,1,1), (0,2,2), (1,0,1), (1,1,2), (1,2,0), (2,0,2), (2,1,0), (2,2,1)\}$.

3. Prove that the propositions
$$\forall x \forall z \exists! y [x \circ y = z]$$
$$\forall y \forall z \exists! y [x \circ y = z]$$
are true in any group $(S, \circ, e)$.

4. Prove that the proposition "$\forall x [\exists y (x \circ y = y) \rightarrow x = e]$" is true in any group $(S, \circ, e)$.

5. A group, say $(S, \circ, e)$, is said to be *abelian* or *commutative* iff $\circ$ is commutative. Present an example of an abelian group. Present an example of a group which is not abelian.

6. Show that $(\wp S, \dotdiv, \varnothing)$ is an abelian group, where S is a set.

7. The ordered pair $(S, \circ)$ is said to be a *quasigroup* iff S is a nonempty set and $\circ$ is a binary operation on S such that
(i) $\forall x \forall z \exists! y [x \circ y = z]$,
(ii) $\forall y \forall z \exists! x [x \circ y = z]$.
   a. Characterize the notion of a quasigroup in terms of conditions on the table for $\circ$.
   b. Show that the algebraic system $(I, -)$ is a quasigroup, where I is the set of all integers and "$-$" denotes the binary operation of subtraction.
   c. Show that the algebraic system $(I, -, 0)$ is *not* a group.
   d. Show that the algebraic system $(I, \circ)$ is *not* a quasigroup, where I is the set of all integers and $x \circ y = |x - y|$ whenever $x \in I$ and $y \in I$.

8. The ordered triple $(S, \circ, e)$ is said to be a *loop* iff $(S, \circ)$ is a quasigroup and "$\forall x [x \circ e = x \wedge e \circ x = x]$" is true in $(S, \circ, e)$.
   a. Characterize the notion of a loop in terms of conditions on the table for $\circ$.
   b. Prove that each group is a loop.
   c. Show that $(\{0, 1, 2, 3\}, +, 0)$ is a loop, where the table for $+$ is as follows:

+	0	1	2	3
0	0	1	2	3
1	1	0	3	2
2	2	3	0	1
3	3	2	1	0

   d. Show that the algebraic system of part **c** is a group.

9. Present a loop whose basic set has five members and which is not a group.

10. Let $(S, \circ)$ be a quasigroup such that $\forall x \forall y \forall z [x \circ (y \circ z) = (x \circ y) \circ z]$.
   a. Show that $\forall x \forall y \forall z [x \circ z = y \circ z \rightarrow x = y]$.

b. Show that $\forall x \forall y \forall z [z \circ x = z \circ y \rightarrow x = y]$.

c. Show that $\forall x \exists! z [x \circ z = x \land z \circ x = x]$.

d. Show that $\exists! z \forall x [x \circ z = x \land z \circ x = x]$.

e. Show that $(S, \circ, e)$ is a group, where $e \in S$ and "$\forall x [x \circ e = x]$" is true in $(S, \circ)$.

11. Let $(S, \circ, e)$ be any group and let a be any member of S; the expression "a^n", where n is any integer, is defined as follows: $a^1 = a$ and $a^{n+1} = a^n \circ a$ whenever n is a positive integer; moreover, $a^0 = e$ and $a^{-n} = (a^{-1})^n$ whenever n is a positive integer. Prove the following:

a. $a^n \circ a^m = a^{n+m}$ whenever n and m are integers.

b. $a^n \circ a^m = a^m \circ a^n$ whenever n and m are integers.

c. $(a^n)^m = a^{n \cdot m}$ whenever n and m are integers.

12. Let $(S, \circ, e)$ and $(S', \circ', e')$ be groups such that $S' \subset S$ and $\circ' \subset \circ$; then $(S', \circ', e')$ is said to be a *subgroup* of $(S, \circ, e)$. Prove that $e' = e$.

13. Given that $(S, \circ, e)$ is a group, $S' \subset S$, and $\circ' \subset \circ$, prove that $(S', \circ', e)$ is a subgroup of $(S, \circ, e)$ iff (i) $\circ'$ is a binary operation on S', (ii) $\forall x [x \in S' \rightarrow x^{-1} \in S']$.

14. Let $(S, \circ, e)$ be a group and let $a \in S$. Prove that $(S', \circ', e)$ is a subgroup of $(S, \circ, e)$, where $S' = \{a^n | n$ is an integer$\}$ and $\circ'$ is $\circ$ restricted to S'. Prove that $(S', \circ', e)$ is an abelian group.

15. Let $(G, \circ, e)$ be a group whose basic set is finite, and let S be the basic set of a subgroup of $(G, \circ, e)$. Let $a \in G$; then $\{x \circ a | x \in S\}$ is denoted by "Sa" and is said to be a *right coset* of S in G. Similarly, $\{a \circ x | x \in S\}$ is denoted by "aS" and is said to be a *left coset* of S in G.

a. Prove that $Sa = Sb$ or else $Sa \cap Sb = \emptyset$ whenever $a \in G$ and $b \in G$.

b. Prove that $\{Sa | a \in G\}$ is a partition of G.

16. Let $(S', \circ', e)$ be a subgroup of $(S, \circ, e)$, where S is a finite set with m members and S' has n members. Prove that m is a multiple of n.

17. Let $(G, +, 0)$ be any group. Prove that $(M, \circ, \varphi)$ is a group where M is the set of all mappings of G into G, "$\mu \circ \nu$" denotes the mapping that associates $\mu(t) + \nu(t)$ with t whenever $t \in G$, and $\varphi = \{(t, 0) | t \in G\}$. Show that $\circ$ is commutative iff $+$ is commutative.

3.5   More Examples of Groups

We now present two methods of generating groups. The first method that we shall discuss produces abelian groups, whereas the second method results in groups for which the commutative law fails, i.e., nonabelian groups.

Consider a circle whose circumference has been divided into three equal parts by means of three points labeled "0", "1", and "2". Suppose that a pointer is pivoted at the center of the circle so that it is free to point at any one of the three numbers on the circumference (see Fig. 3.5.1). Let us use this device to construct an algebraic system which, in fact, is an abelian group. The basic set of our algebraic system is $\{0,1,2\}$. We introduce $+$, a binary operation on $\{0,1,2\}$, as follows: let x and y be any members of $\{0,1,2\}$; then $x+y$ is found by first setting the pointer at the number x and then turning the pointer clockwise through y parts; the number the pointer stops at is defined to be $x+y$. Finally, we display 0, a member of our basic set. Thus, the algebraic system we have

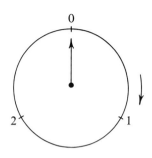

Figure 3.5.1

constructed by using the above device is $(\{0,1,2\},+,0)$. We want to show that the following four propositions are true in this algebraic system:

$$\forall x \forall y \forall z[x + (y + z) = (x + y) + z].$$
$$\forall x[x + 0 = x].$$
$$\forall x \exists y[x + y = 0].$$
$$\forall x \forall y[x + y = y + x].$$

First, we shall demonstrate that $+$ is commutative. To this purpose, we observe that the procedure of setting the pointer at a number, say x, can be broken down into two parts: namely, first set the pointer at 0 and then move the pointer clockwise through x parts. This means that $x + y$ can be found by first setting the pointer at 0, then moving the pointer clockwise through x parts, and finally moving the pointer clockwise through y parts — where x and y are any members of $\{0,1,2\}$. Now, $y + x$ is found by setting the pointer at 0, moving the pointer clockwise through y parts, and then moving the pointer clockwise through x parts. Thus, in both cases the pointer is moved through x parts and through y parts (the pointer does not care about the *order* in which the movements are performed); therefore, $x + y = y + x$ whenever x and y are members of $\{0,1,2\}$. This establishes the truth of "$\forall x \forall y[x + y = y + x]$" in our algebraic system.

Next, we shall establish that $+$ is associative. Let x, y, and z be any members of $\{0,1,2\}$; we want to show that $x + (y + z) = (x + y) + z$. But $x + (y + z) = (y + z) + x$, since $+$ is commutative. So $x + (y + z)$ is the number obtained by setting the pointer at 0, then moving it clockwise through y parts, then through z parts (so that the pointer now points at the number $y + z$), and finally through x parts. On the other hand, $(x + y) + z$ is the number obtained by setting the pointer at 0, then moving the pointer clockwise through x parts, then through y parts (so that the pointer now points at the number $x + y$), and finally through z parts. Notice that in each case the pointer was moved through the sum of x, y, and z parts, so that the pointer came to rest at the same number in both cases. This establishes the truth of "$\forall x \forall y \forall z[x + (y + z) = (x + y) + z]$" in our algebraic system.

We now consider the proposition "$\forall x[x + 0 = x]$". Of course, this is true here, since setting the pointer at a number and then moving the pointer through no parts leaves the pointer where it was.

Finally, let us consider the proposition "$\forall x \exists y[x + y = 0]$". This proposition is easily established by eliminating quantifiers; note that $1 + 2 = 0$, $2 + 1 = 0$, and $0 + 0 = 0$ in this algebraic system. This completes our demonstration that the ordered triple $(\{0, 1, 2\}, +, 0)$ is an abelian group.

The binary operation $+$ discussed above is actually of mathematical interest; this operation is called *addition modulo 3*. We point out that by dividing the circumference of a circle into n equal parts, where n is any natural number, we can construct an abelian group by defining a binary operation $+$ as above, on the basic set $\{0, 1, \cdots, n - 1\}$ and displaying 0 as the third term of the algebraic system.

We now present another method of generating a group, a method which produces nonabelian groups. Let M be the set of all mappings of $\{1, 2, 3\}$ onto $\{1, 2, 3\}$; then M has six members as follows:

$$\{(1, 1), (2, 2), (3, 3)\}, \quad \{(1, 1), (2, 3), (3, 2)\}, \quad \{(1, 2), (2, 1), (3, 3)\},$$

$$\{(1, 2), (2, 3), (3, 1)\}, \quad \{(1, 3), (2, 1), (3, 2)\}, \quad \{(1, 3), (2, 2), (3, 1)\}.$$

The set M is to be the basic set of our algebraic system. Next, let us construct a binary operation on M, which we shall denote by "$\circ$". Let μ and ν be any members of M; then "$\mu \circ \nu$" denotes the mapping of $\{1, 2, 3\}$ onto $\{1, 2, 3\}$ which associates $\mu(\nu(x))$ with x whenever $x \in \{1, 2, 3\}$. For example,

$$\{(1, 2), (2, 1), (3, 3)\} \circ \{(1, 3), (2, 2), (3, 1)\} = \{(1, 3), (2, 1), (3, 2)\}.$$

It is easily seen that if μ and ν are any mappings of $\{1, 2, 3\}$ onto $\{1, 2, 3\}$, then $\mu \circ \nu$ is also a mapping of $\{1, 2, 3\}$ onto $\{1, 2, 3\}$. Finally, for the third term of our ordered triple we take the identity mapping $\{(1, 1), (2, 2), (3, 3)\}$, which we shall denote by "φ". Thus, our algebraic system is $(M, \circ, \varphi)$.

Let us show that the binary operation $\circ$ is associative. Let λ, μ, and ν be any members of M; then

$$[\lambda \circ (\mu \circ \nu)](x) = \lambda[(\mu \circ \nu)(x)] = \lambda(\mu(\nu(x)))$$

and
$$[(\lambda \circ \mu) \circ \nu](x) = [\lambda \circ \mu](\nu(x)) = \lambda(\mu(\nu(x))).$$

Therefore, $\lambda \circ (\mu \circ \nu) = (\lambda \circ \mu) \circ \nu$. This demonstrates that $\circ$ is associative.

Clearly, $\mu \circ \varphi = \mu$ whenever $\mu \in M$; therefore, $\forall x[x \circ \varphi = x]$ in our algebraic system.

Moreover, $\{(1,a),(2,b),(3,c)\} \circ \{(a,1),(b,2),(c,3)\} = \{(1,1),(2,2),(3,3)\}$, provided that $\{a,b,c\} = \{1,2,3\}$. This proves that "$\forall x \exists y[x \circ y = \varphi]$" is true in our algebraic system.

We conclude that the algebraic system $(M, \circ, \varphi)$ is a group.

Finally, we point out that this is a nonabelian group. We must show that the commutative law fails here. But

$$\{(1,2),(2,1),(3,3)\} \circ \{(1,3),(2,2),(3,1)\} = \{(1,3),(2,1),(3,2)\}$$
and $\{(1,3),(2,2),(3,1)\} \circ \{(1,2),(2,1),(3,3)\} = \{(1,2),(2,3),(3,1)\}$.

Thus, $\{(1,2),(2,1),(3,3)\} \circ \{(1,3),(2,2),(3,1)\}$
$$\neq \{(1,3),(2,2),(3,1)\} \circ \{(1,2),(2,1),(3,3)\}.$$

EXERCISES

1. Exhibit the table for the binary operation called *addition modulo 3*.
2. Exhibit the table for the operation of the group based on dividing the circumference of a circle into four equal parts (this operation is called *addition modulo 4*).
3. Present an abelian group whose basic set has five members.
4. Let the set of all integers from 1 to 10 inclusive be the basic set of an algebraic system whose second term is the binary operation + based on dividing the circumference of a circle into five equal parts (i.e., $x + y$ is calculated by setting the pointer at 0, then moving it clockwise through x parts, and then through y parts), and whose third term is 0.
   a. Display the table for the binary operation.
   b. Is the operation associative?
   c. Is the operation commutative?
   d. Is the proposition "$\forall x [x + 0 = x]$" true in this algebraic system?
   e. Is this algebraic system a group?
   f. Is this algebraic system a loop?
5. Prove that if n is any natural number greater than 2, there is a nonabelian group whose basic set has $n!$ members.
6. Present a nonabelian group whose basic set has 24 members.
7. a. Let n be any natural number and let "$\oplus$" denote the binary operation on the set of all natural numbers based on dividing the circumference of a circle into n equal parts (i.e., $x \oplus y$ is computed by setting the pointer at 0, then moving the pointer clockwise through x parts, and then through y parts). This operation is called *addition modulo n*. Given that x and y are any natural numbers, show that $x \oplus y = r$, where q is a natural number such that $nq \leq x + y < n(q + 1)$

and $x + y = nq + r$ (i.e., r is the remainder on dividing $x + y$ by n). (*Note:* The proposition "$x \oplus y = r$" is given by writing "$x + y \equiv r \pmod{n}$".)

b. Let n be any natural number and let "$\circ$" denote the binary operation on the set of all nonnegative integers such that $x \circ y = r$, where r is the remainder on dividing $x \cdot y$ by n; more precisely, $x \circ y = r$ iff there is a natural number q such that $n \cdot q \leq x \cdot y < n \cdot (q + 1)$ and $x \cdot y = n \cdot q + r$. The operation $\circ$ is called *multiplication modulo n.*

  (i) Display the table for $\circ$, given that $n = 3$.

  (ii) Display the table for $\circ$, given that $n = 4$.

  Note: The proposition "$x \circ y = r$" is given by writing "$x \cdot y \equiv r \pmod{n}$".

8. A group, say $(S, \circ, e)$, is said to be *cyclic* iff there is a member of S, say a, such that $S = \{a^n | n \text{ is an integer}\}$; moreover, a is said to *generate* the group.

a. Show, intuitively, that the group $(I, +, 0)$, where I is the set of all integers and $+$ is addition, is cyclic and is generated by 1.

b. Prove that for each positive integer k, the group $(\{0, 1, 2, \cdots, k - 1\}, +, 0)$ is cyclic with generator 1, where "$+$" denotes addition modulo k.

3.6 Rings; Integral Domains

In this section we shall see how the concept of a group can be used to build up, or describe, more complex mathematical entities.

DEFINITION 3.6.1.   An algebraic system, say $(R, +, \cdot, 0)$, where $+$ and $\cdot$ are binary operations on R and $0 \in R$, is said to be a *ring* iff

     (i) $(R, +, 0)$ is an abelian group,

     (ii) $(R, \cdot)$ is a semigroup,

     (iii) $\forall x \forall y \forall z [x \cdot (y + z) = x \cdot y + x \cdot z]$,

     (iv) $\forall x \forall y \forall z [(y + z) \cdot x = y \cdot x + z \cdot x]$.

Propositions (iii) and (iv) are called *distributive* laws.

Recalling the definitions of a group and a semigroup, we see that the algebraic system $(R, +, \cdot, 0)$ is a ring iff:

$$\forall x \forall y \forall z [x + (y + z) = (x + y) + z],$$
$$\forall x [x + 0 = x],$$
$$\forall x \exists y [x + y = 0],$$
$$\forall x \forall y [x + y = y + x],$$
$$\forall x \forall y \forall z [x \cdot (y \cdot z) = (x \cdot y) \cdot z],$$
$$\forall x \forall y \forall z [x \cdot (y + z) = x \cdot y + x \cdot z],$$
$$\forall x \forall y \forall z [(y + z) \cdot x = y \cdot x + z \cdot x].$$

For example, the ordered 4-tuple $(\mathcal{P}S, \doteq \cap, \emptyset)$ is a ring, where S is a set; this is easy to see in view of the properties of the *symmetric difference* and *intersection*.

As another example of a ring, we present the algebraic system $(\{0, 1, 2, 3\}, +, \cdot, 0)$, where the binary operations $+$ and $\cdot$ are given by Tables 3.6.1 and

<table>
<tr><td colspan="5" align="center">TABLE 3.6.1</td></tr>
<tr><td>+</td><td>0</td><td>1</td><td>2</td><td>3</td></tr>
<tr><td>0</td><td>0</td><td>1</td><td>2</td><td>3</td></tr>
<tr><td>1</td><td>1</td><td>2</td><td>3</td><td>0</td></tr>
<tr><td>2</td><td>2</td><td>3</td><td>0</td><td>1</td></tr>
<tr><td>3</td><td>3</td><td>0</td><td>1</td><td>2</td></tr>
</table>

<table>
<tr><td colspan="5" align="center">TABLE 3.6.2</td></tr>
<tr><td>·</td><td>0</td><td>1</td><td>2</td><td>3</td></tr>
<tr><td>0</td><td>0</td><td>0</td><td>0</td><td>0</td></tr>
<tr><td>1</td><td>0</td><td>1</td><td>2</td><td>3</td></tr>
<tr><td>2</td><td>0</td><td>2</td><td>0</td><td>2</td></tr>
<tr><td>3</td><td>0</td><td>3</td><td>2</td><td>1</td></tr>
</table>

3.6.2. Here, $+$ represents *addition modulo 4*, and $\cdot$ represents *multiplication modulo 4*. In view of Section 3.5, it is clear that $(\{0, 1, 2, 3\}, +, 0)$ is an abelian group. To see that we have a ring, note that $\cdot$ can be expressed in terms of $+$ as follows:

(1) $\forall x[0 \cdot x = 0],$
(2) $\forall x[1 \cdot x = x],$
(3) $\forall x[2 \cdot x = x + x],$
(4) $\forall x[3 \cdot x = (x + x) + x].$

These statements are easily verified by examining the tables for $+$ and $\cdot$. Moreover, from the table for $\cdot$, we see that $\cdot$ is commutative, i.e., $\forall x \forall y[x \cdot y = y \cdot x]$. We can now establish the *distributive* laws. Since $\cdot$ is commutative, it is enough to demonstrate one distributive law, say $\forall x \forall y \forall z[x \cdot (y + z) = x \cdot y + x \cdot z]$. Eliminating the first quantifier, we must establish the following:

$$\forall y \forall z[0 \cdot (y + z) = 0 \cdot y + 0 \cdot z],$$
$$\forall y \forall z[1 \cdot (y + z) = 1 \cdot y + 1 \cdot z],$$
$$\forall y \forall z[2 \cdot (y + z) = 2 \cdot y + 2 \cdot z],$$
$$\forall y \forall z[3 \cdot (y + z) = 3 \cdot y + 3 \cdot z].$$

In view of statements (1), (2), (3), and (4) above and the fact that $+$ is associative and commutative, we readily demonstrate these four propositions. This establishes our distributive law.

Finally, we must prove that $\cdot$ is associative, i.e., $\forall x \forall y \forall z[x \cdot (y \cdot z) = (x \cdot y) \cdot z]$. Eliminating the first quantifier, we must establish the following:

$$\forall y \forall z[0 \cdot (y \cdot z) = (0 \cdot y) \cdot z],$$
$$\forall y \forall z[1 \cdot (y \cdot z) = (1 \cdot y) \cdot z],$$
$$\forall y \forall z[2 \cdot (y \cdot z) = (2 \cdot y) \cdot z],$$
$$\forall y \forall z[3 \cdot (y \cdot z) = (3 \cdot y) \cdot z].$$

These propositions are easily verified by applying statements (1), (2), (3), and (4) above and the distributive laws. We conclude that $(\{0,1,2,3\}, +, \cdot, 0)$ is a ring.

At an intuitive level, we observe that $(I, +, \cdot, 0)$ is a ring, where I is the set of all integers, $+$ and $\cdot$ represent addition and multiplication respectively, and 0 is the integer zero.

We now establish two theorems about rings.

THEOREM 3.6.1. $\forall x[0 \cdot x = 0]$.

Proof: Let $(R, +, \cdot, 0)$ be any ring. We must show that if a is any member of R, then $0 \cdot a = 0$. Now,

$$0 \cdot a = (0 + 0) \cdot a \qquad \text{since } 0 + 0 = 0$$
$$= 0 \cdot a + 0 \cdot a \qquad \text{by a distributive law.}$$

Let $y = -(0 \cdot a)$; then $0 \cdot a + y = (0 \cdot a + 0 \cdot a) + y$; i.e.,

$$0 = 0 \cdot a + (0 \cdot a + y) \qquad \text{since } + \text{ is associative}$$
$$= 0 \cdot a + 0$$
$$= 0 \cdot a.$$

This establishes Theorem 3.6.1.

THEOREM 3.6.2. $\forall x \forall y[-(x \cdot y) = (-x) \cdot y]$.

Proof: Let $(R, +, \cdot, 0)$ be any ring. We must show that if a and b are any members of R, then $-(a \cdot b) = (-a) \cdot b$, where "$-x$" denotes the additive inverse of x. But

$$a \cdot b + (-a) \cdot b = (a + -a) \cdot b \qquad \text{by a distributive law}$$
$$= 0 \cdot b$$
$$= 0 \qquad\qquad\qquad \text{by Th. 3.6.1.}$$

Thus, $(-a) \cdot b$ is the inverse of $a \cdot b$. This completes the proof.

If $(R, +, \cdot, 0)$ is a ring such that $\cdot$ is commutative, then this algebraic system is said to be a *commutative ring*.

If $(R, +, \cdot, 0)$ is a ring such that $\exists y \forall x [x \cdot y = x \wedge y \cdot x = x]$, then this algebraic system is said to be a *ring with identity;* moreover, if e is a member of R such that $\forall x [x \cdot e = x \wedge e \cdot x = x]$, then e is said to be an *identity*.

THEOREM 3.6.3.   Each ring has at most one identity.

Proof: We indicate a proof, leaving the details as an exercise. Suppose that a particular ring has two identities; this will quickly lead you to a contradiction.

To illustrate the notions that we have just introduced, we note that the ring $(\mathscr{P}S, \doteq, \cap, \varnothing)$ is a commutative ring with identity; the identity, here, is S. Considering the ring $(\{0, 1, 2, 3\}, +, \cdot, 0)$ given above, we see that this ring is commutative and has an identity, namely 1.

A commutative ring with unit, say $(R, +, \cdot, 0)$, is said to be an *integral domain* iff 0 has no proper divisors, i.e., iff $\forall x \forall y [x \cdot y = 0 \rightarrow x = 0 \vee y = 0]$.

Notice that $(\{0, 1, 2, 3\}, +, \cdot, 0)$ is *not* an integral domain, since $2 \cdot 2 = 0$ — thus 2 is a divisor of 0. Moreover, the ring $(\mathscr{P}\{1, 2\}, \doteq, \cap, \varnothing)$ is not an integral domain since $\{1\} \cap \{2\} = \varnothing$.

The prime example of an integral domain is the ring of integers $(I, +, \cdot, 0)$. Another example is the ring $(\{0, 1\}, +, \cdot, 0)$, where $+$ and $\cdot$ are given as foliows:

+	0	1
0	0	1
1	1	0

$\cdot$	0	1
0	0	0
1	0	1

Clearly, this algebraic system is an integral domain.

We now establish one theorem about integral domains.

THEOREM 3.6.4. $\forall x \forall y \forall z [z \neq 0 \wedge x \cdot z = y \cdot z \rightarrow x = y]$.

Proof: Let $(R, +, \cdot, 0)$ be any integral domain. We want to show that "$\forall x \forall y \forall z [z \neq 0 \wedge x \cdot z = y \cdot z \rightarrow x = y]$" is true in $(R, +, \cdot, 0)$. We must show that if $c \neq 0$ and $a \cdot c = b \cdot c$, then $a = b$. Now,

$$-(a \cdot c) = -(b \cdot c) \qquad \text{since } a \cdot c = b \cdot c;$$

thus $a \cdot c + (-b) \cdot c = 0$; so $(a - b) \cdot c = 0$, by a distributive law. But $c \neq 0$

and there are no proper divisors of 0; hence, $a - b = 0$. Thus, $a = b$. This establishes Theorem 3.6.4.

EXERCISES

1. Prove that $\forall x[x \cdot 0 = 0]$ in any ring $(R, +, \cdot, 0)$.

2. **a.** Present a ring whose basic set has exactly five members.
   b. Is your solution to part **a** also an integral domain?

3. Present a ring which is *not* commutative.

4. Show that $(R, +, \cdot, 0)$ is a ring, where R is the set of all 2×2 real matrices, $+$ and $\cdot$ represent matrix addition and matrix multiplication respectively, and "0" denotes the null matrix.

5. It is sometimes convenient to display the identity of an integral domain; thus, we shall say that $(R, +, \cdot, 0, 1)$ is an integral domain, provided that $(R, +, \cdot, 0)$ is an integral domain with identity 1. Given that $(R, +, \cdot, 0, 1)$ is an integral domain, show the following:
   a. $\forall x[-x = (-1) \cdot x]$.
   b. $-1 \cdot -1 = 1$.
   c. $\forall x \forall y[(-x) \cdot (-y) = x \cdot y]$.

6. Show that the algebraic system $(\{0\}, \{(0,0,0)\}, \{(0,0,0)\}, 0, 0)$ is an integral domain.

7. Prove that the algebraic system $(\{0, 1, 2, \cdots, k - 1\}, +, \cdot, 0, 1)$, where $+$ and $\cdot$ represent *addition modulo k* and *multiplication modulo k* respectively, is an integral domain iff k is prime.

8. Let $(S, +, \cdot, 0, 1)$ be any integral domain; by the *characteristic* of a, where a is any nonzero member of S, we mean the smallest natural number k such that $0 = a + a + \cdots + a$ (k "a"'s). In case $0 \neq a + a + \cdots + a$ (k "a"'s) for each natural number k, we say that the characteristic of a is zero.
   a. Prove that any two nonzero members of S have the same characteristic. (Hint: Consider the characteristic of 1.)
   b. Let $k, k \neq 0$, be the characteristic of 1; prove that k is prime.

9. Let $(R, +, \cdot, 0)$ be any ring, and let S be any subset of R such that $(S, +', 0)$ is a group where $+'$ is $+$ restricted to S, and $\forall x \forall y[x \in S \wedge y \in R \rightarrow x \cdot y \in S \wedge y \cdot x \in S]$. Then S is said to be an *ideal* of the given ring.
   a. List the ideals of the ring $(\{0, 1, 2, 3, 4, 5\}, +, \cdot, 0)$, where $+$ and $\cdot$ represent addition modulo 6 and multiplication modulo 6 respectively.
   b. Show that for each integer k, $\{a \cdot k | a \in I\}$, the set of all multiples of k, is an ideal of the ring of integers $(I, +, \cdot, 0)$.
   c. Prove that the only ideals of the ring of integers are those given by part **b**.

10. Given that $(R, +, \cdot, 0)$ is a ring with identity 1 and that $\forall x[x \neq 0 \rightarrow \exists y[x \cdot y = 1]]$, prove that the only ideals of this ring are R and $\{0\}$.

3.7 Fields; Ordered Fields

We now introduce the notion of a *field*.

DEFINITION 3.7.1. An algebraic system, say $(S, +, \cdot, 0, 1)$, is said to be a *field* iff

(i) $(S, +, \cdot, 0, 1)$ is an integral domain,
(ii) "$\forall x \exists y [x \neq 0 \rightarrow x \cdot y = 1]$" is true in $(S, +, \cdot, 0, 1)$,
(iii) $0 \neq 1$.

For example, $(\{0, 1\}, +, \cdot, 0, 1)$ is a field where the binary operations $+$ and $\cdot$ are given by Tables 3.7.1 and 3.7.2.

TABLE 3.7.1

+	0	1
0	0	1
1	1	0

TABLE 3.7.2

·	0	1
0	0	0
1	0	1

Again, $(\{0, 1, 2\}, +, \cdot, 0, 1)$ is a field where $+$ and $\cdot$ are given by Tables 3.7.3 and 3.7.4.

TABLE 3.7.3

+	0	1	2
0	0	1	2
1	1	2	0
2	2	0	1

TABLE 3.7.4

·	0	1	2
0	0	0	0
1	0	1	2
2	0	2	1

At an intuitive level, we observe that the algebraic system $(Rt, +, \cdot, 0/1, 1/1)$ is a field, where Rt is the set of all rational numbers, $+$ and $\cdot$ are the operations of addition and multiplication respectively, and $0/1$ and $1/1$ are the rational numbers 0 and 1.

Since there are nine postulates for an integral domain, we see that there are eleven postulates for a field. However, it is easy to show that the integral domain postulate "$\forall x \forall y [x \cdot y = 0 \rightarrow x = 0 \lor y = 0]$" follows from the other field postulates. Thus, we have the following theorem, which displays the necessary field postulates in detail.

THEOREM 3.7.1.   The algebraic system $(S, +, \cdot, 0, 1)$ is a field, where $+$ and $\cdot$ are binary operations on S, $0 \in S$, and $1 \in S$, iff

1. $\forall x \forall y \forall z [x + (y + z) = (x + y) + z]$,
2. $\forall x [x + 0 = x]$,
3. $\forall x \exists y [x + y = 0]$,
4. $\forall x \forall y [x + y = y + x]$,
5. $\forall x \forall y \forall z [x \cdot (y \cdot z) = (x \cdot y) \cdot z]$,
6. $\forall x [x \cdot 1 = x]$,
7. $\forall x \exists y [x \neq 0 \rightarrow x \cdot y = 1]$,
8. $\forall x \forall y [x \cdot y = y \cdot x]$,
9. $\forall x \forall y \forall z [x \cdot (y + z) = x \cdot y + x \cdot z]$,
10. $0 \neq 1$

are each true in the algebraic system $(S, +, \cdot, 0, 1)$.

Next, we introduce the notion of an ordered field.

DEFINITION 3.7.2.   An algebraic system, say $(S, +, \cdot, <, 0, 1)$, where $<$ is a binary relation on S, is said to be an *ordered field* iff $(S, +, \cdot, 0, 1)$ is a field and the following propositions are true in the given algebraic system $(S, +, \cdot, <, 0, 1)$:

11. $\forall x \forall y \forall z [x < y \land y < z \rightarrow x < z]$,
12. $\forall x [x = 0 \, \ⓥ \, 0 < x \, \ⓥ \, x < 0]$,
13. $\forall x \forall y \forall z [x < y \rightarrow x + z < y + z]$,
14. $\forall x \forall y \forall z [x < y \land 0 < z \rightarrow x \cdot z < y \cdot z]$.

(Recall that "$p \, \ⓥ \, q \, \ⓥ \, r$" is true iff exactly one of p, q, r is true.)

Although we had no trouble constructing a simple example of a field, it is not easy to illustrate the notion of an ordered field. In fact, there is no ordered field whose basic set is finite; this is a consequence of Postulates 10, 11, 12, and 13. However, at an intuitive level we point out that the algebraic system $(Rt, +, \cdot, <, 0/1, 1/1)$ is an ordered field, where Rt is the set of all rational numbers, and $+, \cdot, <, 0/1, 1/1$ are interpreted in the usual way.

We now establish some theorems about ordered fields.

THEOREM 3.7.2. $\forall x [x < 0 \rightarrow 0 < -x]$.

Proof: Assume $x < 0$; by Postulate 12, exactly one of the following propositions is true: $-x = 0$, $0 < -x$, $-x < 0$. If $-x = 0$, then $x + -x = x + 0$, hence $x = 0$; this is impossible by Postulate 12. If $-x < 0$, then $-x + x <$

$0 + x$ by Postulate 13, i.e., $0 < x$; this is impossible by Postulate 12. We conclude, again by Postulate 12, that $0 < -x$.

THEOREM 3.7.3. $0 < 1$.

Proof: From Postulate 10, $0 \neq 1$; therefore, from Postulate 12, either $0 < 1$ or $1 < 0$. Suppose $1 < 0$; then, by Theorem 3.7.2, $0 < -1$. Now, $1 < 0$; hence, by Postulate 14, $1 \cdot -1 < 0 \cdot -1$, i.e., $-1 < 0$. Thus, $0 < -1$ and $-1 < 0$; this contradicts Postulate 12. We conclude that $0 < 1$.

THEOREM 3.7.4. $\forall x[x \neq 0 \rightarrow 0 < x \cdot x]$.

Proof: Assume $x \neq 0$; then, by Postulate 12, $x < 0$ or else $0 < x$. If $x < 0$, then by Theorem 3.7.2, $0 < -x$; hence, by Postulate 14, $0 \cdot -x < -x \cdot -x$. But, by Theorem 3.6.1, $0 \cdot -x = 0$, and by Exercise 5c, page 106, $-x \cdot -x = x \cdot x$; hence, $0 < x \cdot x$. If $0 < x$, then, by Postulate 14, $0 \cdot x < x \cdot x$; hence, by Theorem 3.6.1, $0 < x \cdot x$. This establishes Theorem 3.7.4.

Finally, we wish to state what is meant by a *complete* ordered field. Consider any ordered field, say $(S, +, \cdot, <, 0, 1)$. Suppose that K is any nonempty subset of S and that b is a member of S, not necessarily in K, such that $\forall x[x \in K \rightarrow x < b \lor x = b]$; then we call b an *upper bound of K*. Now, suppose that L is an upper bound of K such that $L < b \lor L = b$ whenever b is an upper bound of K; then we call L a *least upper bound of K*. A word of warning about language; it is customary to say "K possesses an upper bound" when we mean "an upper bound of K exists"; similarly, we say "K possesses a least upper bound" when we mean "a least upper bound of K exists". Do not interpret "K *possesses* an upper bound" as meaning that an upper bound of K *is a member of K*.

To illustrate these concepts, consider again the system of rational numbers $(Rt, +, \cdot, <, 0/1, 1/1)$, which is an ordered field, interpreting $+$, $\cdot$, $<$, $0/1$, and $1/1$ in the usual way. The set of all negative rational numbers, namely $\{x | x \in Rt \land x < 0\}$, possesses many upper bounds — in fact, each rational number not in the set is an upper bound of the set. Furthermore, $0/1$ is a least upper bound of this set.

Now we can state what is meant by a complete ordered field.

DEFINITION 3.7.3.   Let $(S, +, \cdot, <, 0, 1)$ be any ordered field; then this algebraic system is said to be a *complete ordered field* iff each nonempty subset of S which possesses an upper bound also possesses a least upper bound.

It is easy to show that the system of rational numbers is *not* a complete ordered field; on the other hand, the system of real numbers is a complete ordered field (we are speaking intuitively here). Furthermore, there is essentially just one complete ordered field; i.e., any two complete ordered fields are isomorphic.

EXERCISES

1. Show that the algebraic system $(\{0,1,2,3,4\},+,\cdot,0,1)$ is a field, where the binary operations $+$ and $\cdot$ are given by the following tables:

+	0	1	2	3	4
0	0	1	2	3	4
1	1	2	3	4	0
2	2	3	4	0	1
3	3	4	0	1	2
4	4	0	1	2	3

$\cdot$	0	1	2	3	4
0	0	0	0	0	0
1	0	1	2	3	4
2	0	2	4	1	3
3	0	3	1	4	2
4	0	4	3	2	1

2. List the field postulates contained in Definition 3.7.1.

3. Prove Theorem 3.7.1.

4. Prove that "$\forall x \forall y [x = y \oslash x < y \oslash y < x]$" is true in any ordered field $(S,+,\cdot,<,0,1)$.

5. Show that $(\{0,1\},+,\cdot,<,0,1)$ is *not* an ordered field, given that $+ = \{(0,0,0),(0,1,1),(1,0,1),(1,1,0)\}$, $\cdot = \{(0,0,0),(0,1,0),(1,0,0),(1,1,1)\}$, and $< = \{(0,1)\}$. Which postulate is false?

6. Present an example, at least on an intuitive level, of an algebraic system in which each of the postulates of an ordered field is true, with the exception of Postulate 14.

7. Prove that "$\forall x \forall y [x < y \leftrightarrow -y < -x]$" is true in each ordered field $(S,+,\cdot,<,0,1)$.

8. Prove that "$\forall x \forall y \forall z [x < y \land z < 0 \rightarrow y \cdot z < x \cdot z]$" is true in each ordered field $(S,+,\cdot,<,0,1)$.

9. Prove that "$\forall x \forall y \forall z \forall w [x < y \land z < w \rightarrow x + z < y + w]$" is true in each ordered field $(S,+,\cdot,<,0,1)$.

10. Prove that "$\forall x \forall y \forall z \forall w [0 < x \land x < y \land 0 < z \land z < w \rightarrow x \cdot z < y \cdot w]$" is true in each ordered field $(S,+,\cdot,<,0,1)$.

11. Prove that "$\forall x \forall y \exists ! z [x \neq 0 \rightarrow x \cdot z = y]$" is true in each field $(S,+,\cdot,0,1)$.

12. Let $(S,+,\cdot,<,0,1)$ be any ordered field, and suppose that K is a nonempty subset of S. Show that K does not possess *two* least upper bounds.

13. Suppose that $(S,+,\cdot,<,0,1)$ is an ordered field, K is a nonempty subset of S, and $b \in S$. Then b is called a *lower bound of K* iff $\forall x [x \in K \rightarrow b < x \lor b = x]$; furthermore, G is called a *greatest lower bound of K* iff G is a lower bound of

K and $b < G \lor b = G$ whenever b is a lower bound of K. Assuming that $(S, +, \cdot, <, 0, 1)$ is complete, prove that each nonempty subset of S which possesses a lower bound also possesses a greatest lower bound. (*Hint:* Consider $\{x | -x \in K\}$.)

14. Prove that the ordered field $(S, +, \cdot, <, 0, 1)$ is complete iff each nonempty subset of S which possesses a lower bound also possesses a greatest lower bound.

15. Prove that the basic set of each ordered field is infinite.

16. Prove that any two complete ordered fields are isomorphic.

17. Prove that the algebraic system $(\{0, 1, 2, \cdots, k - 1\}, +, \cdot, 0, 1)$, where $+$ and $\cdot$ represent *addition modulo k* and *multiplication modulo k* respectively, is a field iff k is prime.

3.8   Vector Spaces

Algebraic systems can be used to characterize a more complex mathematical structure — the notion of a *vector space*.

DEFINITION 3.8.1.   The ordered triple $(\mathcal{F}, \mathcal{V}, \circ)$, where $\mathcal{F} = (F, +, \cdot, 0, 1)$ and $\mathcal{V} = (V, +, \mathbf{0})$, is said to be a *vector space* iff:

    (i) $\mathcal{F}$ is a field,
    (ii) $\mathcal{V}$ is an abelian group,
    (iii) $\circ$ is a mapping of $F \times V$ into V,
    (iv) $\forall a \forall x \forall y [a \in F \land x \in V \land y \in V \to a \circ (x + y) = a \circ x + a \circ y]$,
    (v) $\forall a \forall b \forall x [a \in F \land b \in F \land x \in V \to (a + b) \circ x = a \circ x + b \circ x]$,
    (vi) $\forall a \forall b \forall x [a \in F \land b \in F \land x \in V \to (a \cdot b) \circ x = a \circ (b \circ x)]$,
    (vii) $\forall x [x \in V \to 1 \circ x = x]$.

The members of V are called *vectors* and the members of F are called *scalars*. The mapping $\circ$ is called *scalar multiplication*. It is customary to denote $a \circ x$, where a is a scalar and x is a vector, by writing "ax"; indeed, $a \cdot b$ is customarily denoted by "ab", where a and b are scalars. We rely on the context to distinguish between field multiplication and scalar multiplication.

We now present some vector spaces.

EXAMPLE 1.   Let $(F, +, \cdot, 0, 1)$ be any field, let $V = F \times F$, let $(a, b) + (c, d) = (a + c, b + d)$ whenever $(a, b) \in V$ and $(c, d) \in V$, let $\mathbf{0} = (0, 0)$, and let $c \circ (a, b) = (c \cdot a, c \cdot b)$ whenever $c \in F$ and $(a, b) \in V$.

EXAMPLE 2.   Let $(F, +, \cdot, 0, 1)$ be any field, let V be the set of all mappings of

$\{0,1\}$ into F, let $f+g=\{(0,f(0)+g(0)),(1,f(1)+g(1))\}$ whenever $f\in V$ and $g\in V$, let $\mathbf{0}=\{(0,0),(1,0)\}$, and let $c\circ f=\{(0,c\cdot f(0)),(1,c\cdot f(1))\}$ whenever $c\in F$ and $f\in V$.

EXAMPLE 3.   Let $(F,+,\cdot,0,1)$ be any field, let V be the set of all mappings of F into F, let $f+g=\{(t,f(t)+g(t))|t\in F\}$ whenever $f\in V$ and $g\in V$, let $\mathbf{0}=\{(t,0)|t\in F\}$, and let $c\circ f=\{(t,c\cdot f(t))|t\in F\}$ whenever $c\in F$ and $f\in V$.

EXAMPLE 4.   Let $(F,+,\cdot,0,1)$ be any field, let V be the set of all $m\times n$ matrices over F, let vector addition be the usual matrix addition, let $\mathbf{0}$ be the null matrix, and let $\circ$ be the operation of multiplying each entry of the matrix by the given scalar.

We now establish some theorems about vector spaces.

THEOREM 3.8.1. $\forall x[x\in V\rightarrow 0\circ x=\mathbf{0}]$.

Proof: Let $(\mathcal{F},\mathcal{V},\circ)$ be any vector space, and let $v\in V$; then, by (v), $(0+0)\circ v=0\circ v+0\circ v$. By (i), $0+0=0$, so $0\circ v=0\circ v+0\circ v$. Hence, by (ii), $0\circ v=\mathbf{0}$. This establishes Theorem 3.8.1.

THEOREM 3.8.2. $\forall x[x\in V\rightarrow (-1)\circ x=-x]$.

Proof: Let $(\mathcal{F},\mathcal{V},\circ)$ be any vector space, and let $v\in V$. By (v), $(1+-1)\circ v=1\circ v+(-1)\circ v$. By (i), $(1+-1)=0$; by (vii), $1\circ v=v$. Therefore, $0\circ v=v+(-1)\circ v$. Hence, by Theorem 3.8.1, $v+(-1)\circ v=\mathbf{0}$. Therefore, $(-1)\circ v$ is the inverse of v, i.e., $(-1)\circ v=-v$. This establishes Theorem 3.8.2.

THEOREM 3.8.3. $\forall a[a\in F\rightarrow a\circ\mathbf{0}=\mathbf{0}]$.

Proof: Apply (iv); the details are left as an exercise.

Let $(\mathcal{F},\mathcal{V},\circ)$ be any vector space, and suppose that W is any nonempty subset of V such that

$$\forall x\forall y[x\in W\wedge y\in W\rightarrow x+y\in W]$$
and
$$\forall a\forall x[a\in F\wedge x\in W\rightarrow a\circ x\in W].$$

Then the mathematical structure $(\mathcal{F},\mathcal{W},\circ|F\times W)$ is said to be a *subsystem* of $(\mathcal{F},\mathcal{V},\circ)$, where $\mathcal{W}=(W,+|W\times W,\mathbf{0})$.   (*Note:* "$\circ|S$" denotes $\circ$ restricted to S.)

THEOREM 3.8.4. $(\mathcal{F},\mathcal{W},\circ|F\times W)$ is a vector space.

Proof: First, we must show that $(W,+|W\times W,\mathbf{0})$ is an abelian group; next, we must show that the remaining conditions of Definition 3.8.1 have been met. The details are left as an exercise.

Since vector addition is associative, we are entitled to suppress parentheses when summing three vecotrs: more precisely, $x + (y + z) = (x + y) + z$; therefore there is no ambiguity in writing "$x + y + z$". Now, consider the expression "$x + y + z + w$", where x, y, z, and w are vectors. To make sense of this expression, we insert parentheses in all possible ways. It is easy to see that no matter how we insert parentheses, we obtain the same vector: for example, $(x + y) + z + w = x + (y + z + w) = (x + y + z) + w = x + (y + z) + w$. For this reason, we agree to suppress parentheses and write "$x + y + z + w$". It is easy to generalize this convention. Indeed, let n be any natural number and let $x_1, x_2, \cdots, x_n$ be any vectors; then there is no ambiguity in writing "$x_1 + x_2 + \cdots + x_n$". No matter how we insert parentheses in this expression, we end up with the same vector.

DEFINITION 3.8.2. Let $v_1, v_2, \cdots, v_n$ be any vectors and let $a_1, a_2, \cdots, a_n$ be any scalars; then the vector

$$a_1 v_1 + a_2 v_2 + \cdots + a_n v_n$$

is said to be a *linear combination* of the vectors $v_1, v_2, \cdots, v_n$.

THEOREM 3.8.5. Let $(\mathcal{F}, \mathcal{V}, \circ)$ be any vector space and suppose $\{v_1, v_2, \cdots, v_n\} \subset V$. Let W be the set of all linear combinations of $v_1, v_2, \cdots, v_n$; then $(\mathcal{F}, \mathcal{W}, \circ | F \times W)$ is a subspace of $(\mathcal{F}, \mathcal{V}, \circ)$, where $\mathcal{W} = (W, + | W \times W, \mathbf{0})$.
Proof: The details are left as an exercise.

DEFINITION 3.8.3. The vectors $v_1, v_2, \cdots, v_n$ are said to be *linearly dependent* iff there are scalars $a_1, a_2, \cdots, a_n$, not all zero, such that $a_1 v_1 + a_2 v_2 + \cdots + a_n v_n = \mathbf{0}$.

DEFINITION 3.8.4. The vectors $v_1, v_2, \cdots, v_n$ are said to be *linearly independent* iff they are not linearly dependent.

Considering the vector space of Example 1, we note that the vectors $(1, 0)$ and $(-1, 0)$ are linearly dependent, since $1 \circ (1, 0) + 1 \circ (-1, 0) = (0, 0) = \mathbf{0}$. In this same vector space, the vectors $(1, 0)$ and $(0, 1)$ are linearly independent. To see this, let a and b be scalars such that

$$a \circ (1, 0) + b \circ (0, 1) = \mathbf{0};$$

then $(a, b) = \mathbf{0}$, i.e., $a = 0$ and $b = 0$.

DEFINITION 3.8.5.   The *dimension* of a vector space is the largest natural number t such that there are t linearly independent vectors in the vector space; if there is no such natural number, the vector space is said to have infinite dimension.

Notice that the vector space of Example 1 has dimension 2, since any three or more vectors of this vector space are linearly dependent.

DEFINITION 3.8.6.   Let $\mathcal{V}$ be a finite-dimensional vector space; then $\{v_1, v_2, \cdots, v_n\}$ is said to be a *basis* for $\mathcal{V}$ iff
(i) V is the set of all linear combinations of $v_1, v_2, \cdots, v_n$,
(ii) $v_1, v_2, \cdots, v_n$ are linearly independent.

For example, $\{(1,0), (0,1)\}$ is a basis for the vector space of Example 1; notice that $c \circ (1,0) + d \circ (0,1) = (c,d)$ whenever c and d are scalars of the vector space.

E X E R C I S E S

1. Let $\mathcal{F} = (F, +, \cdot, 0, 1)$ be any field; show that $(\mathcal{F}, \mathcal{V}, \cdot)$ is a vector space where $\mathcal{V} = (F, +, 0)$.

2. **a.** Let $\mathcal{F} = (F, +, \cdot, 0, 1)$ be any field, and let n be any natural number. Show that $(\mathcal{F}, \mathcal{V}, \circ)$ is a vector space where V is the set of all ordered n-tuples of members of F,
$$(a_1, a_2, \cdots, a_n) + (b_1, b_2, \cdots, b_n) = (a_1 + b_1, a_2 + b_2, \cdots, a_n + b_n),$$
$$0 = (0, 0, \cdots, 0),$$
and $c \circ (a_1, a_2, \cdots, a_n) = (c \cdot a_1, c \cdot a_2, \cdots, c \cdot a_n).$
   b. Present n linearly independent vectors of this vector space.
   c. If $t > n$, prove that any t vectors of this vector space are linearly dependent.

3. **a.** Let $\mathcal{F} = (F, +, \cdot, 0, 1)$ be any field, and let n be any natural number. Show that $(\mathcal{F}, \mathcal{V}, \circ)$ is a vector space where V is the set of all mappings of $\{1, 2, \cdots, n\}$ into F,
$$f + g = \{(t, f(t) + g(t)) \mid t \in \{1, 2, \cdots, n\}\},$$
$$0 = \{(t, 0) \mid t \in \{1, 2, \cdots, n\}\},$$
and $c \circ f = \{(t, c \cdot f(t)) \mid t \in \{1, 2, \cdots, n\}\}.$
   b. Present n linearly independent vectors of this vector space.
   c. If $t > n$, prove that any t vectors of this vector space are linearly dependent.

4. Given that any t vectors of a vector space are linearly dependent, prove that any $t + n$ vectors of the vector space are linearly dependent, where n is any natural number.

5. Prove Theorem 3.8.3.

6. Prove Theorem 3.8.4.

7. Prove Theorem 3.8.5.

8. Given that a is a nonzero scalar and that v is a vector, prove that $a \circ v = 0$ iff $v = 0$.

9. Prove that $v_1, v_2, \cdots, v_n$ are linearly dependent if $v_1 = v_2$.

10. Show that the vector spaces of Examples 1 and 2 are algebraically the same.

11. Show that the vector spaces of Exercises 2 and 3 are algebraically the same.

12. Let $(\mathcal{F}, \mathcal{V}, \circ)$ be any vector space, let V be the set of all linear combinations of the vectors $v_1, v_2, \cdots, v_t$, and let $x_1, x_2, \cdots, x_m$ be linearly independent vectors of V. Prove that there are $t - m$ of the v's, say $v_{m+1}, v_{m+2}, \cdots, v_t$, such that V is the set of all linear combinations of $x_1, x_2, \cdots, x_m, v_{m+1}, v_{m+2}, \cdots, v_t$.

13. Let $v_1, v_2, \cdots, v_t$ be vectors of a given vector space. Prove that the vectors $x_1, x_2, \cdots, x_{t+1}$ are linearly dependent if each of these vectors is a linear combination of $v_1, v_2, \cdots, v_t$.

14. Let $\{x_1, x_2, \cdots, x_s\}$ be a basis for a vector space, and let $\{y_1, y_2, \cdots, y_t\}$ be a basis for the same vector space. Prove that $s = t$.

15. Let $(\mathcal{F}, \mathcal{V}, \circ)$ be a vector space with dimension t. Prove that any set of t linearly independent vectors of this vector space is a basis for the vector space.

16. Prove that a subsystem of a finite-dimensional vector space differs from the vector space iff they have different dimensions.

17. Present an example of an infinite-dimensional vector space.

3.9   Boolean Algebra

The algebraic systems investigated in the preceding sections are important because of their relationship to the various number systems of mathematics. We turn now to the study of a family of algebraic systems called *Boolean algebras*, an investigation which is largely motivated by the algebra of sets. In Section 2.4, we saw that the name of a set can be simplified by applying a strictly algebraic procedure using seventeen basic laws. Of course, we do not need all seventeen laws, since some of these laws can be established algebraically on the basis of the remaining laws. Furthermore, we do not need all of the operations and relations $\cup, \cap, ', \subset$, since some of these can be defined in terms of the others. Do you see the problem that confronts us? We want to choose certain of the operations and relations $\cup, \cap, ', \subset$ and to list certain of their properties in such a manner that the remaining operations and relations can be defined in terms of the chosen ones and their properties established.

This problem was investigated by the famous American mathematician E. V. Huntington, and in 1904 his solution appeared in print (of course, there are other solutions to this problem). He showed that by selecting the binary operations $\cup$ and $\cap$ and the special sets $\varnothing$ and I, only seven basic laws are needed:

LAW 1. $\forall x \forall y [x \cup y = y \cup x]$.
LAW 2. $\forall x \forall y [x \cap y = y \cap x]$.
LAW 3. $\forall x [x \cup \varnothing = x]$.
LAW 4. $\forall x [x \cap I = x]$.
LAW 5. $\forall x \forall y \forall z [x \cap (y \cup z) = (x \cap y) \cup (x \cap z)]$.
LAW 6. $\forall x \forall y \forall z [x \cup (y \cap z) = (x \cup y) \cap (x \cup z)]$.
LAW 7. $\forall x \exists y [x \cup y = I \wedge x \cap y = \varnothing]$.

We want to demonstrate that the unary operation $'$ and the binary relation $\subset$ can be defined in terms of $\cup$, $\cap$, $\varnothing$, and I; and that each of our seventeen basic laws can be established algebraically by using Huntington's seven laws. For this purpose, it is convenient to consider any algebraic system of the type $(B, +, \cdot, 0, 1)$ — where B is the basic set of the algebraic system, $+$ and $\cdot$ are both binary operations on B, 0 and 1 are distinct members of B — in which Huntington's seven laws are true; i.e.,

(1) $\forall x \forall y [x + y = y + x]$
(2) $\forall x \forall y [x \cdot y = y \cdot x]$
(3) $\forall x [x + 0 = x]$
(4) $\forall x [x \cdot 1 = x]$
(5) $\forall x \forall y \forall z [x \cdot (y + z) = (x \cdot y) + (x \cdot z)]$
(6) $\forall x \forall y \forall z [x + (y \cdot z) = (x + y) \cdot (x + z)]$
(7) $\forall x \exists y [x + y = 1 \wedge x \cdot y = 0]$.

Such an algebraic system is called a *Boolean algebra*. For example, the algebraic system $(\{0, 1\}, +, \cdot, 0, 1)$, where $+ = \{(0,0,0), (0,1,1), (1,0,1), (1,1,1)\}$ and $\cdot = \{(0,0,0), (0,1,0), (1,0,0), (1,1,1)\}$, is a Boolean algebra.

Problem: Demonstrate that Huntington's seven laws are true here!

Of course, the algebraic system $(\mathcal{P}I, \cup, \cap, \varnothing, I)$ — where I is a nonempty set, $\cup$ and $\cap$ are the usual operations on sets, and $\varnothing$ is the empty set — is a Boolean algebra, as is easily checked. It is this Boolean algebra that interests us particularly; we want to show that our seventeen basic laws are true here. We accomplish this by proving that these laws are true in *any* Boolean algebra. Suppose, then, that the algebraic system $(B, +, \cdot, 0, 1)$ is a Boolean algebra. Let us prove the following theorems.

THEOREM 3.9.1. $\forall x[x + x = x]$.

Proof: Suppose $a \in B$; then

$$
\begin{aligned}
a &= a + 0 & &\text{by (3)} \\
&= a + (a \cdot b) & &\text{by (7), for a certain } b \in B \\
&= (a + a) \cdot (a + b) & &\text{by (6)} \\
&= (a + a) \cdot 1 & &\text{by (7)} \\
&= a + a & &\text{by (4).}
\end{aligned}
$$

THEOREM 3.9.2. $\forall x[x + x = x]$.

Proof: The proof parallels the proof of Theorem 3.9.1 and is left as an exercise.

THEOREM 3.9.3. $\forall x[x + 1 = 1]$.

Proof: Suppose $a \in B$; then

$$
\begin{aligned}
1 &= a + b & &\text{by (7), for a certain } b \in B \\
&= a + (b \cdot 1) & &\text{by (4)} \\
&= (a + b) \cdot (a + 1) & &\text{by (6)} \\
&= 1 \cdot (a + 1) & &\text{since } a + b = 1 \\
&= (1 \cdot a) + (1 \cdot 1) & &\text{by (5)} \\
&= (1 \cdot a) + 1 & &\text{by Th. 3.9.2} \\
&= (a \cdot 1) + 1 & &\text{by (2)} \\
&= a + 1 & &\text{by (4).}
\end{aligned}
$$

THEOREM 3.9.4. $\forall x[x \cdot 0 = 0]$.

Proof: The proof parallels the proof of Theorem 3.9.3 and is left as an exercise.

THEOREM 3.9.5. $\forall x \forall y[x + (x \cdot y) = x]$.

Proof: Suppose $a \in B$ and $b \in B$; then

$$
\begin{aligned}
a &= a \cdot 1 & &\text{by (4)} \\
&= a \cdot (b + 1) & &\text{by Th. 3.9.3} \\
&= a \cdot (1 + b) & &\text{by (1)} \\
&= (a \cdot 1) + (a \cdot b) & &\text{by (5)} \\
&= a + (a \cdot b) & &\text{by (4).}
\end{aligned}
$$

THEOREM 3.9.6. $\forall x \forall y [x \cdot (x + y) = x]$.

Proof: The proof parallels the proof of Theorem 3.9.5 and is left as an exercise.

THEOREM 3.9.7. $\forall x \forall y \forall z \forall w [z + w = 1 \wedge z \cdot w = 0 \wedge z \cdot x = z \cdot y \wedge w \cdot x = w \cdot y \rightarrow x = y]$.

Proof: Suppose a, b, c, and d are members of B such that $c + d = 1$, $c \cdot d = 0$, $c \cdot a = c \cdot b$, and $d \cdot a = d \cdot b$; then

$$(c \cdot a) + (d \cdot a) = (c \cdot b) + (d \cdot b),$$

and so
$$(c + d) \cdot a = (c + d) \cdot b,$$

i.e.,
$$1 \cdot a = 1 \cdot b;$$

hence
$$a = b.$$

THEOREM 3.9.8. $\forall x \forall y \forall z [x + (y + z) = (x + y) + z]$.

Proof: Suppose a, b, and c are any members of B. Consider the two members of B, $a + (b + c)$ and $(a + b) + c$, and suppose that e is a member of B such that $a + e = 1$ and $a \cdot e = 0$. Then

$$
\begin{aligned}
a \cdot [a + (b + c)] &= (a \cdot a) + [a \cdot (b + c)] && \text{by (5)}\\
&= a + [a \cdot (b + c)] && \text{by Th. 3.9.2}\\
&= a && \text{by Th. 3.9.5;}
\end{aligned}
$$

and
$$
\begin{aligned}
a \cdot [(a + b) + c] &= [a \cdot (a + b)] + (a \cdot c) && \text{by (5)}\\
&= a + (a \cdot c) && \text{by Th. 3.9.6}\\
&= a && \text{by Th. 3.9.5;}
\end{aligned}
$$

therefore, $a \cdot [a + (b + c)] = a \cdot [(a + b) + c]$.

Also,
$$
\begin{aligned}
e \cdot [a + (b + c)] &= (e \cdot a) + [e \cdot (b + c)]\\
&= 0 + [e \cdot (b + c)]\\
&= e \cdot (b + c),
\end{aligned}
$$

and
$$
\begin{aligned}
e \cdot [(a + b) + c] &= [e \cdot (a + b)] + (e \cdot c)\\
&= [(e \cdot a) + (e \cdot b)] + (e \cdot c)\\
&= [0 + (e \cdot b)] + (e \cdot c)\\
&= (e \cdot b) + (e \cdot c)\\
&= e \cdot (b + c);
\end{aligned}
$$

therefore, $e \cdot [a + (b + c)] = e \cdot [(a + b) + c]$.

Thus, by Theorem 3.9.7, $a + (b + c) = (a + b) + c$.

THEOREM 3.9.9. $\forall x \forall y \forall z [x \cdot (y \cdot z) = (x \cdot y) \cdot z]$.

Proof: The proof of this theorem is parallel to that of Theorem 3.9.8. This means that you must first state and prove a theorem parallel to Theorem 3.9.7.

THEOREM 3.9.10. $\forall x \forall y \forall z [x + y = 1 \wedge x \cdot y = 0 \wedge x + z = 1 \wedge x \cdot z = 0 \rightarrow y = z]$.

Proof: Suppose a, b, and c are members of B such that $a + b = 1$, $a \cdot b = 0$, $a + c = 1$, and $a \cdot c = 0$; then

$$b = (a + c) \cdot b = (a \cdot b) + (c \cdot b) = 0 + (c \cdot b) = c \cdot b$$

and $c = (a + b) \cdot c = (a \cdot c) + (b \cdot c) = 0 + (b \cdot c) = b \cdot c = c \cdot b;$

hence $b = c$.

In view of Theorem 3.9.10, we know that given a member of B, say a, there is exactly one member of B, say b, such that $a + b = 1$ and $a \cdot b = 0$. For this reason, we introduce a unary operation on B, called $'$, as follows:

DEFINITION 3.9.1. $' = \{(a,b) \mid a \in B \wedge b \in B \wedge a + b = 1 \wedge a \cdot b = 0\}$.

As usual, if $(a,b) \in '$, then b is denoted by "a'".

THEOREM 3.9.11. $\forall x [(x')' = x]$.

Proof: Suppose $a \in B$; then $a + a' = 1$ and $a \cdot a' = 0$; therefore, $a' + a = 1$ and $a' \cdot a = 0$, and so $(a')' = a$.

THEOREM 3.9.12. $1' = 0$.

Proof: $1 + 0 = 1$, by (3), and $1 \cdot 0 = 0 \cdot 1 = 0$, by (4); therefore, $1' = 0$.

THEOREM 3.9.13. $0' = 1$.

Proof: $0' = (1')' = 1$, by Theorem 3.9.11.

THEOREM 3.9.14. $\forall x \forall y [(x + y)' = x' \cdot y']$.

Proof: Suppose a and b are members of B. Then

$$(a + b) + (a' \cdot b') = [(a + b) + a'] \cdot [(a + b) + b'] = 1 \cdot 1 = 1,$$

and $(a + b) \cdot (a' \cdot b') = [a \cdot (a' \cdot b')] + [b \cdot (a' \cdot b')] = 0 + 0 = 0;$

therefore, $(a + b)' = a' \cdot b'$.

THEOREM 3.9.15. $\forall x \forall y [(x \cdot y)' = x' + y']$.

Proof: Suppose a and b are members of B. Then

$$(a' + b')' = (a')' \cdot (b')' = a \cdot b;$$

and so $$(a \cdot b)' = [(a' + b')']' = a' + b'.$$

We now introduce a binary relation on B, denoted by "$\leq$".

DEFINITION 3.9.2. $\leq = \{(a, b) | a + b = b\}$.

As usual, the statement "$(a, b) \in \leq$" is denoted by writing "$a \leq b$". The proofs of the following three theorems are straightforward.

THEOREM 3.9.16. $\forall x [x \leq x]$.

THEOREM 3.9.17. $\forall x \forall y [x \leq y \land y \leq x \rightarrow x = y]$.

THEOREM 3.9.18. $\forall x \forall y \forall z [x \leq y \land y \leq z \rightarrow x \leq z]$.

This completes our demonstration that each of our seventeen basic laws can be established algebraically by using Huntington's seven laws.

E X E R C I S E S

1. Show that $(\{0, 1\}, +, \cdot, 1, 0)$ is a Boolean algebra, where $+ = \{(0,0,0), (0,1,0), (1,0,0), (1,1,1)\}$ and $\cdot = \{(0,0,0), (0,1,1), (1,0,1), (1,1,1)\}$.

2. Show that the algebraic system $(\{a, b, c, d\}, +, \cdot, a, b)$ is a Boolean algebra, where the binary operations are defined by the following tables:

+	a	b	c	d
a	a	b	c	d
b	b	b	b	b
c	c	b	c	b
d	d	b	b	d

·	a	b	c	d
a	a	a	a	a
b	a	b	c	d
c	a	c	c	a
d	a	d	a	d

Prove that the following propositions are true in each Boolean algebra:

3. $\forall x \forall y [x + (y \cdot x') = x + y]$.

4. $\forall x \forall y \forall z [(x \cdot y \cdot z) + (x' + y' + z') = 1]$.

5. $\forall x[0 \le x \wedge x \le 1]$.

6. $\forall x \forall y \forall z[x \le y \rightarrow z + x \le z + y]$.

7. $\forall x \forall y[x \le y \leftrightarrow x \cdot y' = 0]$.

8. $\forall x \forall y[x \le y \leftrightarrow y + x' = 1]$.

9. $\forall x \forall y \forall z[x \le y \wedge x \le z \rightarrow x \le y \cdot z]$.

10. $\forall x \forall y[x \le y \leftrightarrow y' \le x']$.

11. $\forall x \forall y[x \le y \leftrightarrow x \cdot y = x]$.

12. $\forall x \forall y \forall z[x \le y \rightarrow z \cdot x \le z \cdot y]$.

13. Construct a Boolean algebra such that the basic set of the algebraic system has exactly eight members.

14. Show that there is no Boolean algebra whose basic set has exactly three members.

15. Show that $(B, ?, !, a, b)$ is a Boolean algebra whenever $(B, !, ?, b, a)$ is a Boolean algebra.

16. Suppose that I is a nonempty set with an even number of members, and that I has more than three members. Show that $(B, \cup, \cap, \varnothing, I)$ is *not* a Boolean algebra, where "B" denotes the collection of all subsets of I that have an even number of members, $\cup$ and $\cap$ are the usual operations on sets, and $\varnothing$ is the empty set.

17. Suppose that I is a nonempty set and that B is a collection of subsets of I. Prove that $(B, \cup, \cap, \varnothing, I)$ is a Boolean algebra, where $\cup$ and $\cap$ are the usual operations on sets — provided that $\cup$ and $\cap$ are binary operations on B, $\varnothing \in B$, and $I \in B$.

18. Show that no algebraic system is both a field and a Boolean algebra.

19. a. Show that $(B, +, \cdot, (0,0), (1,1))$ is a Boolean algebra, where $B = \{(0,0), (0,1), (1,0), (1,1)\}$, $(a,b) + (c,d) = (\max\{a,c\}, \max\{b,d\})$, and $(a,b) \cdot (c,d) = (a \cdot c, b \cdot d)$.

   b. Construct a Boolean algebra whose basic set has 2^n members, given that n is a natural member.

20. Show that $(P, \vee, \wedge, f, t)$ is a Boolean algebra, where for each proposition p, $\{q | q$ is a proposition and "$q \leftrightarrow p$" is logically true$\} \in P$, "$\vee$" and "$\wedge$" denote the logical connectives discussed in Chapter 1, "f" denotes the equivalence class consisting of logically false propositions, and "t" denotes the equivalence class consisting of logically true propositions.

Chapter 4

Number Systems

4.1 The Peano System

Our purpose in this chapter is to study some of the important number systems of mathematics. We shall begin with the axiomatic presentation of a rudimentary system which we call the Peano System. A great achievement of the Italian mathematician G. Peano, in the latter part of the nineteenth century, was the discovery that the natural number system $(N, +, \cdot, <, 1)$ can be constructed from the much simpler algebraic system $(N, ', 1)$, where $'$ is a unary operation on N known as the *successor* operation, and $1 \in N$. Using the axiomatic approach, Peano characterized his rudimentary number system by listing three of its properties. Essentially, this means that Peano discovered three fundamental properties of the natural number system which could be expressed in terms of the successor operation and the special number 1. From these three properties flow all the number systems of mathematics.

We now introduce the notion of a Peano System.

> **DEFINITION 4.1.1.** Let $(N, ', 1)$ be any algebraic system—where $'$ is a unary operation on N, and $1 \in N$—such that
>
> 1. $\forall x[x' \neq 1]$,
> 2. $\forall x \forall y[x \neq y \rightarrow x' \neq y']$,
> 3. $S = N$ whenever S is a subset of N such that
>   a. $1 \in S$,
>   b. $\forall x[x \in S \rightarrow x' \in S]$.
>
> Then $(N, ', 1)$ is said to be a Peano System.

Propositions 1, 2, and 3 are known as the *Peano Postulates*.

Let us pause to consider the intuitive content of the Peano Postulates. First, we interpret the successor operation as the operation "add one".

Intuitively, then, x' stands for $x + 1$. In these terms, we easily see that the Peano Postulates express our innate ideas about the system of natural numbers. The first postulate asserts that adding 1 to a given natural number produces a number different from 1. The second postulate asserts that $x + 1 \neq y + 1$ whenever $x \neq y$. The third postulate, known as the *Induction Postulate,* states that each natural number is a member of a given set of natural numbers which has the following properties:

    a. 1 is a member of the given set,
    b. if x is a member of the given set, then so is $x + 1$.

We observe that the first two postulates work together to ensure that N is large. Let us prove that no two of 1, $1'$, $(1')'$, $[(1')']'$ are the same. By Postulate 1, $1 \neq 1'$; therefore, by Postulate 2, $1' \neq (1')'$. Hence, by Postulate 1, no two of 1, $1'$, $(1')'$ are the same. We show $[(1')']'$ is different from each of 1, $1'$, $(1')'$. By Postulate 1, $[(1')']' \neq 1$; since $(1')' \neq 1$, it follows from Postulate 2 that $[(1')']' \neq 1'$. Finally, since $(1')' \neq 1'$, it follows from Postulate 2 that $[(1')']' \neq (1')'$. This establishes that no two of 1, $1'$, $(1')'$, $[(1')']'$ are the same.

Next, let us consider the function of Peano's third postulate, the Induction Postulate. Since the first two postulates ensure that N is large, we would like the remaining postulate to restrict the size of N. In fact, this is the case. Consider the set S constructed as follows:

$$S = \{1, 1', (1')', [(1')']', ([(1')']')', \text{ and so on}\}.$$

We have extended our code for naming sets; however, the construction should be clear. We put 1 in S and then apply the successor operation repeatedly to obtain more members of S. By construction, then, $x' \in S$ whenever $x \in S$. Applying the Induction Postulate, we conclude that $S = N$. Thus, the size of N is restricted by this postulate.

It is customary to call the members of N *natural numbers.* There is an important proof technique, known as *mathematical induction,* which we have used informally on several occasions (for example, see Sec. 1.3 and Sec. 2.5). It is time, now, to formalize the procedure involved. Let $P(x)$ be a propositional form which generates a proposition whenever a natural number is substituted for "x"; we shall say that a natural number, say k, has property P iff $P(k)$ is true.

THEOREM 4.1.1 (Mathematical Induction). Each natural number has property P iff
    (i) 1 has property P,

(ii) k' has property P whenever k is a natural number which has property P.

Proof: Let $S = \{k | k \in N \wedge P(k)\}$. By (i), $1 \in S$; furthermore, by (ii), $\forall x [x \in S \rightarrow x' \in S]$. Therefore by the Induction Postulate, $S = N$, i.e., $\forall k [k \in N \rightarrow P(k)]$. This means that each natural number has property P.

To illustrate this method of proving theorems, consider the following theorem.

THEOREM 4.1.2. $\forall x \exists y [x = 1 \vee x = y']$.

Proof: We must show that each natural number is 1 or is the successor of a natural number. Clearly 1 has the property. Suppose k has the property. But certainly k' has the property, since k' is the successor of k. Therefore, by mathematical induction, each natural number has the property.

THEOREM 4.1.3. $\forall x [x \neq x']$.

Proof: We must show that each natural number has the property that it is different from its successor. But 1 has the property, since $1 \neq 1'$ by Peano Postulate 1. Suppose k is a natural number with the property; then $k \neq k'$. Therefore, by Peano Postulate 2, $k' \neq (k')'$. Thus, k' has the property. By mathematical induction, each natural number has the property.

THEOREM 4.1.4. $\forall y \forall z [y' = z' \rightarrow y = z]$.

Proof: Suppose there are natural numbers a and b such that $a' = b'$, yet $a \neq b$. By Peano Postulate 2, $a' \neq b'$ since $a \neq b$. Contradiction! Notice that this theorem asserts that each natural number has at most one predecessor.

We shall now demonstrate that there is essentially just one Peano System; i.e., we wish to prove that $\mathfrak{N} \cong \mathfrak{B}$ whenever $\mathfrak{N} = (N, ', 1)$ and $\mathfrak{B} = (B, *, e)$ are Peano Systems.

Let μ be a mapping of N into B defined as follows:

(i) $\mu(1) = e$,
(ii) $\mu(k') = [\mu(k)]^*$ whenever $k \in N$.

We intend to use μ to establish that $\mathfrak{N} \cong \mathfrak{B}$. Hold on! Does μ exist? We have presented two properties of a supposed mapping; how do we know that there is a mapping with these properties? We may regard (i) and (ii) as instructions which are intended to associate a member of B with each member of N. The question is: are the given instructions adequate to the purpose? In other words is there a member of N which is not supplied with an image? We shall use mathematical induction to establish the existence of μ; indeed, we shall prove that μ is unique.

Lemma 1:   There is a unique mapping μ of N into B such that

> (i) $\mu(1) = e$,
> (ii) $\mu(k') = [\mu(k)]^*$ whenever $k \in N$.

Proof: We shall regard (i) and (ii) as constituting an instruction μ. Let $t \in N$; we shall say that t has property P iff a unique member of B is associated with t by μ. First, we note, by (i), that 1 has property P. Next, suppose that k has property P; then the instruction μ associates a unique member of B with k, which we denote by "$\mu(k)$". Therefore, by (ii), μ associates a unique member of B with k', namely $[\mu(k)]^*$. Hence, by mathematical induction, each member of N has property P. This establishes Lemma 1.

Now that we know that μ is a mapping of N into B, let us prove that μ is a one–one mapping of N onto B.

Lemma 2: μ is a one–one mapping of N onto B.
Proof: We shall sketch a proof and leave the details as an exercise. First, note that each member of B is an image, under μ, of at least one member of N; this is easy to prove by mathematical induction. Next, we must show that each member of B is the image of exactly one member of N. But e has this property; furthermore, if b has the property, then so has b^*. This establishes Lemma 2.

Finally, we can come to grips with our main theorem.

THEOREM 4.1.5. $(N,',1) \cong (B,*,e)$, provided that these are Peano Systems.
Proof: We show that $\mu(N,',1)$ is $(B,*,e)$. By Lemma 2, $\mu N = B$; moreover, $\mu(1) = e$ by definition. It remains to prove that μ transforms the unary operation $'$ into $*$. Let $(a,b) \in '$; then $\mu(a,b) = (\mu a, \mu b) = (\mu a, \mu a') = (\mu a, (\mu a)^*)$ by definition. Since $(\mu a, (\mu a)^*) \in *$, it follows that $\mu' \subset *$. But each member of B is a first term of exactly one ordered pair in $*$; therefore, $\mu' = *$. This establishes Theorem 4.1.5.

To facilitate the study of the Peano System $(N, ', 1)$, we introduce an efficient method of naming the members of N. We have established that $N = \{1, 1', (1')', [(1')']', ([(1')']')', \ldots\}$. We shall construct names of members of N from the symbols "0", "1", "2", "3", "4", "5", "6", "7", "8", "9" — the so-called digits. Let us agree to denote $1'$ by "2", $2'$ by "3", $3'$ by "4", $4'$ by "5", $5'$ by "6", $6'$ by "7", $7'$ by "8", and $8'$ by "9". To construct a name for $9'$ we juxtapose the digits "1" and "0", thereby obtaining "10". Continuing in this way, we construct a name for each member of N by juxtaposing digits. Using these names, we display the following partial table for the successor operation:

a	1	2	3	4	5	6	7	8	9	10	11	12	$\cdots$
a'	2	3	4	5	6	7	8	9	10	11	12	13	$\cdots$

In this table the first term of an ordered pair in $'$ is written above the line, and the corresponding second term is written below the line.

We turn now to the basic idea underlying the *less than* relation on N. Now, each natural number can be constructed from 1 by applying the successor operation first to 1, then to the object that results, and so on. For example, we can obtain 10 by starting with 1 and applying the successor operation repeatedly (in fact, nine times) as follows:

$$1' = 2, \ 2' = 3, \ 3' = 4, \ 4' = 5, \ 5' = 6, \ 6' = 7, \ 7' = 8, \ 8' = 9, \ 9' = 10.$$

What has this to do with the *less than* relation on N? Let us consult our intuition. We regard x as being less than y iff x precedes y in the list for y; i.e. when we construct y by applying the successor operation repeatedly to 1 we obtain x before we obtain y.

Our job is to characterize mathematically the set of all natural numbers that are used to construct k, where $k \in N$, in this way. Unfortunately, this is not as easy as it sounds. First, we need the notion of a *chain*. By a *chain* we mean a subset of N such that the *predecessor* of each member of the set is also a member of the set (y is said to be a predecessor of x iff $y' = x$). Notice that if x has a predecessor then x has a unique predecessor.

DEFINITION 4.1.2.   A subset of N, say S, is said to be a *chain*, iff

$$\forall x \forall y [x \in S \wedge x = y' \rightarrow y \in S].$$

We point out that this concept is related to the induction postulate in the sense that the predecessor of each member of a chain is also in the chain, whereas the set referred to in the induction postulate has the property that the successor of each member of the set is also a member of the set.

THEOREM 4.1.6. Let k be any natural number; then there is a chain, say S, such that $k \in S$.

Proof: Clearly $\{1\}$ is a chain and $1 \in \{1\}$; therefore, 1 has the property. Suppose t is a natural number with the property; then there is a chain S such that $t \in S$. But $S \cup \{t'\}$ is a chain! To see this, let $a \in S \cup \{t'\}$; if $a \in S$ and $a = b'$, then $b \in S$ since S is a chain. Moreover, $t \in S$ by assumption. So, $S \cup \{t'\}$ is a chain. This establishes that t' has the property whenever t has the property. By mathematical induction, each natural number has the property. This establishes Theorem 4.1.6.

Let us associate with a given natural number, say k, the family of chains to which k belongs. Actually, we want to select a particular chain in the family and associate that chain with k. Intuitively, the idea is to associate with k the *smallest* chain in the family. Consider the intersection of all the chains in the family; this is a set which we shall denote by "C_k".

DEFINITION 4.1.3. Let $k \in N$; $C_k = \bigcap_{\alpha} S_{\alpha}$ where S_{α} is a chain and $k \in S_{\alpha}$.

THEOREM 4.1.7. Let $k \in N$; then C_k is a chain and $k \in C_k$.

Proof: $k \in C_k$, since $k \in S_{\alpha}$ for each α. Suppose $x \in C_k$ and $x = y'$; then $x \in S_{\alpha}$ for each α, and $y \in S_{\alpha}$ for each α, since each S_{α} is a chain. Hence, $y \in C_k$. This proves that C_k is a chain.

THEOREM 4.1.8. Let S be any chain; then $\forall k[k \in S \rightarrow C_k \subset S]$.

Proof: Clearly, $1 \in S \rightarrow \{1\} \subset S$; but $C_1 = \{1\}$. Thus, 1 has the property. Suppose t has the property; i.e., $t \in S \rightarrow C_t \subset S$. We shall show that t' has the property. Suppose $t' \in S$; then $t \in S$, since S is a chain. Therefore, $C_t \subset S$ by assumption. Hence, $C_t \cup \{t'\} \subset S$. But $C_t \cup \{t'\}$ is a chain containing t'; therefore, $C_{t'} \subset C_t \cup \{t'\}$, since $C_{t'}$ is the intersection of all chains containing t'. Thus, $C_{t'} \subset S$. We conclude that t' has the property whenever t has the property. By mathematical induction, each natural number has the property.

THEOREM 4.1.9. $\forall k[C_k \subset C_{k'}]$.

Proof: $C_1 = \{1\}$, $C_{1'} = \{1, 1'\}$; therefore, 1 has the property. Suppose t has the property; i.e., $C_t \subset C_{t'}$. We must show that $C_{t'} \subset C_{(t')'}$. But $(t')' \in C_{(t')'}$; therefore, $t' \in C_{(t')'}$, since $C_{(t')'}$ is a chain. Hence, by Theorem

4.1.8, $C_{t'} \subset C_{(t')'}$. We conclude that t' has the property whenever t has the property. Hence, by mathematical induction, each natural number has the property.

THEOREM 4.1.10. $\forall k[C_{k'} = C_k \cup \{k'\}]$.

Proof: $C_{1'} = \{1, 1'\} = \{1\} \cup \{1'\} = C_1 \cup \{1'\}$; therefore, 1 has the property. Assume t has the property; then $C_{t'} = C_t \cup \{t'\}$. Consider $C_{t'} \cup \{(t')'\} = S$. Clearly, S is a chain containing $(t')'$. Therefore, $C_{(t')'} \subset S$. But $C_{t'} \subset C_{(t')'}$ by Theorem 4.1.9, and $(t')' \in C_{(t')'}$ by definition. Therefore, $C_{t'} \cup \{(t')'\} \subset C_{(t')'}$; i.e., $S \subset C_{(t')'}$. Hence, $C_{(t')'} = S = C_{t'} \cup \{(t')'\}$. We conclude that t' has the property whenever t has the property. By mathematical induction, each natural number has the property.

THEOREM 4.1.11. $\forall k[k' \bar{\in} C_k]$.

Proof: $1' \bar{\in} \{1\}$; therefore, 1 has the property. Assume t has the property; then $t' \bar{\in} C_t$. We show t' has the property. But $C_{t'} = C_t \cup \{t'\}$ by Theorem 4.1.10; if $(t')' \in C_{t'}$, then $(t')' \in C_t$, since $(t')' \neq t'$ by Theorem 4.1.3. But C_t is a chain; hence, $t' \in C_t$. This contradiction demonstrates that t' has the property whenever t has the property. By mathematical induction, each natural number has the property.

Next, we want to bring out an important property of chains contained in Theorem 4.1.12. To this purpose, we need the notion of equinumerous sets. Let A and B be any sets; intuitively, A and B have the same number of members, i.e., are equinumerous, iff we can pair off the members of B with the members of A in such a fashion that each member of both sets is used exactly once in the pairing process. In mathematical language, A and B are equinumerous iff there is a one–one mapping of A onto B. The technical term used here is *equivalent*; i.e., equinumerous sets are said to be equivalent.

DEFINITION 4.1.4.   Let A and B be any sets; then A is said to be equivalent to B iff there is a one–one mapping of A onto B. If A is equivalent to B, we write "$A \equiv B$".

For example, $\{1, 2, 3\} \equiv \{2, 5, 10\}$, since $\{(1, 2), (2, 5), (3, 10)\}$ is a one–one mapping of $\{1, 2, 3\}$ onto $\{2, 5, 10\}$.

THEOREM 4.1.12. $\forall k[C_k$ is the only subset of C_k equivalent to $C_k]$.
Proof: $C_1 = \{1\}$, and $\varnothing$ is not equivalent to $\{1\}$. Therefore, 1 has the

property. Assume t has the property; then no proper subset of C_t is equivalent to C_t. We show t' has the property. Suppose that A is a proper subset of $C_{t'}$ equivalent to $C_{t'}$. Then there is a member of $C_{t'}$ not in A; clearly we may assume that $t' \in A$. Since $C_{t'} = C_t \cup \{t'\}$, we see that $A \subset C_t$. Now, let μ be a one–one mapping of A onto $C_{t'}$ and let $\mu(a) = t'$, where $a \in A$. Then $\mu(A - \{a\}) = C_t$. This means that $A - \{a\}$ is equivalent to C_t. But $A - \{a\}$ is a proper subset of C_t. This contradiction demonstrates that t' has the property whenever t has the property. By mathematical induction, each natural number has the property.

THEOREM 4.1.13. $\forall y[C_1 = C_y \rightarrow 1 = y]$.

Proof: Suppose $C_y = C_1$; but $C_1 = \{1\}$. Therefore, $y = 1$ since $y \in C_y$ by Theorem 4.1.7.

THEOREM 4.1.14. $\forall x \forall y[C_x = C_y \rightarrow x = y]$.

Proof: In view of Theorem 4.1.13 and Theorem 4.1.2, we need only show that $x' = y'$ whenever $C_{x'} = C_{y'}$. But $C_{x'} = C_x \cup \{x'\}$ and $C_{y'} = C_y \cup \{y'\}$. If $x' \neq y'$, then $x' \in C_y$; therefore, by Theorem 4.1.8, $C_{x'} \in C_y$. But $y' \in C_y$ by Theorem 4.1.11; hence, $y' \in C_{x'}$. Thus, $C_{x'} \neq C_{y'}$. This contradiction establishes Theorem 4.1.14.

COROLLARY 4.1.1. $\forall x \forall y[C_x = C_y \leftrightarrow x = y]$.

Proof: Apply Theorem 4.1.14.

We now list some properties of chains which we shall need later. First, we note that if k is a natural number, then $k \in C_k$ and $k' \in C_k$; thus $\forall x \exists y[y \in C_x \wedge y' \in C_x]$. In fact we can prove that there is just one member of C_x with this property.

THEOREM 4.1.15. $\forall x \exists! y[y \in C_x \wedge y' \in C_x]$.

Proof: Use mathematical induction; the details are left as an exercise.

COROLLARY 4.1.2. $\forall x \forall y[y \in C_x \wedge y' \in C_x \rightarrow y = x]$.

Proof: Theorem 4.1.15.

THEOREM 4.1.16. $\forall x \forall y[x \in C_y \vee y \in C_x]$.

Proof: Use mathematical induction and Corollary 4.1.2.

THEOREM 4.1.17. $\forall x \forall y[C_x \subset C_y \vee C_y \subset C_x]$.

Proof: Let $x \in N$ and let $y \in N$. By Theorem 4.1.16 $x \in C_y$ or $y \in C_x$.

If $x \in C_y$ then $C_x \subset C_y$ by Theorem 4.1.8. If $y \in C_x$ then $C_y \subset C_x$ by Theorem 4.1.8. This establishes our result.

We can now establish a trichotomy law for chains. To this purpose we shall use the *proper subset* relation. Let us agree to denote $A \subset B \wedge A \neq B$ by writing "$A \underset{p}{\subset} B$" (read "$A$ is a proper subset of B").

THEOREM 4.1.18. $\forall x \forall y [C_x = C_y \vee C_x \underset{p}{\subset} C_y \vee C_y \underset{p}{\subset} C_x]$.

Proof: Let $x \in N$ and let $y \in N$. There are just two possibilities: $x = y$ or $x \neq y$.

1. Suppose $x = y$; then $C_x = C_y$ by Corollary 4.1.1. Therefore C_x is not a proper subset of C_y, and C_y is not a proper subset of C_x.

2. Suppose $x \neq y$; then $C_x \neq C_y$ by Corollary 4.1.1. But, by Theorem 4.1.17, $C_x \subset C_y \vee C_y \subset C_x$. Since $C_x \neq C_y$ these are proper subsets; i.e., $C_x \underset{p}{\subset} C_y \vee C_y \underset{p}{\subset} C_x$. Moreover, if $C_x \underset{p}{\subset} C_y \wedge C_y \underset{p}{\subset} C_x$, then $C_x = C_y$, which is impossible. Therefore, $C_x \underset{p}{\subset} C_y \vee C_y \underset{p}{\subset} C_x$. This establishes our result.

Finally, we point out that chains possess a practical and important application. The statement "Set A has exactly n members", where n is a natural number, can be given a precise meaning, as follows.

DEFINITION 4.1.5.   Let $n \in N$ and let A be any set. Then we shall say that A has exactly n members iff $A \equiv C_n$.

For example, {sun, moon, Mars} has exactly 3 members since {sun, moon, Mars} $\equiv C_3$.

EXERCISES

1. Use mathematical induction to prove that $\forall x [x \neq (x')']$ is true in any Peano System $(N, ', 1)$.

2. **a.** Prove that "$\forall x [x = 1 \vee \exists! y [x = y']]$" is true in any Peano System $(N, ', 1)$.
   b. Show that "$\forall x \exists! y [x = 1 \vee x = y']$" is false in any Peano System $(N, ', 1)$.

3. Prove Lemma 2.

4. Prove that each natural number has property P iff
   (i) 1 has property P,
   (ii) k' has property P whenever each member of C_k has property P.

5. Is the empty set a chain?

6. Let S and T be chains.
  a. Prove that $S \cup T$ is a chain.
  b. Prove that $S \cap T$ is a chain.
  c. Is the complement of S necessarily a chain?
7. a. Prove that $\forall k [1 \in C_k]$.
  b. Prove that $\forall k [1' \in C_{k'}]$.
8. a. Prove Theorem 4.1.15.
  b. Prove Corollary 4.1.2.
9. Prove that $\forall x \forall k [x \in C_k \to x' \in C_{k'}]$.
10. Prove Theorem 4.1.16.
11. Show that there is exactly one mapping of $N \times N$ into N, say μ, such that
  (i) $\mu(n, 1) = n'$ whenever $n \in N$,
  (ii) $\mu(n, k') = [\mu(n, k)]'$ whenever $n \in N$ and $k \in N$.
12. Let A be any set. We shall say A is *finite* iff $A = \varnothing$ or $\exists k [k \in N \wedge A \equiv C_k]$. A set which is not finite is said to be *infinite*.
  a. Prove that no finite set is equivalent to one of its *proper* subsets.
  b. Show that N is equivalent to one of its proper subsets. Is N finite?
  c. Suppose T is a superset of N (i.e., $N \subset T$); prove that T is equivalent to one of its proper subsets.
13. Prove that a set, say A, is infinite iff A is equivalent to one of its proper subsets.
14. Let "B" denote the set of all objects constructed by juxtaposing a finite number of 1's, e.g., 1, 11, 111, 1111, and so on. Show that $(B, *, 1)$ is a Peano System, where $x^* = x1$ whenever $x \in B$.
15. Let $(N, ', 1)$ be any Peano System, let ν be any mapping of S into S, where S is a nonempty set, and let $a \in S$. Prove that there is a unique mapping of N into S, say μ, such that
  (i) $\mu(1) = a$,
  (ii) $\mu(k') = \nu[\mu(k)]$ whenever $k \in N$.
16. Let $(N, ', 1)$ be any Peano System, and let λ and ν be mappings of N into N. Prove that there is a unique mapping of $N \times N$ into N, say μ, such that
  (i) $\mu(m, 1) = \lambda(m)$ whenever $m \in N$,
  (ii) $\mu(m, k') = \nu[\mu(m, k)]$ whenever $m \in N$ and $k \in N$.
17. Let $(N, ', 1)$ be any Peano System, let λ be a mapping of N into N, and let ν be a mapping of $N \times N$ into N. Prove that there is a unique mapping of $N \times N$ into N, say μ, such that
  (i) $\mu(m, 1) = \lambda(m)$ whenever $m \in N$,
  (ii) $\mu(m, k') = \nu[\mu(m, k), m]$ whenever $m \in N$ and $k \in N$.
18. Given that A and B are sets, prove the following:
  a. $A \equiv A$.
  b. $B \equiv A$ if $A \equiv B$.
  c. $A \equiv C$ if $A \equiv B$ and $B \equiv C$.
  Express the preceding statements in intuitive language.

4.2   The Natural Number System

Our purpose in this section is to *construct* the natural number system from the Peano System. The basic set of the natural number system is N, the basic set of the Peano System. We shall construct two binary operations on N called *addition* and *multiplication*, and one binary relation on N called *less than*.

Let $(N, ', 1)$ be the Peano System; we define $+$, a mapping of $N \times N$ into N, as follows:

DEFINITION 4.2.1.   The sum of two natural numbers is computed by applying the following construction steps:
(i) $a + 1$ is defined to be a' — whenever $(a, 1) \in N \times N$.
(ii) $a + b'$ is defined to be $(a + b)'$, provided $a + b$ is defined — whenever $(a, b) \in N \times N$.

For example, $3 + 1 = 4$ by (i); $3 + 2 = 3 + 1' = (3 + 1)'$ by (ii); hence, $3 + 2 = 4' = 5$. Similarly, $3 + 3 = 3 + 2' = (3 + 2)' = 5' = 6$.

We now establish directly that Definition 4.2.1 actually defines a mapping of $N \times N$ into N; alternatively, we may apply Exercise 16, page 131.

THEOREM 4.2.1. $+$ is a binary operation on N.

Proof: Suppose there is a member of $N \times N$ which does not have a unique member of N associated with it under $+$, say (m, n). We shall show, using mathematical induction, that each ordered pair with first term m has associated with it a unique natural number. Let us be clear about the property that is involved. A natural number, say t, has the property iff $m + t$ is defined. Clearly, 1 has the property, since $m + 1 = m'$ by (i). Furthermore, if k has the property (so $m + k$ is defined), then k' has the property, since $m + k' = (m + k)'$ by (ii). This demonstrates that $m + t$ is defined whenever $t \in N$. In particular, $+$ associates a unique natural number with the ordered pair (m, n). This contradiction establishes Theorem 4.2.1.

We now introduce multiplication.

DEFINITION 4.2.2.   The product of two natural numbers is computed by applying the following construction steps:
(i) $a \cdot 1$ is defined to be a — whenever $(a, 1) \in N \times N$.
(ii) $a \cdot b'$ is defined to be $a \cdot b + a$, provided $a \cdot b$ is defined — whenever $(a, b) \in N \times N$.

For example, $3 \cdot 1 = 3$ by (i); $3 \cdot 2 = 3 \cdot 1' = 3 \cdot 1 + 3$ by (ii); hence, $3 \cdot 2 = 3 + 3 = 6$. Similarly, $3 \cdot 3 = 3 \cdot 2' = 3 \cdot 2 + 3 = 6 + 3$; but $6 + 3 = 6 + 2' = (6 + 2)' = (6 + 1')' = ([6 + 1]')' = ([6']')' = (7')' = 8' = 9$; so, $3 \cdot 3 = 9$.

By using mathematical induction or applying Exercise 17, page 131, it is easy to prove the following theorem.

THEOREM 4.2.2. $\cdot$ is a binary operation on N.

Next, we introduce the important binary relation on N called *less than* and denoted by "$<$".

DEFINITION 4.2.3.   Suppose $(a, b) \in N \times N$; then $a < b$ iff $a' \in C_b$.

For example, $3 < 5$ since $3' \in C_5$. (Note that $C_5 = \{1, 2, 3, 4, 5\}$.)

Now to work. We have constructed the important algebraic system $(N, +, \cdot, <, 1)$, called the *natural number system*, and must now demonstrate some of its properties.

THEOREM 4.2.3. $\forall x \forall y \forall z [(x + y) + z = x + (y + z)]$.

Proof: Proof is by mathematical induction on z; i.e., we shall say that t has property P iff $\forall x \forall y [(x + y) + t = x + (y + t)]$. We show 1 has property P. Let x and y be any natural numbers; then

$$(x + y) + 1 = (x + y)' = x + y' \qquad \text{by Def. 4.2.1}$$
and
$$x + (y + 1) = x + y' \qquad \text{by Def. 4.2.1.}$$

Now, suppose k has property P; then $\forall x \forall y [(x + y) + k = x + (y + k)]$. But

$$(x + y) + k' = [(x + y) + k]' \qquad \text{by Def. 4.2.1}$$
$$= [x + (y + k)]' \qquad \text{by assumption}$$
and
$$x + (y + k') = x + (y + k)' = [x + (y + k)]' \qquad \text{by Def. 4.2.1.}$$

Thus, k' has property P whenever k has property P. By mathematical induction, it follows that each natural number has property P; i.e., $\forall z \forall x \forall y [(x + y) + z = x + (y + z)]$. So, $\forall x \forall y \forall z [(x + y) + z = x + (y + z)]$.

THEOREM 4.2.4. $\forall y [1 + y = y + 1]$.

Proof: We shall establish this theorem by mathematical induction. The property of natural numbers involved here is this: we shall say a natural number t has property P iff $1 + t = t + 1$. Clearly, 1 has property P. Suppose k has property P; then $1 + k = k + 1$. We wish to show that k' has property P. But

$$
\begin{aligned}
k' + 1 &= (k + 1) + 1 && \text{by Def. 4.2.1} \\
&= (1 + k) + 1 && \text{by assumption} \\
&= 1 + (k + 1) && \text{by Th. 4.2.3} \\
&= 1 + k' && \text{by Def. 4.2.1.}
\end{aligned}
$$

Hence, k' has property P whenever k has property P. By mathematical induction, then, each natural number has property P; i.e., "$\forall y[1 + y = y + 1]$" is true in $(N, +, \cdot, <, 1)$.

We now generalize Theorem 4.2.4 to the commutative law.

THEOREM 4.2.5. $\forall x \forall y[x + y = y + x]$.

Proof: Again, we use mathematical induction. We shall say that a natural number t has property P iff $\forall y[t + y = y + t]$. By Theorem 4.2.4, 1 has property P. Suppose k has property P; then $\forall y[k + y = y + k]$. We must show that k' has property P. Let m be any natural number; then

$$
\begin{aligned}
k' + m &= (k + 1) + m && \text{by Def. 4.2.1} \\
&= (1 + k) + m && \text{by Th. 4.2.4} \\
&= 1 + (k + m) && \text{by Th. 4.2.3} \\
&= 1 + (m + k) && \text{by assumption} \\
&= (m + k) + 1 && \text{by Th. 4.2.4} \\
&= (m + k)' && \text{by Def. 4.2.1} \\
&= m + k' && \text{by Def. 4.2.1.}
\end{aligned}
$$

Hence, k' has the property whenever k has the property. Thus, each natural number has the property. We conclude that "$\forall x \forall y[x + y = y + x]$" is true in $(N, +, \cdot, <, 1)$.

We now establish that multiplication distributes over addition.

THEOREM 4.2.6. $\forall x \forall y \forall z[(y + z) \cdot x = y \cdot x + z \cdot x]$.

Proof: We say t has property P iff $\forall y \forall z[(y + z) \cdot t = y \cdot t + z \cdot t]$. But $(m + n) \cdot 1 = m + n$ by Definition 4.2.2, and $m \cdot 1 + n \cdot 1 = m + n$ by Definition 4.2.2, whenever $m \in N$ and $n \in N$. Thus, $\forall y \forall z[(y + z) \cdot 1 = y \cdot 1 + z \cdot 1]$; so 1 has property P. Suppose k has property P; then $\forall y \forall z[(y + z) \cdot k$

$= y \cdot k + z \cdot k]$. We show k' has property P. Let m and n be any natural numbers; then

$$
\begin{aligned}
(m + n) \cdot k' &= (m + n) \cdot k + (m + n) && \text{by Def. 4.2.2} \\
&= (m \cdot k + n \cdot k) + (m + n) && \text{by assumption} \\
&= (m \cdot k + m) + (n \cdot k + n) && \text{by Th. 4.2.3 and Th. 4.2.5} \\
&= m \cdot k' + n \cdot k' && \text{by Def. 4.2.2.}
\end{aligned}
$$

Therefore, $\forall y \forall z[(y + z) \cdot k' = y \cdot k' + z \cdot k']$; hence, k' has property P whenever k has property P. We conclude that all natural numbers have property P. Thus, "$\forall x \forall y \forall z[(y + z) \cdot x = y \cdot x + z \cdot x]$" is true in $(N, +, \cdot, <, 1)$.

In each of the preceding theorems, the proof depends upon observing that the theorem in question asserts that each natural number possesses a certain property. By using this technique, it is easy to establish the following theorems.

THEOREM 4.2.7. $\forall y[1 \cdot y = y \cdot 1]$.

THEOREM 4.2.8. $\forall x \forall y[x \cdot y = y \cdot x]$.

THEOREM 4.2.9. $\forall x \forall y \forall z[(x \cdot y) \cdot z = x \cdot (y \cdot z)]$.

Turning now to our binary relation on N, let us establish some of the algebraic properties of $<$.

THEOREM 4.2.10 (The Transitive Law). $\forall x \forall y \forall z[x < y \wedge y < z \rightarrow x < z]$.
Proof: Let a, b, and c be any natural numbers such that $a < b$ and $b < c$. Since $a' \in C_b$, it follows that $C_{a'} \subset C_b$. Since $b' \in C_c$, we see that $b \in C_c$, and so $C_b \subset C_c$. Therefore, $C_{a'} \subset C_c$; hence, $a' \in C_c$. We conclude that $a < c$. This establishes Theorem 4.2.10.

THEOREM 4.2.11. $\forall k[\sim(k < k)]$.
Proof: By Theorem 4.1.11 $\forall k[k' \overline{\in} C_k]$.

THEOREM 4.2.12. $\forall x[1 = x \vee 1 < x]$.
Proof: We say t has property P iff $1 = t \vee 1 < t$. By Theorem 4.2.11, 1 has property P. Suppose k has property P; then $1 = k \vee 1 < k$. If $k = 1$, then $C_{k'} = \{1, 1'\}$; hence, $1 < k'$. If $1 < k$, then $1' \in C_k$; thus, $1' \in C_{k'}$, and it follows from Definition 4.2.3 that $1 < k'$. Recalling that $1 \neq k'$ by the Peano

Postulates, we conclude that k' has property P whenever k has property P. Hence, each natural number has property P. This establishes Theorem 4.2.12.

THEOREM 4.2.13. $\forall x \forall y[x < y \rightarrow \sim (y < x)]$.

Proof: Suppose the theorem is false; then there are natural numbers, say a and b, such that $a < b$ and $b < a$. Therefore, by Theorem 4.2.10, $a < a$. This contradicts Theorem 4.2.11.

THEOREM 4.2.14 (The Trichotomy Law). $\forall x \forall y[x = y \bigvee x < y \bigvee y < x]$.

Proof: Apply Theorem 4.1.18.

THEOREM 4.2.15. $\forall x[x < x + 1]$.

Proof: $t' \in C_{t'}$ whenever $t \in N$.

THEOREM 4.2.16. $\forall x \forall y[x < x + y]$.

Proof: We say t has property P iff $\forall y[y < y + t]$. But 1 has property P, by Theorem 4.2.15. Suppose k has property P; then $\forall y[y < y + k]$. By Theorem 4.2.15, $y + k < (y + k) + 1$, i.e., $y + k < y + k'$. Hence, by Theorem 4.2.10, $y < y + k'$. Thus, k' has the property whenever k has the property. This establishes Theorem 4.2.16.

In several of the following theorems, e.g., Theorems 4.2.17 and 4.2.25, we shall prove that natural numbers x and y satisfy certain conditions whenever $x < y$; i.e., we shall demonstrate a proposition of the form "$\forall x \forall y[x < y \rightarrow q(x,y)]$", where $q(x,y)$ is a propositional form involving x and y. A theorem of this sort can sometimes be established by mathematical induction over y; i.e., we shall prove that each natural number has property P, given that t has property P iff $\forall x[x < t \rightarrow q(x,t)]$. To prove that 1 has property P, we must establish $\forall x[x < 1 \rightarrow q(x, 1)]$. Consider any proposition generated by the propositional form "$x < 1 \rightarrow q(x, 1)$", say "$a < 1 \rightarrow q(a, 1)$". In view of Theorem 4.2.12 and the Trichotomy Law, the proposition "$a < 1$" is false; therefore, "$a < 1 \rightarrow q(a, 1)$" is true. In other words, 1 has property P because there is no natural number less than 1. Thus, to establish a theorem of this sort, we have only to prove that k' has property P whenever k has property P.

THEOREM 4.2.17. $\forall a \forall b[a < b \rightarrow \exists x[b = a + x]]$.

Proof: We say t has property P iff $\forall a[a < t \rightarrow \exists x[t = a + x]]$. Clearly, 1 has the property. Suppose k has the property; then $\forall a[a < k \rightarrow \exists x[k =$

$a + x]]$. We show k' has the property. Suppose $a < k$; by assumption, there is a natural number, say x, such that $k = a + x$. Then $k' = (a + x)' = a + x'$. Next, suppose $a < k'$ and $\sim(a < k)$. If $a \neq k$, then $a' \neq k'$; hence, $a' \in C_k$ (since $a' \in C_{k'}$ and $C_{k'} = C_k \cup \{k'\}$). This contradiction shows that $a = k$. But $k' = k + 1 = a + 1$. We conclude that k' has the property whenever k has the property. This completes our proof.

THEOREM 4.2.18. $\forall x \forall y \forall z [x < y \rightarrow x + z < y + z]$.

Proof: Given $a < b$ and $c \in N$, we show $a + c < b + c$. Since $a < b$, by Theorem 4.2.17 there exists a natural number t such that $b = a + t$. Therefore, $b + c = (a + t) + c = (a + c) + t$. Hence, by Theorem 4.2.16, $a + c < b + c$.

THEOREM 4.2.19. $\forall x \forall y \forall z [x < y \leftrightarrow x + z < y + z]$.

Proof: Suppose $a + c < b + c$, but not $a < b$. By the Trichotomy Law, it follows that $b < a$ (if $a = b$, then $a + c = b + c$). Therefore, $b + c < a + c$, by Theorem 4.2.18. This contradiction proves $\forall x \forall y \forall z [x + z < y + z \rightarrow x < y]$. Together with Theorem 4.2.18, we have our proof.

THEOREM 4.2.20. $\forall x \forall y \forall z [x < y \rightarrow x \cdot z < y \cdot z]$.
Proof: Apply Theorem 4.2.17.

THEOREM 4.2.21. $\forall x \forall y \forall z [x < y \leftrightarrow x \cdot z < y \cdot z]$.
Proof: Follow the pattern of the proof of Theorem 4.2.19.

We can now establish the *Cancellation Laws.*

THEOREM 4.2.22 (The Cancellation Law for +). $\forall x \forall y \forall z [x + z = y + z \rightarrow x = y]$.
Proof: Given $x + z = y + z$, suppose $x \neq y$, say $x < y$. Then, by Theorem 4.2.18, $x + z < y + z$. If $y < x$, then $y + z < x + z$. This contradiction establishes Theorem 4.2.22.

THEOREM 4.2.23 (The Cancellation Law for $\cdot$). $\forall x \forall y \forall z [x \cdot z = y \cdot z \rightarrow x = y]$.
Proof: Given $x \cdot z = y \cdot z$, suppose $x \neq y$. Applying Theorem 4.2.20, if $x < y$, then $x \cdot z < y \cdot z$, whereas if $y < x$, then $y \cdot z < x \cdot z$. In either case, we conclude from the Trichotomy Law that $x \cdot z \neq y \cdot z$. This contradiction establishes Theorem 4.2.23.

It is convenient to introduce the binary relation on N denoted by "$\leq$" and defined as follows:

DEFINITION 4.2.4. $x \leq y$ iff $x < y \lor x = y$.

To be precise, $\leq$ is $\{(a,b)|(a,b) \in N \times N \land a < b \lor a = b\}$.

THEOREM 4.2.24. $\forall x \forall y[x < y' \rightarrow x \leq y]$.

Proof: By Theorem 4.2.17, there is a natural number, say k, such that $x + k = y' = y + 1$. Either $k = 1$ or there is a natural number t such that $k = t'$. In the former case, $x + 1 = y + 1$; hence, $x = y$ by a Cancellation Law. In the latter case, $x + t' = y + 1$, i.e., $(x + t) + 1 = y + 1$; so, by a Cancellation Law, $x + t = y$. Thus, by Theorem 4.2.16, $x < y$. This establishes Theorem 4.2.24.

THEOREM 4.2.25. $\forall x \forall y \exists q \exists r[y < x \rightarrow x = q \cdot y + r \land r \leq y]$.

Proof: We shall say t has property P iff $\forall y \exists q \exists r[y < t \rightarrow t = q \cdot y + r \land r \leq y]$. Clearly, 1 has property P. Suppose k has property P; we wish to show that k' has property P. We must show that if $a < k'$ there exist natural numbers q and r such that $k' = q \cdot a + r \land r \leq a$. By Theorem 4.2.24, there are two cases: $a < k$ and $a = k$.

1. Suppose $a < k$. Then, by assumption, there are natural numbers q and r such that $k = q \cdot a + r \land r \leq a$. Therefore, $k + 1 = (q \cdot a + r) + 1 = q \cdot a + (r + 1)$. If $r < a$, then $r + 1 \leq a$. If $r = a$, then $k + 1 = (q \cdot a + a) + 1 = (q + 1) \cdot a + 1$ and $1 \leq a$.

2. Suppose $a = k$. Then $k + 1 = 1 \cdot k + 1 \land 1 \leq k$.

We conclude that k' has property P whenever k has property P. Applying mathematical induction, we have Theorem 4.2.25.

THEOREM 4.2.26 (The Division Theorem). $\forall x \forall y[y < x \rightarrow \exists! q \exists! r[x = q \cdot y + r \land r \leq y]]$.

Proof: We have only to show the uniqueness of q and r. Assume $x = q_1 \cdot y + r_1$, $r_1 \leq y$, $x = q_2 \cdot y + r_2$, $r_2 \leq y$. Then $q_1 \cdot y + r_1 = q_2 \cdot y + r_2$. If $q_1 = q_2$, then $r_1 = r_2$ by a Cancellation Law. Suppose $q_1 \neq q_2$. If $q_1 < q_2$, then there is a natural number k such that $q_1 + k = q_2$ (see Theorem 4.2.17). Hence, $q_1 \cdot y + r_1 = (q_1 + k) \cdot y + r_2 = q_1 \cdot y + (k \cdot y + r_2)$. Thus, by a Cancellation Law, $r_1 = k \cdot y + r_2$. Therefore, $k \cdot y + r_2 \leq y$. But $y < k \cdot y + r_2$. Contradiction! Notice that the same argument applies if $q_2 < q_1$. This establishes Theorem 4.2.26.

We now demonstrate that each nonempty set of natural numbers has a smallest member.

THEOREM 4.2.27 (Law of Well-Ordering).   Suppose $S \subset N$ and $S \neq \emptyset$; then $\exists x[x \in S \land \forall y[y \in S \rightarrow x \leq y]]$.

Proof: Let $T = \{t | \forall x[x \in S \rightarrow t < x]\}$. If $1 \overline{\in} T$, then $1 \in S$; but $\forall y[1 \leq y]$. So we suppose $1 \in T$. Now we apply mathematical induction in an unusual way. Suppose that $k' \in T$ whenever $k \in T$; then, by mathematical induction, $T = N$; it follows from this that $S = \emptyset$. This contradiction demonstrates the existence of a natural number, say t, such that $t \in T$ and $t' \overline{\in} T$. This means that $\forall x[x \in S \rightarrow t < x]$ and $\exists x[x \in S \land x \leq t']$. Applying Theorem 4.2.24 and the Trichotomy Law, we readily establish that $t' \in S$ and $\forall x[x \in S \rightarrow t' \leq x]$. This completes our proof.

It is convenient to introduce $>$, a binary relation on N which we define as follows.

DEFINITION 4.2.5. $x > y$ iff $y < x$.

EXERCISES

1. Let μ be a mapping of N into N such that
     (i) $\mu(1) = 1$,
     (ii) $\mu(k + 1) = \mu(k) + (k + 1)$ whenever $k \in N$.
   a. Prove that μ is unique.
   b. Describe μ in intuitive terms.
   c. Prove that $2\mu(n) = n \cdot (n + 1)$ whenever $n \in N$.
2. Let μ be a mapping of N into N such that
     (i) $\mu(1) = 2$,
     (ii) $\mu(k + 1) = \mu(k) + 2 \cdot (k + 1)$.
   a. Prove that μ is unique.
   b. Describe μ in intuitive terms.
   c. Prove that $\mu(n) = n \cdot (n + 1)$ whenever $n \in N$.
3. Let μ be a mapping of N into N such that
     (i) $\mu(1) = 1$,
     (ii) $\mu(k + 1) = \mu(k) + (2 \cdot k + 1)$ whenever $k \in N$.
   a. Prove that μ is unique.
   b. Describe μ in intuitive terms.
   c. Prove that $\mu(n) = n \cdot n$ whenever $n \in N$.
4. Let μ be a mapping of N into N such that
     (i) $\mu(1) = 1$,
     (ii) $\mu(k + 1) = \mu(k) + (k + 1) \cdot (k + 1)$.

    a. Prove that μ is unique.

    b. Describe μ in intuitive terms.

    c. Prove that $6\mu(n) = n \cdot (n + 1) \cdot (2 \cdot n + 1)$ whenever $n \in N$.

5. a. Given $a < b$, prove $\exists!x[b = a + x]$.

    b. It is customary to denote the unique x such that $b = a + x$ by writing "$b - a$". Prove that $\forall x \forall y[x < y \rightarrow x + (y - x) = y]$.

    c. Prove that $\forall x \forall y[(x + y) - x = y]$.

6. Let a^n, where $a \in N$ and $n \in N$, be defined as follows:

$$\text{(i) } a^1 = a,$$
$$\text{(ii) } a^{k+1} = a^k \cdot a \text{ whenever } k \in N.$$

Prove that $a^{m+n} = a^m \cdot a^n$, $(a \cdot b)^n = a^n \cdot b^n$, $(a^m)^n = a^{m \cdot n}$ whenever $a \in N$, $b \in N$, $m \in N$, and $n \in N$.

7. Suppose that we obtain names for the natural numbers by juxtaposing the digits 0 and 1, so that $1'$ is denoted by "10", $10'$ is denoted by "11", $11'$ is denoted by "100", $100'$ is denoted by "101", $101'$ is denoted by "110", $110'$ is denoted by "111", $111'$ is denoted by "1000", and so on. Apply the definition of + given in the text to prove that $101 + 11 = 1000$ and $11101 + 110 = 100011$.

8. Let S by any nonempty set of natural numbers such that

$$\text{(i) } \forall x \forall y[x \in S \wedge y \in S \rightarrow x + y \in S],$$
$$\text{(ii) } \forall x \forall y[x \in S \wedge y \in S \wedge x < y \rightarrow y - x \in S].$$

Show that there is a natural number, say t, such that $S = \{n \cdot t | n \in N\}$.

9. Prove that the algebraic system $(N, +)$ is a semigroup.

10. Show that $\leq$ is $< \cup \{(a, a) | a \in N\}$.

11. Let $(N, ', 1)$ be any Peano System, and let P be a property such that

$$\text{(i) } 1 \text{ has property } P,$$
$$\text{(ii) } k' \text{ has property } P \text{ if } \forall t[t < k' \rightarrow t \text{ has property } P].$$

Prove that n has property P whenever $n \in N$.

12. Let $(N, ', 1)$ be a Peano System, and let P be a property such that

$$\text{(i) } m \text{ has property } P,$$
$$\text{(ii) } k' \text{ has property } P \text{ whenever } k \text{ has property } P.$$

Prove that n has property P whenever $m \leq n$.

13. Prove that "$\forall x \forall y \exists z[x < y \cdot z]$" is true in the natural number system.

14. Show that "$\forall x \forall y \exists! q \exists! r[y < x \rightarrow x = q \cdot y + r \wedge r \leq y]$" is false in the natural number system.

4.3   The System of Integers

    An obvious disadvantage of the natural number system $(N, +, \cdot, <, 1)$ is that it lacks an additive identity: i.e., there is no natural number, say k, such that $\forall x[x + k = x]$. Furthermore, the possibility of subtraction is limited. In particular, "$\forall x \forall y \exists z[x + z = y]$" is false in the natural number system; note, for example, that there is no ordered triple in $+$ whose first term is 3 and whose third term is 1.

The system of integers is an extension of the natural number system which is free of the above defects. We shall construct this richer number system from the material available in the algebraic system $(N, +, \cdot, <, 1)$. First, consider the set $N \times N$ and the binary relation on $N \times N$, denoted by "$\equiv$" and defined as follows:

DEFINITION 4.3.1.   Let $(a, b) \in N \times N$ and let $(c, d) \in N \times N$; then $(a, b) \equiv (c, d)$ iff $a + d = b + c$.

For example, $(3, 1) \equiv (5, 3)$ and $(2, 5) \equiv (3, 6)$.

THEOREM 4.3.1. $\equiv$ is an equivalence relation on $N \times N$.

Proof: The proof is left as an exercise.

Using the equivalence relation $\equiv$, we partition $N \times N$. Let "I" denote the resulting set of subsets of $N \times N$; the members of I are called *integers*.

DEFINITION 4.3.2. $\{(m, n) \mid (m, n) \equiv (a, b)\}$ is said to be an *integer* and is denoted by "$[a, b]$".

In view of Theorem 2.9.1 (p. 73), $[a, b] = [c, d]$ iff $(a, b) \equiv (c, d)$.

You will note that we consistently call the binary operations of a number system *addition* and *multiplication*, and denote these operations by "$+$" and "$\cdot$" respectively. Similarly, we consistently call the order relation of a number system *less than* and denote it by "$<$". It is convenient to adopt this uniform system of naming the components of a number system; furthermore, there is no possibility of ambiguity since we always know from the context to which number system the operation or relation belongs.

We now introduce two binary operations on I — addition and multiplication.

DEFINITION 4.3.3.   Let $[a, b] \in I$ and let $[c, d] \in I$; then

$$\text{(i) } [a, b] + [c, d] = [a + c, \; b + d],$$
$$\text{(ii) } [a, b] \cdot [c, d] = [a \cdot c + b \cdot d, \; a \cdot d + b \cdot c].$$

Let $x \in I$ and let $y \in I$; then, in view of Definition 4.3.3, $x + y$ is found by performing certain operations on a member of x and a member of y. There is a question here: can we be sure that we obtain the *same* member of I

no matter which representatives of x and of y we work with? To see the problem, one might think of two nations settling an international dispute by a meeting attended by a representative of each nation. One wonders whether the outcome of the meeting is affected by the particular representatives at the meeting.

Fortunately, in the case of mathematics, we can prove that the sum of x and y (or the product of x and y) is independent of the representatives of x and y used in applying Definition 4.3.3. Consider the following theorem.

THEOREM 4.3.2.   If $(a_1, b_1) \in [a, b]$ and $(c_1, d_1) \in [c, d]$, then $(a_1 + c_1, b_1 + d_1) \in [a + c, b + d]$.

Proof: We are given that $a_1 + b = b_1 + a$ and $c_1 + d = d_1 + c$; we must show that $(a_1 + c_1) + (b + d) = (b_1 + d_1) + (a + c)$. Since addition is associative and commutative in $(N, +, \cdot, <, 1)$, it follows that

$$(a_1 + b) + (c_1 + d) = (a_1 + c_1) + (b + d)$$

and

$$(b_1 + a) + (d_1 + c) = (b_1 + d_1) + (a + c).$$

But $(a_1 + b) + (c_1 + d) = (b_1 + a) + (d_1 + c)$, by assumption. This completes our proof.

THEOREM 4.3.3.   If $(a_1, b_1) \in [a, b]$ and $(c_1, d_1) \in [c, d]$, then $(a_1 \cdot c_1 + b_1 \cdot d_1, \; a_1 \cdot d_1 + b_1 \cdot c_1) \in [a \cdot c + b \cdot d, \; a \cdot d + b \cdot c]$.

Proof: We are given:

$$(1) \; a_1 + b = b_1 + a,$$
$$(2) \; c_1 + d = d_1 + c.$$

Multiply (1) by c_1; multiply (2) by b; multiply (1) by d_1; multiply (2) by a. Add appropriate sides of the resulting equations; finally, apply the Cancellation Law for $+$ (Theorem 4.2.22). This establishes Theorem 4.3.3.

Next, we introduce an order relation on I.

DEFINITION 4.3.4.   Let $[a, b] \in I$ and let $[c, d] \in I$; then $[a, b] < [c, d]$ iff $a + d < b + c$.

For example, $[1, 3] < [5, 2]$, since $1 + 2 < 3 + 5$.

We must show that the criterion for membership in $<$ is independent of the representatives of the integers involved.

THEOREM 4.3.4. Suppose $a + d < b + c$ and $(a_1, b_1) \equiv (a, b)$ and $(c_1, d_1) \equiv (c, d)$; then $a_1 + d_1 < b_1 + c_1$.

Proof: By assumption, $a_1 + b = b_1 + a$ and $c_1 + d = d_1 + c$. Therefore, $(a_1 + b) + (d_1 + c) = (b_1 + a) + (c_1 + d)$. Since $+$ is associative and commutative in $(N, +, \cdot, <, 1)$, it follows that $(a_1 + d_1) + (b + c) = (b_1 + c_1) + (a + d)$. By Theorem 4.2.17, there is a natural number k such that $(a + d) + k = b + c$; therefore, $(a_1 + d_1) + [(a + d) + k] = (b_1 + c_1) + (a + d)$; hence, by Theorem 4.2.22, $(a_1 + d_1) + k = b_1 + c_1$. Thus, by Theorem 4.2.16, $a_1 + d_1 < b_1 + c_1$.

Theorem 4.3.4 assures us that Definition 4.3.4 actually defines a binary relation on I. We now show that our binary relation is an order relation on I.

THEOREM 4.3.5. $\forall x \forall y \forall z [x < y \wedge y < z \rightarrow x < z]$.

Proof: Let $[a, b] \in I$, let $[c, d] \in I$, let $[e, f] \in I$, and suppose that $[a, b] < [c, d]$ and $[c, d] < [e, f]$. Then $a + d < b + c$ and $c + f < d + e$. Therefore, by Theorem 4.2.18,

$$a + d + f < b + c + f \quad \text{and} \quad c + f + b < d + e + b.$$

But $<$ is transitive in the natural number system; therefore, $a + d + f < d + e + b$. Hence, by Theorem 4.2.19, $a + f < b + e$; thus, $[a, b] < [e, f]$.

THEOREM 4.3.6. $\forall x \forall y [x = y \bigvee x < y \bigvee y < x]$.

Proof: Let $[a, b] \in I$ and let $[c, d] \in I$. Consider the natural numbers $a + d$ and $b + c$. By Theorem 4.2.14 (the Trichotomy Law for the natural number system) $a + d = b + c \bigvee a + d < b + c \bigvee b + c < a + d$. Hence, $[a, b] = [c, d] \bigvee [a, b] < [c, d] \bigvee [c, d] < [a, b]$. This establishes the Trichotomy Law for the system of integers.

Consider the integers $[1, 1]$ and $[2, 1]$. It turns out that these integers possess important properties; indeed, let us show that $[1, 1]$ is an additive identity and that $[2, 1]$ is a multiplicative identity.

THEOREM 4.3.7. $\forall x [x + [1, 1] = x]$.

Proof: Let $[a, b] \in I$. By Definition 4.3.3, $[a, b] + [1, 1] = [a + 1, b + 1]$. But $(a + 1, b + 1) \equiv (a, b)$, since $a + 1 + b = b + 1 + a$. Therefore, $[a, b] + [1, 1] = [a, b]$.

THEOREM 4.3.8. $\forall x[x \cdot [2,1] = x]$.

Proof: Let $[a,b] \in I$. By Definition 4.3.3, $[a,b] \cdot [2,1] = [2 \cdot a + b, a + 2 \cdot b]$.   But $(2 \cdot a + b, a + 2 \cdot b) \equiv (a,b)$,   since $(2 \cdot a + b) + b = (a + 2 \cdot b) + a$. Therefore, $[a,b] \cdot [2,1] = [a,b]$.

THEOREM 4.3.9.   The additive identity is unique.

Proof: Suppose there is an integer $[t_1, t_2]$ such that $\forall x[x + [t_1, t_2] = x]$. Let $[a,b] \in I$; then $[a,b] + [t_1, t_2] = [a,b]$. Therefore, $(a + t_1, b + t_2) \equiv (a,b)$; hence, $(a + t_1) + b = (b + t_2) + a$. Thus, by the Cancellation Law for + (Theorem 4.2.22), $t_1 = t_2$. We conclude that $[t_1, t_2] = [1,1]$.

THEOREM 4.3.10.   The multiplicative identity is unique.

Proof: Suppose there is an integer $[t_1, t_2]$ such that $\forall x[x \cdot [t_1, t_2] = x]$. Then $[2,1] \cdot [t_1, t_2] = [2,1]$. Hence, $2 \cdot t_1 + t_2 + 1 = 2 \cdot t_2 + t_1 + 2$. Applying the Cancellation Law for + (Theorem 4.2.22), it follows that $t_1 = t_2 + 1$. Therefore, $[t_1, t_2] = [t_2 + 1, t_2] = [2,1]$. This establishes Theorem 4.3.10.

It is customary to denote the additive identity of a number system by "0".

DEFINITION 4.3.5. $0 = [1,1]$.

At last we are ready to define the system of integers!

DEFINITION 4.3.6.   By the *system of integers,* we mean the algebraic system $(I, +, \cdot, <, 0, [2,1])$.

Let us establish some properties of the system of integers. First, we consider the algebraic system $(I, +, 0)$, which is constructed from the system of integers by an obvious maneuver.

THEOREM 4.3.11. $(I, +, 0)$ is an abelian group.

Proof: We begin by showing that + is commutative. Let $[a,b] \in I$, and let $[c,d] \in I$; then $[a,b] + [c,d] = [a + c, b + d]$ and $[c,d] + [a,b] = [c + a, d + b] = [a + c, b + d]$, since + is commutative in the natural number system. This demonstrates that "$\forall x \forall y[x + y = y + x]$" is true in $(I, +, 0)$. In the same way, it is easily seen that the proof that + is associative relies upon the corresponding property of + in the natural number system. Finally, we demonstrate the existence of an inverse. Let $[a,b] \in I$; then

$[a, b] + [b, a] = [a + b, b + a] = 0$.   Hence,   "$\forall x \exists y [x + y = 0]$"   is   true   in $(I, +, 0)$. We conclude that $(I, +, 0)$ is an abelian group.

It is now convenient to introduce the unary operation "$-$" on I.

DEFINITION 4.3.7.   Let $[a, b] \in I$; then $-[a, b] = [b, a]$.

Since $\forall x [x + -x = 0]$, we say that $-[a, b]$ is an additive inverse of $[a, b]$. We now list some properties of $-$; these are easily demonstrated by applying Definition 4.3.7.

THEOREM 4.3.12. $\forall x [-(-x) = x]$.

THEOREM 4.3.13. $\forall x \forall y [-(x + y) = -x + -y]$.

THEOREM 4.3.14. $\forall x \forall y [-(x \cdot y) = (-x) \cdot y]$.

THEOREM 4.3.15. $\forall x [-x = [1, 2] \cdot x]$.

THEOREM 4.3.16. $\forall x [0 < x \rightarrow -x < 0]$.

It may be helpful to summarize the above concepts as shown in Table 4.3.1, which displays the intuitive content of each idea.

TABLE 4.3.1

Formal Concept	Intuitive Idea
$[a, b]$	$a - b$
$[a, b] = [c, d]$	$a - b = c - d$ or $a + d = b + c$
$[1, 1]$	0
$[2, 1]$	1
$[a, b] + [c, d] = [a + c, b + d]$	$(a - b) + (c - d) = (a + c) - (b + d)$
$[a, b] \cdot [c, d] = [a \cdot c + b \cdot d, a \cdot d + b \cdot c]$	$(a - b) \cdot (c - d) = (ac + bd) - (ad + bc)$
$-[a, b] = [b, a]$	$-(a - b) = b - a$

We now show that the system of integers is an extension of the natural number system. Let $P = \{x \mid x \in I \wedge 0 < x\}$ and consider the algebraic system $(P, +, \cdot, <, [2, 1])$, where $+, \cdot$, and $<$ are the sets obtained from the corresponding operations and relations of the system of integers by throwing out all ordered triples and pairs which involve integers not in P.

THEOREM 4.3.17. $(N, +, \cdot, <, 1) \cong (P, +, \cdot, <, [2, 1])$.

Proof: We must find a one–one mapping of N onto P, say μ, such that

$$\mu(N, +, \cdot, <, 1) = (P, +, \cdot, <, [2, 1]).$$

We define μ as follows: let $\mu(n) = [1 + n, 1]$ whenever $n \in N$. Clearly, μ is a one–one mapping of N onto P. Now consider any ordered triple in the $+$ of $(N, +, \cdot, <, 1)$, say $(m, n, m + n)$. Then

$$\mu(m, n, m + n) = ([m', 1], [n', 1], [(m + n)', 1]).$$

But in $(P, +, \cdot, <, [2, 1])$,

$$[m', 1] + [n', 1] = [m' + n', 2] = [(m + n)', 1].$$

Furthermore, since our mapping is *onto*, it follows that no member of the $+$ of $(P, +, \cdot, <, [2, 1])$ is left out. Similarly,

$$\mu(m, n, m \cdot n) = ([m', 1], [n', 1], [(m \cdot n)', 1]);$$

but $\quad [m', 1] \cdot [n', 1] = [m' \cdot n' + 1, m' + n'] = [m \cdot n + 1, 1].$

Next, we observe that $m < n$ in $(N, +, \cdot, <, 1)$ iff $[m', 1] < [n', 1]$ in $(P, +, \cdot, <, [2, 1])$; this follows from Theorem 4.2.19. Finally, we note that $\mu(1) = [2, 1]$. Hence,

$$\mu(N, +, \cdot, <, 1) = (P, +, \cdot, <, [2, 1]).$$

This establishes Theorem 4.3.17.

Since the positive integers are algebraically the same as the natural numbers, it is customary to denote the positive integer $[1 + k, 1]$ by the corresponding natural number, namely k. This convention enables us to eliminate the clumsy "$[a,b]$" notation altogether. Let us find a simple name for the negative integer $[1, 1 + k]$. Now,

$$[1, 1 + k] = -[1 + k, 1] = -k.$$

Therefore, "$-k$" denotes $[1, 1 + k]$. For example, "-3" is a name of the negative integer $[2, 2 + 3]$.

THEOREM 4.3.18. $\forall x \forall y \forall z [0 < z \rightarrow (x \cdot z < y \cdot z \leftrightarrow x < y)].$

Proof: Assume $0 < z$; then there is a natural number k such that $z = [k', 1]$. But

$[a,b] \cdot [k',1] < [c,d] \cdot [k',1]$ iff $[a \cdot k' + b, a + b \cdot k'] < [c \cdot k' + d, c$
$$+ d \cdot k']$$
$$\text{iff } (a \cdot k' + b) + (c + d \cdot k') < (a + b \cdot k')$$
$$+ (c \cdot k' + d)$$
$$\text{iff } (a \cdot k + a + b) + (c + d \cdot k + d)$$
$$< (a + b \cdot k + b) + (c \cdot k + c + d)$$
iff $a \cdot k + d \cdot k < b \cdot k + c \cdot k$, by Th. 4.2.19
iff $a + d < b + c$, by Th. 4.2.21
iff $[a,b] < [c,d]$, by Def. 4.3.4.

This establishes Theorem 4.3.18.

THEOREM 4.3.19. $\forall x \forall y \forall z [x + z < y + z \leftrightarrow x < y]$.
Proof: Follow the pattern of the proof of Theorem 4.2.19.

Let us establish the Cancellation Laws.

THEOREM 4.3.20. $\forall x \forall y \forall z [x + z = y + z \rightarrow x = y]$.
Proof: Apply Theorem 4.3.19 and the Trichotomy Law.

THEOREM 4.3.21. $\forall x \forall y \forall z [0 < z \wedge x \cdot z = y \cdot z \rightarrow x = y]$.
Proof: Apply Theorem 4.3.18 and the Trichotomy Law.

We now introduce the operation of subtraction.

DEFINITION 4.3.8. $x - y = x + -y$ whenever $x \in I$ and $y \in I$.

For example, $[3,5] - [1,2] = [3,5] + [2,1] = [5,6] = -1$.
It is convenient to introduce the binary relation on I, denoted by "$\leq$" and defined as follows:

DEFINITION 4.3.9. $x \leq y$ iff $x < y \vee x = y$.

We shall need the notion of the *absolute value* of an integer.

DEFINITION 4.3.10. $|x| = \begin{cases} x \text{ if } 0 \leq x \\ -x \text{ if } x < 0 \end{cases}$ whenever x is an integer.

We shall now establish the Division Theorem for the system of integers. First, we need two lemmas and two theorems.

Lemma 1: $\forall r \forall y [0 < r \leq y \rightarrow 0 \leq y - r < y]$.

Proof: This is easy to establish from first principles; alternatively, apply the Trichotomy Law to the integers $y - r$ and 0, and then to the integers $y - r$ and y; this will require using Theorem 4.3.19.

Lemma 2: $\forall x \forall y [x < 0 \wedge |x| \leq y \rightarrow 0 \leq y + x < y]$.

Proof: Apply Lemma 1 (this is actually another form of Lemma 1).

THEOREM 4.3.22. $\forall x \forall y \exists q \exists r [0 < y \rightarrow x = q \cdot y + r \wedge 0 \leq r < y]$.

Proof: By the Trichotomy Law, there are three possibilities regarding the integers y and $|x|$.

1. $y < |x|$. Then, by Theorem 4.2.25, there exist integers q and r such that $|x| = q \cdot y + r$ and $0 \leq r < y$. If $0 < x$, then $|x| = x$, and we have the desired result. If $x < 0$, then $|x| = -x$; hence, $-x = q \cdot y + r$. Thus, $x = -(q \cdot y + r) = (-q - 1) \cdot y + (y - r)$ and $0 \leq y - r < y$, by Lemma 1.

2. $y = |x|$. Then $|x| = 1 \cdot y + 0$.

3. $|x| < y$. Then $|x| = 0 \cdot y + |x|$ and $0 \leq |x| < y$. If $0 < x$, our result holds. If $x < 0$, then $|x| = -x$; hence, $-x = (-1) \cdot y + (y + x)$. But $0 \leq y + x < y$ by Lemma 2. This establishes Theorem 4.3.22.

THEOREM 4.3.23. $\forall x \forall y \exists q \exists r [y \neq 0 \rightarrow x = q \cdot y + r \wedge 0 \leq r < |y|]$.

Proof: We apply the Trichotomy Law to y and 0.

1. $0 < y$. Here, Theorem 4.3.22 gives us our result.

2. $y < 0$. Consider $-y$; by Theorem 4.3.22, $\forall x \exists q \exists r [x = q \cdot (-y) + r \wedge 0 \leq r < -y]$. Noting that $q \cdot (-y) = (-q) \cdot y$, we have our result.

3. $y = 0$. Here, there is nothing to prove.

THEOREM 4.3.24 (The Division Theorem). $\forall x \forall y [y \neq 0 \rightarrow \exists! q \exists! r [x = q \cdot y + r \wedge 0 \leq r < |y|]]$.

Proof: Follow the pattern of the proof of Theorem 4.2.26.

The Division Theorem associates with an ordered pair of integers, say (y, x), where $y \neq 0$, the ordered pair (q, r). Intuitively, we are *dividing* x by y; we obtain the quotient q and the remainder r. The quotient and remainder are unique. The situation in which $r = 0$ (i.e., the remainder is 0) is of special significance.

DEFINITION 4.3.11. We say y *divides* x, or y is a *divisor* of x, iff $\exists q [x = q \cdot y]$.

For example, 3 is a divisor of 6, since $6 = 2 \cdot 3$.

Notice that Definition 4.3.11 introduces a binary relation on I; denoting this relation by "$|$", we have the following definition.

DEFINITION 4.3.12. $y|x$ iff $\exists q[x = q \cdot y]$.

For example, $3|6$, since $6 = 2 \cdot 3$; again, $-3|6$, since $6 = -2 \cdot -3$.
We list some obvious properties of $|$.

THEOREM 4.3.25. $\forall x[x|x \wedge -x|x]$.

THEOREM 4.3.26. $\forall x[1|x \wedge -1|x]$.

THEOREM 4.3.27. $\forall x[x|0]$.

THEOREM 4.3.28. $\forall x \forall y[y|x \rightarrow y|-x \wedge -y|x]$.

THEOREM 4.3.29. $\forall x \forall y \forall z[x|y \wedge y|z \rightarrow x|z]$.

THEOREM 4.3.30. $\forall x[x|1 \rightarrow x = 1 \vee x = -1]$.

THEOREM 4.3.31. $\forall x \forall y[x \neq 0 \wedge y|x \rightarrow |y| \leq |x|]$.

THEOREM 4.3.32. $\forall x \forall y[x|y \wedge y|x \rightarrow x = y \vee x = -y]$.

We now introduce the notion of a *greatest common divisor* of two integers.

DEFINITION 4.3.13. g is said to be a *greatest common divisor* of x and y iff

(i) $g|x \wedge g|y$,
(ii) $\forall d[d|x \wedge d|y \rightarrow d|g]$.

For example, 6 is a greatest common divisor of 12 and 18; so is -6.
In view of Theorem 4.3.32, if g_1 and g_2 are both greatest common divisors of x and y, then $g_1 = g_2$ or $g_1 = -g_2$. Notice that 0 and 0 have no *largest* common divisor; this is a consequence of Theorem 4.3.27. On the other hand, 0 and 0 possess a greatest common divisor in the sense of Definition 4.3.13, namely 0. Moreover, any other pair of integers possesses a greatest common divisor; this is a consequence of Theorem 4.3.31 and Theorem 4.3.26. In short, 0 and 0 have exactly one greatest common divisor, whereas any other pair of integers possesses two greatest common divisors. We are

particularly interested in the larger of the two possible greatest common divisors of a pair of integers.

DEFINITION 4.3.14.   Let a and b be any integers; then by "(a,b)" we denote the nonnegative greatest common divisor of a and b.

Notice that (a,b) is the largest integer in the set $\{g|g$ is a greatest common divisor of a and $b\}$. For example, $(12,18) = 6$ and $(-12,18) = 6$.

THEOREM 4.3.33. $\forall x[(x,0) = |x|]$.
Proof: The proof is obvious.

We now establish formally the existence of (a,b); furthermore, we present a useful way of representing (a,b).

THEOREM 4.3.34.   Let a and b be any integers; then (a,b) exists; moreover, $\exists x \exists y[(a,b) = a \cdot x + b \cdot y]$.
Proof: 1. Suppose one or both of a and b are zero; then (a,b) is given by Theorem 4.3.33. In particular, if $b = 0$, then $(a,b) = |a|$; hence, $(a,b) = a \cdot x + b \cdot 0$, where $x = 1$ if $a \geq 0$ and $x = -1$ if $a < 0$.
2. Suppose $a \neq 0$ and $b \neq 0$. Let $S = \{a \cdot x + b \cdot y \mid 0 < a \cdot x + b \cdot y\}$. Since $S \neq \emptyset$ (notice that $|a| \in S$), it follows from Theorem 4.2.27 that S has a smallest member, say t, where $t = a \cdot x + b \cdot y$. We shall show that $(a,b) = t$. By the Division Theorem, there exist unique integers q and r such that $a = q \cdot t + r$ and $0 \leq r < t$; if $r \neq 0$, then $r \in S$, since

$$r = a - q \cdot t = a - q \cdot (a \cdot x + b \cdot y) = a \cdot (1 - q \cdot x) + b \cdot (-q \cdot y).$$

Hence, $r \in S$ and $r < t$. But t is the smallest member of S; this contradiction demonstrates that $r = 0$; thus, $t|a$. Similarly, it is easily seen that $t|b$. Now, suppose that $d|a$ and $d|b$; then $a = q_1 \cdot d$ and $b = q_2 \cdot d$. Thus, $t = a \cdot x + b \cdot y = q_1 \cdot d \cdot x + q_2 \cdot d \cdot y = (q_1 \cdot x + q_2 \cdot y) \cdot d$; therefore, $d|t$. Hence, t is a greatest common divisor of a and b; since $0 < t$, $(a,b) = t$. This establishes Theorem 4.3.33.
We come now to an important concept—the notion of a prime integer. We have seen that $\forall x[1|x \land -1|x \land x|x \land -x|x]$; if x has *exactly* four divisors, then x is said to be a *prime*.

DEFINITION 4.3.15.   Let $p \in I$; then p is *prime* iff $\forall y[y|p \rightarrow y = 1 \bigvee y = -1 \bigvee y = p \bigvee y = -p]$.

For example, $-3, -2, 5, 7$ are primes; on the other hand, $-1, 1, 0$, and 4 are not primes.

THEOREM 4.3.35. Suppose p is prime and $p|a \cdot b$; then $p|a$ or $p|b$.

Proof: If p is not a divisor of a, then $(p, a) = 1$. Therefore, by Theorem 4.3.34, there are integers x and y such that $p \cdot x + a \cdot y = 1$. Hence, $b = p \cdot b \cdot x + a \cdot b \cdot y$. But p is a divisor of $p \cdot b \cdot x + a \cdot b \cdot y$, since $p|a \cdot b$. Thus, $p|b$. This establishes Theorem 4.3.35.

THEOREM 4.3.36. Suppose $1 < |a|$; then $\exists p[p$ is prime $\wedge 0 < p \wedge p|a]$.

Proof: Let $S = \{x \mid x|a \wedge 1 < x\}$; then $|a| \in S$; so S is nonempty. Therefore, by Theorem 4.2.27, S has a smallest member, say t. By Theorem 4.3.29, any divisor of t is also a divisor of a. Since t is the smallest member of S, it follows that $1 < t$ and the only divisors of t are $1, -1, t$, and $-t$. Hence, t is prime. This demonstrates Theorem 4.3.36.

Since -1 has no prime divisors, and since $-a = (-1) \cdot a$, it follows from Theorem 4.3.35 that the prime divisors of $-a$ are precisely the prime divisors of a. For this reason, we concentrate our attention on the positive integers.

We shall now establish the following theorem.

THEOREM 4.3.37. Suppose $1 < a$; then there is a finite number of positive primes, not necessarily different, say $p_1, p_2, \cdots, p_n$, such that $a = p_1 \cdot p_2 \cdot \ldots \cdot p_n$.

Proof: Suppose the theorem is false; then there exists an integer x such that $1 < x$ and x is not the product of a finite number of positive primes. Therefore, by Theorem 4.2.27, there is a smallest integer a such that $1 < a$ and a is not the product of a finite number of positive primes. By Theorem 4.3.36, there is a positive prime p such that $p|a$. Therefore, $a = q \cdot p$; but $q < a$ and $1 < q$, so q is the product of a finite number of positive primes, not necessarily different, say $p_1, p_2, \cdots, p_k$. Thus,

$$a = q \cdot p = p_1 \cdot p_2 \cdot \ldots \cdot p_k \cdot p.$$

This contradicts our assumption that a is not the product of a finite number of positive primes. Thus, Theorem 4.3.37 is established.

THE FUNDAMENTAL THEOREM OF ARITHMETIC. Suppose $1 < a$; then a can be represented uniquely, except for order, as the product of a finite number of positive primes.

Proof: We know, by Theorem 4.3.37, that a can be represented as the product of a finite number of positive primes, not necessarily different. We must show that there is essentially just one such representation. If there is not, then there is a smallest integer, say a, such that $1 < a$ and a possesses two essentially distinct representations; so

$$a = p_1 \cdot p_2 \cdot \ldots \cdot p_m = q_1 \cdot q_2 \cdot \ldots \cdot q_n,$$

where the p's and the q's are positive primes. Since $p_1 | a$ and $a = q_1 \cdot q_2 \cdot \ldots \cdot q_n$, it follows from Theorem 4.3.35 that $p_1 | q_i$ for some i. But p_1 and q_i are both positive primes; therefore $p_1 = q_i$. For convenience, suppose $i = 1$, i.e., $q_i = q_1$. Then $a = p_1 \cdot p_2 \cdot p_3 \cdot \ldots \cdot p_m = p_1 \cdot q_2 \cdot q_3 \cdot \ldots \cdot q_n$. Now consider the integer $p_2 \cdot p_3 \cdot \ldots \cdot p_m$; since $p_2 \cdot p_3 \cdot \ldots \cdot p_m < a$, it follows that $p_2 \cdot p_3 \cdot \ldots \cdot p_m$ can be represented uniquely as a product of positive primes. Therefore, the product $q_2 \cdot q_3 \cdot \ldots \cdot q_n$ is merely a rearrangement of the product $p_2 \cdot p_3 \cdot \ldots \cdot p_m$ (in particular, it follows that m is n). It follows that $q_1 \cdot q_2 \cdot q_3 \cdot \ldots \cdot q_n$ is merely a rearrangement of $p_1 \cdot p_2 \cdot p_3 \cdot \ldots \cdot p_m$. Thus, a has a unique representation as a product of positive primes. This contradiction demonstrates our theorem.

E X E R C I S E S

Show that the following propositions are true:
1. $[2,5] = [7,10]$.
2. $[4,1] = [8,5]$.
3. $[2,5] + [4,1] = [7,10] + [8,5]$.
4. $[3,1] + [7,7] = [3,1]$.
5. $[4,7] \cdot [1,1] = [4,7]$.
6. $([10,2] + [1,5]) \cdot [3,1] = [9,1]$.
7. $[2,5] < [5,2]$.
8. $[4,2] < [5,2]$.
9. $[2,5] \cdot [4,1] < [5,2] \cdot [4,1]$.
10. Find an integer y such that $[3,5] + y = [4,1]$.
11. Find an integer y such that $[2,5] + y = [1,7]$.
12. Prove that $\forall x \forall y \forall y [z < 0 \rightarrow (y \cdot z < x \cdot z \leftrightarrow x < y)]$ in the system of integers.
13. Prove that $\forall x \forall y \forall z \forall w [x < y \wedge z < w \rightarrow x + z < y + w]$ in the system of integers.
14. Show that the algebraic system $(I, \cdot, [2,1])$ is *not* a group.
15. Prove that $\forall x \forall y [-(x - y) = y - x]$ in the system of integers.

16. Suppose that a is any positive integer, and suppose that n is any natural number. Define a^n as follows:

$\quad$ (i) $a^1 = a$,

$\quad$ (ii) $a^{k+1} = a^k \cdot a$ whenever $k \in N$.

Prove that $a^{m+n} = a^m \cdot a^n$, $(a \cdot b)^n = a^n \cdot b^n$, and $(a^m)^n = a^{m \cdot n}$ whenever a and b are positive integers and m and n are natural numbers.

17. Show that the algebraic system $(I, \cdot, [2,1])$ is a semigroup.

18. Show that the algebraic system $(I, +, \cdot, 0, [2,1])$ is an integral domain.

4.4   The Rational Number System

Just as we constructed the system of integers from the natural number system, so we shall now construct the rational number system from the system of integers. The rational number system is of some importance because of its algebraic properties; in fact, this algebraic system is an ordered field.

Using a technique similar to that of Section 4.3, we shall construct the rational number system from the system of integers. First, we construct the rational numbers. We consider $\{(a,b) | a \in I \wedge b \in I \wedge b \neq 0\}$, the set of all ordered pairs of integers with second term not zero. We think of a member of this set, say (a,b), as representing the rational number a/b of our intuition! Permitting our intuition to guide us, we observe that $a/b = c/d$ iff $a \cdot d = b \cdot c$; this suggests that we introduce a binary relation on $\{(a,b) | a \in I \wedge b \in I \wedge b \neq 0\}$, which we shall denote by "$\equiv$" and define as follows:

DEFINITION 4.4.1. $(a, b) \equiv (c, d)$ iff $a \cdot d = b \cdot c$.

For example, $(3, 2) \equiv (9, 6)$, since $3 \cdot 6 = 2 \cdot 9$. It is easy to show that this binary relation is reflexive, symmetric, and transitive; hence, $\equiv$ is an equivalence relation on our set of ordered pairs. Therefore, $\equiv$ partitions $\{(a, b) | a \in I \wedge b \in I \wedge b \neq 0\}$. The resulting sets of ordered pairs are mathematical objects which we shall call *rational numbers*.

DEFINITION 4.4.2. $\{(m, n) | (m, n) \equiv (a, b)\}$ is said to be a rational number, given that $a \in I$, $b \in I$, and $b \neq 0$; this rational number is denoted by "a/b".

Suppose that $(c, d) \equiv (e, f)$; then

$$\{(m, n) \mid (m, n) \equiv (c, d)\} = \{(m, n) \mid (m, n) \equiv (e, f)\}.$$

Therefore, $c/d = e/f$, provided that $(c, d) \equiv (e, f)$. In other words, if (c, d) and (e, f) are members of the same equivalence class, then $c/d = e/f$.

We now introduce two binary operations and one binary relation on the set of rational numbers.

DEFINITION 4.4.3.   Let a/b and c/d be any rational numbers; then

$$a/b + c/d = (a \cdot d + b \cdot c) / b \cdot d,$$
$$a/b \cdot c/d = a \cdot c / b \cdot d,$$

and $a/b < c/d$ iff $(a \cdot d < b \cdot c \wedge 0 < b \cdot d) \vee (b \cdot c < a \cdot d \wedge b \cdot d < 0)$.

For example, $2/3 + 3/5 = 19/15$, $2/3 \cdot 3/5 = 6/15 = 2/5$, and $3/5 < 2/3$.

We call the operations $+$ and $\cdot$ *addition* and *multiplication* respectively; the relation $<$ is called *less than*.

We must show that $+$ and $\cdot$ are binary operations on the set of rational numbers; i.e., we must show that the sum of x and y (or the product of x and y) is independent of the representatives of x and y used in applying Definition 4.4.3. Of course, the situation is analogous to the case of the system of integers.

THEOREM 4.4.1.   If $(a_1, b_1) \equiv (a, b)$ and $(c_1, d_1) \equiv (c, d)$, then

$$(a_1 \cdot d_1 + b_1 \cdot c_1, \ b_1 \cdot d_1) \equiv (a \cdot d + b \cdot c, \ b \cdot d).$$

Proof: The proof is left as an exercise.

THEOREM 4.4.2.   If $(a_1, b_1) \equiv (a, b)$ and $(c_1, d_1) \equiv (c, d)$, then

$$(a_1 \cdot c_1, b_1 \cdot d_1) \equiv (a \cdot c, b \cdot d).$$

Proof: The proof is left as an exercise.

Next, we show that the criterion for membership in $<$ is independent of the representatives of the rational numbers involved.

THEOREM 4.4.3.   Suppose $a/b < c/d$, $a_1/b_1 = a/b$,   and $c_1/d_1 = c/d$; then $a_1/b_1 < c_1/d_1$.

Proof: In accordance with Definition 4.4.3, there are two cases.
1. $a \cdot d < b \cdot c$ and $0 < b \cdot d$. Here there are two possibilities: $0 < b_1 \cdot d_1$ or $b_1 \cdot d_1 < 0$. We consider the former. Then $a \cdot d \cdot b_1 \cdot d_1 < b \cdot c \cdot b_1 \cdot d_1$, by Theorem 4.3.18. Therefore, $(a_1 \cdot b) \cdot (d \cdot d_1) < (c_1 \cdot d) \cdot (b \cdot b_1)$; i.e., $(a_1 \cdot d_1) \cdot (b \cdot d) < (b_1 \cdot c_1) \cdot (b \cdot d)$. Thus, by Theorem 4.3.18, $a_1 \cdot d_1 < b_1 \cdot c_1$. So $a_1/b_1 < c_1/d_1$. If $b_1 \cdot d_1 < 0$, then $b_1 \cdot d_1 \cdot b \cdot c < b_1 \cdot d_1 \cdot a \cdot d$, by Exercise 12, page 152. Hence, $b_1 \cdot b \cdot d \cdot c_1 < a_1 \cdot b \cdot d \cdot d_1$; i.e., $(b_1 \cdot c_1) \cdot (b \cdot d) < (a_1 \cdot d_1) \cdot (b \cdot d)$. Therefore, $b_1 \cdot c_1 < a_1 \cdot d_1$, by Theorem 4.3.18. So $a_1/b_1 < c_1/d_1$,
2. $b \cdot c < a \cdot d$, and $b \cdot d < 0$. By an argument similar to the preceding demonstration, we can show that $a_1/b_1 < c_1/d_1$.

This establishes Theorem 4.4.3.

The preceding theorem demonstrates that $<$ is a binary relation on the set of all rational numbers; we shall now show that $<$ is an order relation on the set of all rational numbers.

THEOREM 4.4.4. $\forall x \forall y \forall z [x < y \wedge y < z \rightarrow x < z]$.

Proof: Let $x = a/b$, $y = c/d$, and $z = e/f$ — where $0 < b$, $0 < d$, and $0 < f$. By assumption, $a \cdot d < b \cdot c$ and $c \cdot f < d \cdot e$; therefore, by Theorem 4.3.18, $a \cdot d \cdot f < b \cdot c \cdot f$ and $c \cdot f \cdot b < d \cdot e \cdot b$. Hence, by Theorem 4.3.5, $a \cdot d \cdot f < d \cdot e \cdot b$. Applying Theorem 4.3.18, it follows that $a \cdot f < b \cdot e$. Since $0 < b \cdot f$, by Theorem 4.3.18, we conclude that $a/b < e/f$. This proves Theorem 4.4.4.

THEOREM 4.4.5. $\forall x \forall y [x = y \vee x < y \vee y < x]$.

Proof: We sketch the proof. Let a/b and c/d be any rational numbers such that $0 < b$ and $0 < d$. Consider the integers $a \cdot d$ and $b \cdot c$, and apply Theorem 4.3.6. The proof of this theorem should now be apparent.

Denoting the set of all rational numbers by "*Rt*", we note the following corollary.

COROLLARY 4.4.1. $<$ is an order relation on *Rt*.

Next, we select two important members of *Rt*, namely 0/1 and 1/1; these rational numbers are significant because of their algebraic properties.

THEOREM 4.4.6. $(Rt, +, 0/1)$ is a commutative group.

Proof: It is easy to prove that $+$ is associative and commutative, and that 0/1 is an additive identity. Furthermore,

$$a/b + -a/b = (a \cdot b + b \cdot -a)/b \cdot b = b \cdot (a + -a)/b \cdot b = 0/1$$

whenever $a/b \in Rt$; thus, each rational number possesses an additive inverse. This establishes Theorem 4.4.6.

THEOREM 4.4.7. $(Rt, +, \cdot, 0/1, 1/1)$ is a field.

Proof: It is easily seen that $\cdot$ is associative and commutative, and that $1/1$ is a multiplicative identity. Furthermore, $a/b \cdot b/a = a \cdot b \mid b \cdot a = 1/1$ whenever $a/b \in Rt$ and $a \neq 0$; thus, each rational number, other than $0/1$, possesses a multiplicative inverse. Furthermore, the distributive law holds. This establishes Theorem 4.4.7.

We now introduce the rational number system.

DEFINITION 4.4.4.   By the *rational number system,* we mean the algebraic system $(Rt, +, \cdot, <, 0/1, 1/1)$.

THEOREM 4.4.8.   The rational number system is an ordered field.

Proof: In view of the preceding theorems, it remains only to establish $\forall x \forall y \forall z[x < y \rightarrow x + z < y + z]$ and $\forall x \forall y \forall z[x < y \land 0 < z \rightarrow x \cdot z < y \cdot z]$. The details are left as an exercise.

In this section we have presented a well-known method for constructing the rational number system from the system of integers. This construction technique is of extreme importance and merits careful study, for any integral domain can be extended to a field in this way. Note that the rational number system is an extension of the system of integers.

E X E R C I S E S

Show that the following propositions are true in the rational number system:
1. $\forall x[x \cdot 0/1 = 0/1]$.
2. $\forall x \forall y[x + y = y + x]$.
3. $\forall x \forall y[x \cdot y = y \cdot x]$.
4. $\forall x \forall y \forall z[x + (y + z) = (x + y) + z]$.
5. $\forall x \forall y \forall z[x \cdot (y \cdot z) = (x \cdot y) \cdot z]$.
6. $\forall x \forall y \forall z[x \cdot (y + z) = x \cdot y + x \cdot z]$.
7. $\forall x \exists y[x + y = 0/1]$.
8. $\exists x \forall y[x \cdot y = 0/1]$.

9. $\forall x \forall y \forall z [x < y \rightarrow x + z < y + z]$.

10. $\forall x \forall y \forall z [0 < z \wedge x < y \rightarrow x \cdot z < y \cdot z]$.

11. $\forall x \forall y \forall z [z < 0 \wedge x < y \rightarrow y \cdot z < x \cdot z]$.

12. Let $-$ be a unary operation on Rt defined as follows: $-(a/b) = (-a)/b$.
   a. Show that $\forall x [x + -x = 0/1]$ and that $\forall x [-(-x) = x]$.
   b. Show that $\forall x \forall y [x < y \rightarrow -y < -x]$.
   c. Show that $\forall x [-x = (-1/1) \cdot x]$.

13. a. Simplify $a/1 + b/1$.
   b. Simplify $a/1 \cdot b/1$.
   c. Under what condition on a and b is $a/1 < b/1$?
   d. Now show that the algebraic system obtained from the rational number system by considering only rational numbers of the form $x/1$ is algebraically the same as the system of integers.

14. Show that given a rational number, say x, there is a unique integer, say c, such that $(c/1 < x \vee c/1 = x) \wedge x < (c + 1)/1$; c is denoted by "$[x]$". (*Hint:* Consider the properties of $<$ in the system of integers.)

15. A rational number is said to be a *decimal rational* iff it has a name, say a/b, such that $\exists n [n \in N \wedge b = 10^n]$.
   a. Show that $x + y$ is a decimal rational if x and y are decimal rationals.
   b. Show that $x \cdot y$ is a decimal rational if x and y are decimal rationals.
   c. Show that $1/2$, $1/4$, $-1/5$, $1/8$ are decimal rationals, and that $-1/3$, $1/6$, $1/7$, $1/9$ are not decimal rationals.

16. Show that a rational number, say x, is a decimal rational iff there is a natural number n and $n + 1$ integers, say $a_0, a_1, a_2, \cdots, a_n$, such that $x = a_0/1 + a_1/10^1 + a_2/10^2 + \cdots + a_n/10^n$ and $\{a_1, a_2, \cdots, a_n\} \subset \{0, 1, 2, 3, 4, 5, 6, 7, 8, 9\}$. (*Hint:* Take advantage of the $[y]$ notation, and first treat the case $0 < x$.)

17. Show that the algebraic system $(Rt, \cdot, 1/1)$ is *not* a group.

18. Suppose $x \in Rt$ and $x \neq 0/1$; then x possesses a unique multiplicative inverse which is denoted by $\dfrac{\text{``1''}}{x}$. Prove the following:

   a. $\dfrac{1}{\dfrac{1}{x}} = x$ whenever $x \neq 0/1$.

   b. $\dfrac{1}{x \cdot y} = \dfrac{1}{x} \cdot \dfrac{1}{y}$ provided $x \cdot y \neq 0/1$.

19. Suppose that $x \in Rt$, $y \in Rt$, and $x \neq 0/1$; then $y \cdot \dfrac{1}{x}$ is denoted by $\dfrac{\text{``}y\text{''}}{x}$. Prove the following:

   a. $\dfrac{1}{\dfrac{y}{x}} = \dfrac{x}{y}$ provided $x \neq 0/1$ and $y \neq 0/1$.

b. $\dfrac{x+y}{z} = \dfrac{x}{z} + \dfrac{y}{z}$ provided $z \neq 0/1$.

c. $\dfrac{\dfrac{x}{y}}{z} = \dfrac{x \cdot z}{y}$ provided $y \neq 0/1$ and $z \neq 0/1$.

d. $\dfrac{\dfrac{x}{y}}{z} = \dfrac{x}{y \cdot z}$ provided $y \neq 0/1$ and $z \neq 0/1$.

20. Prove that each integral domain can be extended to a field.

Chapter 5

The Real Number System

5.1 Sequences of Decimal Rationals

In an *axiomatic* treatment of the real number system, it is assumed that the real number system is a complete ordered field; on this basis, additional properties of the real number system are readily established. On the other hand, it is possible to *construct* the real number system from a simpler, less sophisticated number system. Since the constructive approach imparts a genuine appreciation of the real number system, and since this number system is vital in mathematics, we shall carry out the constructive approach.

In this chapter, we shall use our intuitive ideas and understanding of infinite decimals to motivate a precise definition of real numbers. We shall appeal to our experience in adding and multiplying infinite decimals to motivate a precise definition of addition and multiplication of real numbers. We shall appeal to our experience in comparing infinite decimals to motivate a precise definition of the *less than* relation on the real numbers. In a conventional treatment of the real number system, real numbers are not infinite decimals: either a real number is said to be a set of rational numbers (in the Dedekind cut approach), or a real number is said to be an equivalence class of convergent sequences of rational numbers (in the Cantor approach). In both of these approaches, infinite decimals are defined in terms of real numbers. We emphasize that in our approach a real number is essentially an infinite decimal.

As stated above, the technique of this chapter is patterned on the layman's concept of the real number system, under which a real number is regarded as an infinite decimal, and the sum or product of two real numbers is obtained by carrying out a well-known, though complicated, computational procedure. The vital point is that it is possible to obtain sums and products of real numbers by carrying out computations within the rational number system. In fact, the celebrated "man in the street" has little difficulty in applying the method. Our job here is to analyze our intuitive ideas about infinite decimals; we must inquire just what we mean by an infinite decimal, just how we add and multiply infinite decimals, and just how we compare infinite decimals. In this way, we shall discover the operations and concepts that are fundamental to this important number system.

As we have suggested, we shall base our construction on the rational number system. First, we need the notion of a *decimal rational*. A rational number, say x, is said to be a decimal rational iff x possesses a name, say "a/b", such that $\exists k[k \in N \wedge b = 10^k]$.

THEOREM 5.1.1.   Let a be any nonnegative integer and let k be any natural number; then there exists a unique integer a_0 and unique digits $a_1, a_2, \cdots, a_k$ such that

$$a/10^k = a_0/1 + a_1/10^1 + a_2/10^2 + \cdots + a_k/10^k.$$

Proof: We apply mathematical induction. We say a natural number t has property P iff $a/10^t$ possesses the property stated in the theorem, whenever a is a nonnegative integer. First, we show that 1 has property P. Let a be any nonnegative integer; by the Division Theorem (Theorem 4.3.24), there exist unique integers, say a_0 and a_1, such that

$$a = 10 \cdot a_0 + a_1 \quad \text{and} \quad 0 \le a_1 < 10.$$

Hence, $a/10 = a_0 + a_1/10$ and a_1 is a digit. This proves that 1 has property P. Next, suppose that t has property P; we shall show that $t + 1$ has property P. Let a be any nonnegative integer; by the Division Theorem, there exist unique integers, say b and c, such that

$$a = 10 \cdot b + c \quad \text{and} \quad 0 \le c < 10.$$

Therefore, $a/10^{t+1} = b/10^t + c/10^{t+1}$. But t has property P; since b is a nonnegative integer (prove this!), there exists a unique integer, say b_0, and unique digits, say $b_1, b_2, \cdots, b_t$, such that

$$b/10^t = b_0/1 + b_1/10 + b_2/10^2 + \cdots + b_t/10^t.$$

Therefore, $a/10^{t+1} = b_0/1 + b_1/10 + b_2/10^2 + \cdots + b_t/10^t + c/10^{t+1}$, where $b_1, b_2, \cdots, b_t, c$ are digits. Thus, $t + 1$ has property P whenever t has property P. This establishes Theorem 5.1.1.

For example, $2492/10^2 = 24/1 + 9/10 + 2/10^2$, and $7130/10^3 = 7/1 + 1/10 + 3/10^2 + 0/10^3$.

COROLLARY 5.1.1.   Let a be any negative integer and let k be any natural number; then there exists a unique integer a_0 and unique digits $a_1, a_2, \cdots, a_k$ such that

$$a/10^k = -(a_0/1 + a_1/10^1 + a_2/10^2 + \cdots + a_k/10^k).$$

For example, $(-2492)/10^2 = -(24/1 + 9/10 + 2/10^2)$.

It is helpful to streamline our notation. Following the conventional practice, we introduce the decimal point. Let a_0 be a nonnegative integer and let $a_1, a_2, \cdots, a_k$ be digits; we shall denote the decimal rational

$$a_0/1 + a_1/10^1 + a_2/10^2 + \cdots + a_k/10^k$$

by writing "$a_0.a_1a_2\cdots a_k$". For example, $23/1 + 2/10^1 + 0/10^2 + 5/10^3 + 6/10^4 + 2/10^5$ is denoted by "23.20562"; it follows that $0/10$ is denoted by "0.0" and that $10/10$ is denoted by "1.0". A streamlined notation for a negative decimal rational is obtained by writing the corresponding positive decimal rational in streamlined form, and prefixing the minus sign. For example, $(-494)/10^4$ is denoted by "-0.0494".

Let "D" denote the set of all decimal rationals; consider the algebraic system constructed from the rational number system by restricting the operations and relations to D, namely $(D, +, \cdot, <, 0.0, 1.0)$. Our goal is to construct the real number system from this algebraic system. Notice that $(D, +, \cdot, 0.0, 1.1)$ is *not* a field, since "$\forall x \exists y [x \neq 0.0 \rightarrow x \cdot y = 1.0]$" is false in this algebraic system; however, it is easy to show that $(D, +, \cdot, 0.0, 1.1)$ is an integral domain.

The basic tool needed in constructing an infinite decimal is the *sequence*. Any mapping of N into D is called a *sequence of decimal rationals*. Recall that a mapping is represented by a set of ordered pairs. Thus, $\{(n, b) | n \in N \wedge b = 1/10^n\}$ is a sequence of decimal rationals; we list a few members of this sequence: $(1, 0.1), (2, 0.01), (3, 0.001), (4, 0.0001)$. Consider the ordered set whose first term is 0.1, whose second term is 0.01, whose third term is 0.001, and whose nth term is $1/10^n$ whenever $n \in N$ —which we denote by writing "$(0.1, 0.01, 0.001, \cdots, 1/10^n, \cdots)$". It is natural to associate this ordered set with the given sequence; in fact, we shall go a step further. We shall *denote* the given sequence by this ordered set. Thus, "$(0.1, 0.01, 0.001, \cdots, 1/10^n, \cdots)$" denotes the sequence $\{(n, b) | n \in N \wedge b = 1/10^n\}$. In general, we shall denote a sequence of decimal rationals by the ordered set whose first term is the decimal rational paired with 1 by the mapping, whose second term is the decimal rational paired with 2 by the mapping, and so on. Thus, the sequence

$\{(n,b)|n \in N \wedge b = a_n\}$, which pairs a_1 with 1, a_2 with 2, and a_n with n whenever $n \in N$, is denoted by "$(a_1,a_2,a_3,\cdots,a_n,\cdots)$". We shall call the terms of this ordered set the *terms* of the sequence, and we shall call a_n the *nth term* of the sequence whenever $n \in N$ (so a_1 is called the *first term* of the sequence, a_2 is called the *second term* of the sequence, and so on).

For example, consider the sequence of decimal rationals $\{(n,b|n \in N \wedge b = n - 3.0\}$; the first term of this sequence is -2.0, the second term is -1.0, the third term is 0.0, and the fourth term is 1.0.

It is convenient to introduce one more abbreviation to help streamline the notation. We shall denote the sequence $(a_1,a_2,a_3,\cdots,a_n,\cdots)$ by writing "(a_n)"; note that only the nth term of the sequence is displayed. This means that we display the *prescription* or *rule* which enables us to compute the nth term of the sequence, whenever $n \in N$. For example, the sequence $(0.1,0.01,0.001,\cdots,1/10^n,\cdots)$ is denoted by "$(1/10^n)$", and the sequence "$\{(n,b)|n \in N \wedge b = 3.0 + 1/10^n\}$ is denoted by "$(3.0 + 1/10^n)$".

Now that we have introduced the concept of a sequence of decimal rationals and have developed a convenient notation, we are ready to do something with sequences. Consider the sequences (a_n) and (b_n); applying the operations of $(D,+,\cdot,<,0.0,1.0)$ to corresponding terms of these sequences, we obtain the sequences $(a_n + b_n)$ and $(a_n \cdot b_n)$. For example, from the sequences of decimal rationals $(1/10^n)$ and $(1/10^{n+1})$, we obtain the sequences of decimal rationals $(11/10^{n+1})$ and $(1/10^{2n+1})$. Again, names can be helpful; we shall call the sequence $(a_n + b_n)$ the *sum* of (a_n) and (b_n), and we shall call the sequence $(a_n \cdot b_n)$ the *product* of (a_n) and (b_n).

We now introduce two families of unary operations on sequences of decimal rationals. Let (a_n) be any sequence of decimal rationals; consider the sequence obtained from (a_n) by blocking out, i.e., throwing out, the first few terms, say the first three terms—namely, the sequence $(a_4,a_5, a_6,\cdots,a_{n+3},\cdots)$. This simple operation is really quite important and warrants a name. Symbolizing the operation of *blocking out* by "B", and inserting the number of terms blocked out as a subscript on B, we obtain "B_3" as a name of this unary operation. Thus, "B_3" prefixed to (a_n) denotes the sequence obtained from (a_n) by omitting the first three terms. Hence, $B_3(a_n) = (a_4,a_5,a_6,\cdots,a_{n+3},\cdots) = (a_{n+3})$. In the same way, if k is any nonnegative integer, the sequence obtained from (a_n) by blocking out the first k terms is denoted by prefixing "B_k" to (a_n).

DEFINITION 5.1.1. $B_k(a_n) = (a_{n+k})$ whenever k is a nonnegative integer.

For example, $B_2(3.1, 3.14, 3.141, 3.1415, 3.14159, \cdots) = (3.141, 3.1415,$

$3.14159, \cdots$), and $B_5\{(n,b)|n \in N \wedge b = 1/10^n\} = \{(n,b)|n \in N \wedge b = 1/10^{n+5}\}$. Notice that $B_0(a_n) = (a_n)$. Clearly, $B_r B_s(a_n) = B_s B_r(a_n) = B_{r+s}(a_n)$ whenever r and s are nonnegative integers.

Now for the second family of unary operations which we shall find useful. Consider the decimal rational 3.14159265; one way of obtaining an approximation to this number is to lop off digits at the extreme right. For example, deleting the last six digits, we obtain the decimal rational 3.14. Alternatively, we can describe this operation on 3.14159265 by observing that we have retained two digits following the decimal point. We shall transform a sequence of decimal rationals by performing this operation on each term of the sequence — retaining two digits following the decimal point. Symbolizing the operation of deleting digits by "D", and inserting, as a subscript on D, the number of digits following the decimal point which are retained, we obtain "D_2" as a name of this unary operation. Thus, "$D_2(a_n)$" denotes the sequence of decimal rationals obtained from (a_n) by carrying out the above operation on each term of (a_n). In the same way, if k is any positive integer, we denote by "D_k" the operation of deleting digits so as to retain k digits following the decimal point. Thus, "$D_k(a_n)$" denotes the sequence of decimal rationals obtained from (a_n) by "simplifying" each term of (a_n) in the manner described.

DEFINITION 5.1.2. Let k be any positive integer; then $D_k(a_n) = (b_n)$, where b_n is obtained from a_n by deleting each digit of a_n following the digit in the kth decimal place; if a_n has less than $k+1$ digits following the decimal point, then $b_n = a_n$.

For example, let a_n be π written out to n decimal places; then

$$D_4(a_n) = (3.1, 3.14, 3.141, 3.1415, 3.1415, 3.1415, \cdots, 3.1415, \cdots).$$

Note that $B_3 D_4(a_n) = (3.1415)$. Also, $D_3(2.534, 3.47853, -15.2489, 0.0007, 6.1, \cdots) = (2.534, 3.478, -15.248, 0.0, 6.1, \cdots)$.

Associated with the *deleting digits* operation, we have the *rounding off* operation which deletes digits and increases the terminal digit by one if the first digit omitted is 5 or greater; we shall use "R" for *rounding off* and a subscript. Notice that this operation can be expressed in terms of the *deleting digits* operation.

DEFINITION 5.1.3. Let k be any positive integer; then $R_k(a_n) = D_k(c_n)$, where

$$c_n = \begin{cases} a_n + 5/10^{k+1} & \text{if } a_n \geq 0 \\ a_n - 5/10^{k+1} & \text{if } a_n < 0 \end{cases}$$

For example, $R_3(2.534, 3.47853, -15.2489, 0.0007, 6.1, \cdots) = D_3(2.5345, 3.47903, -15.2494, 0.0012, 6.1005, \cdots) = (2.534, 3.479, -15.249, 0.001, 6.1, \cdots)$.

We need one more unary operation on sequences of decimal rationals. First, we present a special method of constructing a sequence. Let a be a decimal rational which possesses nonzero digits to the right of the decimal point and whose final nonzero digit is 9. Consider the sequence (b_n) constructed from a as follows: $b_1 = a$, and, for each n, b_{n+1} is constructed from b_n by adjoining the digit 9 to the right of b_n. For example, applying this procedure to the decimal rational 2.09, we obtain the sequence $(2.09, 2.099, 2.0999, \cdots)$; and applying the procedure to the decimal rational -17.9, we obtain the sequence $(-17.9, -17.99, -17.999, \cdots)$. Any sequence which can be constructed in this fashion is called a *9-sequence*. We formalize this notion in the following definition.

DEFINITION 5.1.4. We shall say that (a_n) is a *9-sequence* if

(i) $a_1 = a/10^k + 9/10^{k+1}$, where a and k are nonnegative integers,
(ii) $a_{n+1} = a_n + 9/10^{n+k+1}$ whenever $n \in N$;

furthermore, $(-a_n)$ is said to be a 9-sequence if (a_n) is a 9-sequence.

Clearly, if (b_n) is a 9-sequence, then $B_q(b_n)$ is a 9-sequence whenever q is a nonnegative integer. Generalizing on this property of 9-sequences, consider a sequence (c_n) such that $B_q(c_n)$ is a 9-sequence for at least one nonnegative integer q; we shall call (c_n) an *N-sequence*.

DEFINITION 5.1.5. We shall say that (c_n) is an *N-sequence* iff there is a nonnegative integer, say q, such that $B_q(c_n)$ is a 9-sequence.

For example, $(1.041, 5.1, 3.24, 3.249, 3.2499, 3.24999, \cdots)$ is an N-sequence since $B_3(1.041, 5.1, 3.24, 3.249, 3.2499, 3.24999, \cdots)$ is a 9-sequence.

We are ready to introduce a useful unary operation on sequences of decimal rationals. The idea is to simplify the terms of an N-sequence by throwing out the final block of 9's, and at the same time increasing by one the digit which precedes the block of 9's. We formalize this familiar notion as follows, using "N" to denote the operation.

DEFINITION 5.1.6. Let (a_n) be any N-sequence, let t be the smallest nonnegative integer such that $B_t(a_n)$ is a 9-sequence. Ii $0 < a_{t+1}$, there is a nonnegative integer k such that $a_{t+1} = a/10^k + 9/10^{k+1}$; then we say that $N(a_n) = (b_n)$ where

(i) $b_n = a_n$ whenever $n < t$,
(ii) $b_n = a_n + 1/10^{n+k-t}$ whenever $n \geq t$

If $a_{t+1} < 0$, then we say that $N(a_n)$ is the product of $N(-a_n)$ and (-1). Finally, if (c_n) is not an N-sequence, we say that $N(c_n)$ is (c_n).

For example, $N(1.041, 5.1, 3.24, 3.249, 3.2499, 3.24999, \cdots) = (1.041, 5.1, 3.25, 3.25, 3.25, \cdots)$. Notice that here $t = 3$ and $k = 2$. Also,

$$N(-2.0, -2.09, -2.099, -2.0999, \cdots)$$
$$= (-1) \cdot N(2.0, 2.09, 2.099, 2.0999, \cdots)$$
$$= (-1) \cdot (2.1, 2.1, 2.1, \cdots)$$
$$= (-2.1).$$

In constructing the real number system, we shall make use of the operations and concepts introduced above.

EXERCISES

1. Write down any three members of $\{(n,b) | n \in N \wedge b = 4/10^n\}$.
2. Write down any three members of $\{(n,b) | n \in N \wedge b = 1/10^{n+1}\}$.

   Denote each of the following sequences by an ordered set; in each case, write down the first five terms of the ordered set:

3. $\{(n,b) | n \in N \wedge b = 1/10^{2n+1}\}$.
4. $\{(n,b) | n \in N \wedge b = 5.1 + 1/10^n\}$.
5. $\{(n,b) | n \in N \wedge b = 238/10^{n+2}\}$.
6. $\{(n,b) | n \in N \wedge b = 4/10^{2n-1}\}$.
7. $\{(n,b) | n \in N \wedge b = 3.0\}$.
8. $\{(n,b) | n \in N \wedge b = -12.94\}$.
9. $\{(n,b) | n \in N \wedge b = 7.0 + 4.81\}$.
10. $\{(n,b) | n \in N \wedge b = 10^n/2\}$.
11. $\{(n,b) | n \in N \wedge b = 10^n/5\}$.
12. $\{(n,b) | n \in N \wedge (n < 3 \rightarrow b = 1/10^n) \wedge (2 < n \rightarrow b = 7.0)\}$.
13. $\{(n,b) | n \in N \wedge (n < 4 \rightarrow b = 2/10^{n+1}) \wedge (3 < n \rightarrow b = 2/10^n)\}$.
14. $\{(n,b) | n \in N \wedge (n < 2 \rightarrow b = 10.107) \wedge (1 < n \rightarrow b = 10.107 + 1/10^n)\}$.

15. $\{(n,b)|n \in N \wedge (n<2 \rightarrow b=16.9) \wedge (1<n \rightarrow b=16.9+9/10^n)\}$.

16. $\{(n,b)|n \in N \wedge (n<4 \rightarrow b=7.0) \wedge (3<n \rightarrow b=3.5)\}$.

17. $\{(n,b)|n \in N \wedge (n<2 \rightarrow b=1.1) \wedge (1<n \rightarrow b=1.1+1/10^n)\}$.

18. $\{(n,b)|n \in N \wedge (n<2 \rightarrow b=-1.1) \wedge (1<n \rightarrow b=-1.1-1/10^n)\}$.

19. Compute the sum of $\{(n,b)|n \in N \wedge b=2/10^{2n}\}$ and $\{(n,b)|n \in N \wedge b=3/10^{2n+1}\}$, writing down the first six terms of the sequence.

20. Compute the sum of $\{(n,b)|n \in N \wedge b=5/10^{2n}\}$ and $\{(n,b)|n \in N \wedge b=1/10^{2n-1}\}$, writing down the first six terms of the sequence.

21. Write down the first six terms of the product of $\{(n,b)|n \in N \wedge b=1/10^n\}$ and $\{(n,b)|n \in N \wedge b=4.31\}$.

22. Write down the first six terms of the product of $\{(n,b)|n \in N \wedge b=2/10^{n-1}\}$ and $\{(n,b)|n \in N \wedge b=3/10^{2n}\}$.

Fill in the gaps in the following propositions:

23. $(3, \quad) \in \{(n,b)|n \in N \wedge b=3.1+1/10^n\}$.

24. $(7, \quad) \in \{(n,b)|n \in N \wedge b=3.1+1/10^n\}$.

25. $(\quad,3.11) \in \{(n,b)|n \in N \wedge b=3.1+1/10^n\}$.

26. $(\quad,3.100001) \in \{(n,b)|n \in N \wedge b=3.1+1/10^n\}$.

27. The 4th term of $\{(n,b)|n \in N \wedge b=5/10^n\}$ is _____.

28. The 5th term of $\{(n,b)|n \in N \wedge (n<5 \rightarrow b=1/10^n) \wedge (4<n \rightarrow b=2.1)\}$ is _____.

29. The 3rd term of $(1.21, 1.211, 1.2111, 1.21111, \cdots)$ is _____.

30. The 5th term of $(1.21, 1.211, 1.2111, 1.21111, \cdots)$ is _____.

Compute the following:

31. $B_3(1.1, 1.11, 1.111, 1.1111, \cdots)$.

32. $B_0(a_n)$.

33. $B_1(a_n)$.

34. $B_7(a_n)$.

35. $B_3(3.1, 3.14, 3.141, 3.1415, 3.14159, \cdots)$.

36. $B_2(5.9, 6.01, 5.999, 6.0001, 5.99999, 6.000001, \cdots)$.

37. $D_3(1.7, 1.73, 1.732, 1.7320, 1.73205, 1.732050, 1.7320508, \cdots)$.

38. $D_4(2.49, 2.501, 2.4999, 2.50001, 2.499999, 2.5000001, 2.49999999, \cdots)$.

39. $D_2(1.4, 1.41, 1.414, 1.4142, 1.41421, 1.414213, 1.4142135, 1.41421356, \cdots)$.

40. $D_4(1.4, 1.73, 1.414, 1.7320, 1.41421, 1.732050, 1.4142135, \cdots)$.

41. $B_2 D_3(1.5, 1.42, 1.415, 1.4143, 1.41422, 1.414214, 1.4142136, 1.41421357, \cdots)$.

42. $D_2 B_3(1.8, 1.74, 1.733, 1.7321, 1.73206, 1.732051, 1.7320509, \cdots)$.

43. $B_3(a,b,c,a,b,c,a,b,c,a,b,c, \cdots)$.

44. $B_1(a,b,c,a,b,c,a,b,c,a,b,c, \cdots)$.

45. $B_2 B_4(1.1, 1.11, 1.111, 1.1111, 1.11111, 1.111111, 1.1111111, \cdots)$.

46. $D_2D_4(1.1, 1.11, 1.111, 1.1111, 1.11111, 1.111111, 1.1111111, \cdots)$.

47. $D_4D_2(1.1, 1.11, 1.111, 1.1111, 1.11111, 1.111111, 1.1111111, \cdots)$.

48. $B_3(7.1, 7.2, 7.3, 4.0, 4.0, 4.0, 4.0, 4.0, \cdots)$.

49. $N(5.2, 5.29, 5.299, 5.2999, 5.29999, \cdots)$.

50. $N(23.029, 23.0299, 23.02999, 23.029999, \cdots)$.

51. $N(-5.39, -5.399, -5.3999, -5.39999, \cdots)$.

52. $N(2.9, 3.01, 2.99, 3.001, 2.999, 3.0001, 2.9999, 3.00001, 2.99999, \cdots)$.

53. $N(2.9, 2.999, 2.99999, 2.9999999, \cdots)$.

54. $B_3N(3.1, 3.15, 3.152, 3.1529, 3.15299, 3.152999, \cdots)$.

55. $D_4N(-7.8, -7.89, -7.899, -7.8999, -7.89999, \cdots)$.

56. $B_2D_3N(2.135, 2.1357, 2.13579, 2.135799, 2.1357999, \cdots)$.

57. $R_2(23.029, 23.0299, 23.02999, \cdots)$.

58. $R_3(23.029, 23.0299, 23.02999, \cdots)$.

5.2 The Real Number System

At last we are ready to construct the real number system! First, we shall construct the real numbers. From years of experience in handling infinite decimals, each of us has developed some feeling for and insight into these objects. Perhaps the most important intuitive idea that we possess regarding the concept of a real number is that a real number can be approximated, as closely as desired, by a rational number—in fact, by a decimal rational. It is essential that the meaning of "as closely as desired" be clear. We mean that we can approximate the real number with an error less than $1/10^p$ whenever $p \in N$. For example, consider the square root of 2, i.e., the non-negative number whose square is 2; this number is denoted by "$2^{1/2}$" or "$\sqrt{2}$". Now,

1.4	approximates $2^{1/2}$ with an error less than	$1/10$
1.41	" " " " " " "	$1/10^2$
1.414	" " " " " " "	$1/10^3$
1.4142	" " " " " " "	$1/10^4$
1.41421	" " " " " " "	$1/10^5$
1.414213	" " " " " " "	$1/10^6$

It is a simple matter to compute the next entry in this table.

The question remains: what *is* $2^{1/2}$? Consider a sequence of approximations to $2^{1/2}$, say (a_n) where a_p approximates $2^{1/2}$ with an error less than $1/10^p$ and a_p has exactly p digits to the right of the decimal point whenever

$p \in N$. From a computing point of view, the sequence (a_n) provides complete information about the real number denoted by "$2^{1/2}$". Therefore, we shall say what we mean by "$2^{1/2}$" is the sequence (a_n); the first few terms of an appropriate sequence are given above.

We tend to think of a real number as an *infinite* decimal. For example, we visualize $2^{1/2}$ as the infinite decimal $1.41421357\cdots$, where the three dots stand for infinitely many digits. The infinite decimal is used to generate approximations to the real number involved. By cutting off the infinite decimal at the pth decimal place, we obtain a decimal rational which approximates the real number with an error less than $1/10^p$. The notion of an infinite decimal is a convenient device for representing a real number; unfortunately, an infinite decimal is readily confused with a decimal rational. With or without the three dots, an infinite decimal looks like a decimal rational. Furthermore, the idea of representing infinitely many digits by three dots has the effect of minimizing the *infinite* part of the infinite decimal. For these reasons, we shall represent a real number by a sequence of decimal rationals, as stated above. Notice that the sequence of decimal rationals

$$(1.4, 1.41, 1.414, 1.4142, 1.41421, 1.414213, \cdots)$$

is the mathematical representation of the infinite decimal $1.414213\cdots$.

Clearly, there are many sequences of decimal rationals such that the pth term of the sequence approximates $2^{1/2}$ with an error less than $1/10^p$ whenever $p \in N$. For example, the sequences

$$(1.5, 1.42, 1.415, 1.4143, 1.41422, 1.414214, \cdots)$$
and $$(1.5, 1.41, 1.415, 1.4142, 1.41422, 1.414213, \cdots)$$

possess the stated property. In view of this and keeping the notion of an infinite decimal in mind, we define a real number as follows.

DEFINITION 5.2.1.   A sequence of decimal rationals, say (a_n), is said to be a *real number* if

    (i) $\exists a \exists d [a$ is a nonnegative integer $\wedge d$ is a digit $\wedge a_1 = a + d/10]$,
    (ii) $\forall n \exists d [n \in N \rightarrow a_{n+1} = a_n + d/10^{n+1} \wedge d$ is a digit$]$,
    (iii) (a_n) is not an N-sequence;

furthermore, $(-a_n)$ is said to be a real number if (a_n) is a real number. There are no other real numbers.

The first two of the above restrictions ensure that a real number is patterned on an infinite decimal. To see the necessity for the third restriction, consider the sequences $(1.0, 1.0, 1.0, \cdots, 1.0, \cdots)$ and $(0.9, 0.99, 0.999, \cdots, 1 - 1/10^n, \cdots)$. Intuitively speaking, these sequences generate approximations to the same real number; furthermore, both sequences meet the first two requirements of a real number. Since $(1.0, 1.0, 1.0, \cdots)$ is preferred in practice and is not an N-sequence, whereas $(0.9, 0.99, 0.999, \cdots)$ is an N-sequence, the third restriction is required.

The following examples are intended to illustrate the meaning of Definition 5.2.1. The sequences

$(2.0, 2.01, 2.011, 2.0111, 2.01111, \cdots)$,
$(3.1, 3.14, 3.141, 3.1415, 3.14159, \cdots)$,
$(-15.4, -15.48, -15.489, -15.489, -15.489, \cdots, -15.489, \cdots)$,
$(-2.2, -2.2, -2.2, \cdots, -2.2, \cdots)$,
$(0.0, 0.0, 0.0, 0.0004, 0.00041, 0.00041, 0.00041, \cdots, 0.00041, \cdots)$

are each real numbers, whereas none of the following sequences is a real number:

$(51.8, 51.83, 51.835, 51.8359, 51.83599, 51.835999, \cdots)$,
$(2.01, 2.011, 2.0111, \cdots)$,
$(3.1, 3.14, 3.142, 3.1416, 3.14159, 3.141593, \cdots)$,
$(2.22, 2.22, 2.22, \cdots, 2.22, \cdots)$.

State which of the three restrictions has not been met by these sequences.

Now that we have real numbers, we want to define addition. We know how to add infinite decimals, and shall add real numbers in exactly the same way. Perhaps you regard addition of infinite decimals as a trivial operation; if so, can you define just how two infinite decimals are added? Think about this for a moment. What is needed is an operation, or rule, which when applied to the given infinite decimals produces the first p decimal places of the sum whenever $p \in N$; the one operation must work for any natural number p and for any pair of infinite decimals. In the case of infinite decimals such as $2.222 \cdots 2 \cdots$ and $3.333 \cdots 3 \cdots$, the rule is straightforward: write down the given real numbers to p decimal places and add the resulting decimal rationals. To see the difficulty, consider the infinite decimals $2.222 \cdots 2 \cdots$ and $3.33888 \cdots 8 \cdots$. Applying the stated rule with $p = 1$, we obtain $2.2 + 3.3 = 5.5$, which is correct. Applying the stated rule with $p = 2$, we obtain $2.22 + 3.33 = 5.55$, which is incorrect, since the sum of these infinite decimals is $5.56111 \cdots 1 \cdots$; for $p = 2$, the required answer is 5.56.

From this example it is clear that to obtain the sum of two infinite decimals to p decimal places, it is necessary to write down the given infinite decimals to q decimal places and then add — where q has been chosen so that $p \leq q$ and the digit in the pth decimal place of the sum does not change should q be increased. Finally, the $q - p$ surplus digits at the right of the sum are discarded. There is a difficulty: for one natural number p it may turn out that the required q is $p + 1$, whereas for another natural number p it may turn out that the required q is $p + 10^6$. Can you demonstrate this difficulty by writing down two infinite decimals which possess the stated property?

Fortunately, it is possible to achieve the desired effect with the help of the *blocking out* and *deleting digits* operations introduced in Section 5.1. Let (a_n) and (b_n) be any real numbers. Consider the sequence of decimal rationals $(a_n + b_n)$; this may or may not be a real number. By visualizing the infinite decimals involved, it is easy to see that in either case there exists a unique decimal rational, say d_1, such that $\exists q [\mathbf{B}_q \mathbf{D}_1 (a_n + b_n) = (d_1)]$; similarly, there is a unique decimal rational, say d_2, such that $\exists q [\mathbf{B}_q \mathbf{D}_2 (a_n + b_n) = (d_2)]$; in fact, given any natural number k, there is a unique decimal rational, say d_k, such that $\exists q [\mathbf{B}_q \mathbf{D}_k (a_n + b_n) = (d_k)]$. In this way, we construct the sequence of decimal rationals $(d_1, d_2, d_3, \cdots, d_n, \cdots)$. This sequence has been obtained from the sequence $(a_n + b_n)$ as a result of a definite operation. It is convenient to symbolize this operation by "D", and to denote the resulting sequence by prefixing "D" to the given sequence.

DEFINITION 5.2.2.   Let (c_n) be any sequence of decimal rationals; then

$$\mathbf{D}(c_n) = (e_n) \text{ iff } \forall k \exists q [\mathbf{B}_q \mathbf{D}_k (c_n) = (e_k)].$$

Before illustrating this definition, let us consider the real number (a_n) where each a_t is an approximation to the length of the circumference of the unit semicircle; to be precise, for each t, a_t is less than the length of the circumference of the unit semicircle and differs from this length by less than $1/10^t$. We note that $a_1 = 3.1$, $a_2 = 3.14$, $a_3 = 3.141$, $a_4 = 3.1415$, and $a_5 = 3.14159$. This real number, which is denoted by "π", figures prominently in the history of mathematics; throughout the past two thousand years considerable effort has been devoted to the computation of π. As recently as 1579 the eminent French mathematician François Vieta computed 9 decimal places of π; i.e., he proved that $a_9 = 3.14159\,2653$. In 1593 Adriaen van Roomen (also called Romanus) of the Netherlands computed 15 decimal places of π; i.e., he showed that $a_{15} = 3.14159\,26535$

89793. In the eighteenth and nineteenth centuries, mathematicians did much better by using infinite series. In 1719 the French mathematician De Lagny computed a_{112}, and in 1841 William Rutherford of England calculated π to 208 decimal places (there was an error in the 153rd decimal place, but he made up for this in 1853 by computing a_{400} correctly). After devoting 15 years to the task, William Shanks of England in 1873 claimed to have π to 707 decimal places; however, in 1946 D. F. Ferguson of England found that Shanks's result was in error in the 528th decimal place; the following year, Ferguson computed a_{710} correctly. At this time J. W. Wrench, Jr., of the United States claimed to have a_{808}; Ferguson discovered that Wrench's computation was wrong in the 723rd decimal place. In 1948 Ferguson and Wrench collaborated in computing a_{808} correctly. The following year, an electronic calculator, ENIAC, computed π to 2,035 decimal places, requiring about three days to complete the job. In 1959 an IBM 704 determined π to 16,167 decimal places.

Now, let us use π to illustrate Definition 5.2.2; suppose that, for each n, b_n is π rounded off to n decimal places. Then

$$(b_n) = (3.1, 3.14, 3.142, 3.1416, 3.14159, 3.141593, 3.1415927, \cdots)$$
and $D(b_n) = (3.1, 3.14, 3.141, 3.1415, 3.14159, 3.141592, \cdots) = \pi.$

Of course, D cannot be applied to any sequence of decimal rationals, but we shall not go into this question here.

We now return to the sequence $D(a_n + b_n)$ that we have constructed from the real numbers (a_n) and (b_n). Reviewing the construction of this sequence, we see that $D(a_n + b_n)$ satisfies the first two requirements of a real number. However, it may happen that $D(a_n + b_n)$ is an N-sequence. For example, let $(a_n) = (0.5, 0.55, 0.555, \cdots)$ and let $(b_n) = (0.4, 0.44, 0.444, \cdots)$; then

$$D(a_n + b_n) = D(0.9, 0.99, 0.999, \cdots) = (0.9, 0.99, 0.999, \cdots),$$

which is an N-sequence. But any N-sequence which satisfies the first two requirements of a real number is transformed into a real number by the N operation. For example, $N(0.9, 0.99, 0.999, \cdots) = (1.0)$. Notice that this transformation is patterned on the usual custom of replacing the infinite decimal $0.999 \cdots 9 \cdots$ by 1.0. Thus, the effect of the N operation is to *normalize* the sequence to which it is applied.

We can now characterize the sum of the real numbers (a_n) and (b_n); the number we want is $ND(a_n + b_n)$. As usual, we shall denote the binary operation of addition by "+"; thus, our definition of addition is as follows.

DEFINITION 5.2.3. $(a_n) + (b_n) = \mathrm{ND}(a_n + b_n)$ whenever (a_n) and (b_n) are real numbers.

For example,

$(3.2, 3.24, 3.244, 3.2444, \cdots)$
  $+ (17.6, 17.67, 17.675, 17.6755, 17.67555, \cdots)$
      $= \mathrm{ND}(20.8, 20.91, 20.919, 20,9199, 20.91999, \cdots)$
      $= \mathrm{N}(20.9, 20.91, 20.919, 20.9199, 20.91999, \cdots)$
      $= (20.9, 20.92, 20.92, 20.92, \cdots, 20.92, \cdots);$

and

$(23.2, 23.27, 23.271, 23.2716, 23.27166, 23.271666, \cdots)$
  $+ (-12.1, -12.17, -12.177, -12.1777, \cdots)$
      $= \mathrm{ND}(11.1, 11.1, 11.094, 11.0939, 11.09389, 11.093889,$
                                                                                          $11.0938889, \cdots)$
      $= \mathrm{N}(11.0, 11.09, 11.093, 11.0938, 11.09388, 11.093888, \cdots)$
      $= (11.0, 11.09, 11.093, 11.0938, 11.09388, 11.093888, \cdots).$

Next, we want to introduce multiplication. We know how to multiply infinite decimals, and we shall multiply real numbers in exactly the same way. However, multiplication of infinite decimals is a fairly sophisticated operation, since it is subject to exactly the same complications as addition. Let (a_n) and (b_n) be any real numbers. Recall that the sum of these numbers is obtained from (a_n) and (b_n) as the final result of three operations. First, the sequences (a_n) and (b_n) are added; next, D is applied; finally, N is applied. The operation D smoothes out the sequence $(a_n + b_n)$, and the operation N ensures that the final result is a real number. In the case of multiplication, only the first step is different. We begin by forming the product of the sequences (a_n) and (b_n), obtaining the sequence $(a_n \cdot b_n)$; next, D is applied; finally, N is applied. Again, the operation D smoothes out the sequence $(a_n \cdot b_n)$, and the operation N ensures that the final result is a real number.

As usual, we shall denote the binary operation of multiplication by "$\cdot$"; thus, our definition of multiplication is as follows.

DEFINITION 5.2.4. $(a_n) \cdot (b_n) = \mathrm{ND}(a_n \cdot b_n)$ whenever (a_n) and (b_n) are real numbers.

For example,

$$(0.3, 0.3, 0.3, \cdots) \cdot (2.2, 2.22, 2.222, \cdots)$$
$$= \mathrm{ND}(0.66, 0.666, 0.6666, \cdots)$$
$$= \mathrm{N}(0.6, 0.66, 0.666, \cdots)$$
$$= (0.6, 0.66, 0.666, \cdots),$$

and

$$(0.3, 0.3, 0.3, \cdots) \cdot (2.2, 2.25, 2.253, 2.2533, 2.25333, \cdots)$$
$$= \mathrm{ND}(0.66, 0.675, 0.6759, 0.67599, 0.675999, \cdots)$$
$$= \mathrm{N}(0.6, 0.67, 0.675, 0.6759, 0.67599, 0.675999, \cdots)$$
$$= (0.6, 0.67, 0.676, 0.676, 0.676, \cdots)$$

Now that we have constructed the real numbers and defined addition and multiplication, we need an order relation on the real numbers. We know how to compare infinite decimals, and we shall compare real numbers in exactly the same way. In comparing infinite decimals, we scan the two infinite decimals, looking at corresponding digits, until we reach a decimal place occupied by distinct digits. A parallel procedure works for real numbers. Suppose that (a_n) and (b_n) are any real numbers; we scan the two sequences, comparing corresponding terms, until we find corresponding terms that are different. If there is a natural number k such that a_k is less than b_k, we shall say that (a_n) is less than (b_n) and write "$(a_n) < (b_n)$". Thus, the binary relation $<$ on the real numbers is defined as follows.

DEFINITION 5.2.5. Let (a_n) and (b_n) be any real numbers; then $(a_n) < (b_n)$ iff $\exists k [a_k < b_k]$.

Note that the symbol "$<$" to the right of the "iff" denotes the order relation on the rational numbers. For example,

$$(-21.3, -21.34, -21.344, -21.3444, \cdots)$$
$$< (-21.3, -21.33, -21.333, \cdots)$$

and

$$(5.7, 5.74, 5.746, 5.7468, 5.74688, 5.746888, \cdots)$$
$$< (5.7, 5.74, 5.748, 5.748, 5.748, 5.748, \cdots)$$

The following theorem is easily established.

THEOREM 5.2.1. Let (a_n) and (b_n) be any real numbers; then

$$\exists k[a_k < b_k \to \forall m[k \le m \to a_m < b_m]].$$

Now a word about notation. It is customary to denote a real number, say (a_n), by "a_k", provided that k is the smallest natural number such that $\forall n[k \le n \to a_n = a_k]$. For example, the real number $(5.1, 5.12, 5.128, 5.128, 5.128, \cdots)$ is denoted by "5.128". Furthermore, if the name of a real number ends with the digit 0, then we shall drop out both the 0 and the decimal point that precedes it. Thus, the real numbers $(0.0, 0.0, 0.0, \cdots)$, $(1.0, 1.0, 1.0, \cdots)$, and $(5.0, 5.0, 5.0, \cdots)$ are denoted by "0", "1", and "5" respectively.

Let us denote the set of all real numbers by "R"; then by the *real number system* we mean the algebraic system

$$(R, +, \cdot, <, 0, 1)$$

which we have constructed from the system of decimal rationals.

The demonstration that this algebraic system is a complete ordered field must be postponed to the following sections of this chapter. This is because we require more extensive machinery to establish the associative laws and the distributive law; this machinery will be developed in Section 5.3. The remaining laws, however, are easily established on the basis of the definitions of $+$, $\cdot$, and $<$. For example, we demonstrate that 0 is the additive identity of the real number system.

THEOREM 5.2.2. $\forall x[x + 0 = x]$.
Proof: Let (a_n) be any real number; since $0 = (0.0, 0.0, 0.0, \cdots)$,

$$(a_n) + 0 = (a_n) + (0.0, 0.0, 0.0, \cdots) = \mathrm{ND}(a_n) = \mathrm{N}(a_n) = (a_n).$$

This establishes Theorem 5.2.2.

Similarly, it is easy to show that 1 is the multiplicative identity of the real number system.

Finally, as an illustration, we prove that $<$ is transitive.

THEOREM 5.2.3. $\forall x \forall y \forall z[x < y \wedge y < z \to x < z]$
Proof: Assume that (a_n), (b_n), and (c_n) are real numbers such that $(a_n) < (b_n)$ and $(b_n) < (c_n)$. By Definition 5.2.5, there exist natural numbers, say i and j, such that $a_i < b_i$ and $b_j < c_j$. It follows from Theorem 5.2.1

that $a_{i+j} < b_{i+j}$ and $b_{i+j} < c_{i+j}$. Since $<$ is transitive in the rational number system (see Theorem 4.4.4) it follows that $a_{i+j} < c_{i+j}$; hence, by Definition 5.2.5, $(a_n) < (c_n)$. This establishes Theorem 5.2.3.

EXERCISES

Simplify the following:
1. $D(5.431, 5.4301, 5.43001, 5.430001, \cdots)$.
2. $D(-0.7481, -0.748001, -0.74800001, -0.7480000001, \cdots)$.
3. $D(25.11, 25.1111, 25.111111, \cdots)$.
4. $D(3.09, 3.0909, 3.090909, 3.09090909, \cdots)$.
5. $D(0.34, 0.3434, 0.343434, 0.34343434, \cdots)$.
6. $D(0.1, 0.13, 0.135, 0.1357, 0.13579, 0.135791, 0.1357913, \cdots)$.
7. $D(0.21, 0.221, 0.2221, 0.22221, \cdots)$.
8. $D(0.4, 0.37, 0.367, 0.3667, 0.36667, 0.366667, \cdots)$.
9. $D(3.18, 3.198, 3.1998, 3.19998, \cdots)$.
10. $ND(3.18, 3.198, 3.\lceil 998, 3.19998, \cdots)$.
11. $ND(-2.7, -2.797, -2.7997, -2.79997, -2.799997, \cdots)$.
12. $ND(0.191, 0.1993, 0.19995, 0.199997, 0.1999999, 0.19999991, 0.199999993, \cdots)$.
13. $(0.2, 0.2, 0.2, \cdots) + (0.6, 0.61, 0.615, 0.615, 0.615, \cdots)$.
14. $(0.1, 0.1, 0.1, \cdots) + (4.3, 4.3, 4.308, 4.3088, 4.30888, \cdots)$.
15. $(0.1, 0.11, 0.111, \cdots) + (4.3, 4.3, 4.308, 4.3088, 4.30888, \cdots)$.
16. $(0.1, 0.11, 0.111, \cdots) + (-3.1, -3.12, -3.122, -3.1222, \cdots)$.
17. $(0.1, 0.11, 0.111, \cdots) + (-3.1, -3.1, -3.1, \cdots)$.
18. $(3.2, 3.22, 3.222, \cdots) + (-0.5, -0.55, -0.555, \cdots)$.
19. $(-3.2, -3.22, -3.222, \cdots) + (0.5, 0.55, 0.555, \cdots)$.
20. $(0.1, 0.1, 0.1, \cdots) \cdot (15.2, 15.22, 15.222, \cdots)$.
21. $(0.1, 0.1, 0.101, 0.101, 0.10101, \cdots) \cdot (0.9, 0.9, 0.9, \cdots)$.
22. $(0.1, 0.11, 0.11, 0.11, \cdots) \cdot (0.9, 0.9, 0.909, 0.909, 0.90909, 0.90909, \cdots)$.
23. $(-0.2, -0.2, -0.2, \cdots) \cdot (41.6, 41.63, 41.63, 41.63, \cdots)$.

Show that the following propositions are true in the real number system:
24. $\forall x[x \cdot 1 = x]$.
25. $\forall x[x \cdot 0 = 0]$.
26. $\forall x \forall y[x + y = y + x]$.
27. $\forall x \forall y[x \cdot y = y \cdot x]$.
28. $\forall x \exists y[x + y = 0]$.
29. $\exists x \forall y[x \cdot y = 0]$.

30. $\forall x \forall y \forall z [x < y \rightarrow x + z < y + z]$.

31. $\forall x \forall y \forall z [0 < z \land x < y \rightarrow x \cdot z < y \cdot z]$.

32. $\forall x \forall y \forall z [z < 0 \land x < y \rightarrow y \cdot z < x \cdot z]$.

33. Show that $<$ is an order relation on R.

34. a. Let (a_n) be any real number between 1 and 10, and let (b_n) be a sequence of decimal rationals such that $\forall k [k \in N \rightarrow a_k \cdot b_k \leq 1 \land 1 < a_k \cdot (b_k + 1/10^k)]$; show that $ND(b_n)$ is a real number, and show, by an intuitive argument, that $(a_n) \cdot ND(b_n) = 1$.

b. Prove that $\forall x \exists y [x \neq 0 \rightarrow x \cdot y = 1]$ in the real number system.

c. Assuming that multiplication is associative, prove that each nonzero real number possesses a *unique* multiplicative inverse.

35. Show that there is precisely one decimal rational which occurs infinitely often in the sequence $D_1(a_n + b_n)$ — assuming that (a_n) and (b_n) are real numbers.

36. Show that there is precisely one decimal rational which occurs infinitely often in the sequence $D_1(a_n \cdot b_n)$ — assuming that (a_n) and (b_n) are real numbers.

37. Let "$-$" denote the unary operation on R defined as follows: $-(a_n) = (-a_n)$.

a. Show that $\forall x [x + -x = 0]$.

b. Show that $\forall x [-(-x) = x]$.

c. Show that $\forall x \forall y [x < y \rightarrow -y < -x]$.

d. Show that $\forall x \forall y [-y < -x \rightarrow x < y]$.

e. Show that $\forall x [-x = x \cdot -1]$.

38. Let "S" denote the set of all sequences of decimal rationals defined as follows: $(a_n) \in S$ if

(i) $\exists a \exists d [a$ is a nonnegative integer $\land d$ is a digit $\land a_1 = a + d/10]$,

(ii) $\forall n \exists d [n \in N \rightarrow a_{n+1} = a_n + d/10^{n+1} \land d$ is a digit$]$;

furthermore, $(-a_n) \in S$ if $(a_n) \in S$; S has no other members. Consider the algebraic system $(S, +, 0)$, where $(a_n) + (b_n) = D(a_n + b_n)$ whenever $(a_n) \in S$ and $(b_n) \in S$, and $0 = (0.0, 0.0, 0.0, \cdots)$.

a. Compute $(-0.9, -0.99, -0.999, \cdots) + (1.0, 1.0, 1.0, \cdots)$.

b. Compute $(0.9, 0.99, 0.999, \cdots) + [(-0.9, -0.99, -0.999, \cdots) + (1.0)]$.

c. Compute $[(0.9, 0.99, 0.999, \cdots) + (-0.9, -0.99, -0.999, \cdots)] + (1.0)$.

d. Show that $\forall x \forall y [x + y = y + x]$.

e. Prove that $\forall x [x + 0 = x]$.

f. Prove that $\forall x \exists y [x + y = 0]$.

g. Demonstrate that the proposition "$\forall x \forall y \forall z [x + (y + z) = (x + y) + z]$" is false.

5.3   Almost-Constant Sequences

In order to demonstrate that the real number system is a complete ordered field, we shall need several more concepts and operations.

A sequence of decimal rationals whose terms are the same is said to be *constant*. Thus, we have the following definition.

DEFINITION 5.3.1. A sequence of decimal rationals, say (a_n), is said to be *constant* iff there is a decimal rational, say K, such that

$$(a_n) = (K, K, K, \cdots, K, \cdots).$$

For example, $(5.1, 5.1, 5.1, \cdots, 5.1, \cdots)$ is constant.

Now consider a sequence of decimal rationals such that all its terms are the same with the possible exception of the first few terms of the sequence. We shall describe any such sequence by saying that it is *B-constant*.

DEFINITION 5.3.2. A sequence of decimal rationals, say (a_n), is said to be *B-constant* iff there is a decimal rational, say K, and a nonnegative integer, say q, such that $B_q(a_n) = (K, K, K, \cdots, K, \cdots)$. The decimal rational K is called the *B-limit* of (a_n) and is denoted by "B-lim(a_n)".

For example, $\{(n, b) \mid n \in N \wedge (n < 4 \rightarrow b = 2) \wedge (n > 3 \rightarrow b = 5)\}$ is B-constant and its B-limit is 5.

THEOREM 5.3.1. B-lim(a_n) is unique provided that (a_n) is B-constant.
Proof: Consider Definition 5.3.2.

THEOREM 5.3.2. Let (a_n) be any sequence of decimal rationals such that $\forall k[k \in N \rightarrow D_k(a_n)$ is B-constant]; then $\forall k[$B-lim $D_k(a_n)$ is the kth term of $D(a_n)]$.
Proof: Consider Definition 5.2.2.

We shall now characterize the concept of a *convergent* sequence in terms of the rounding-off operation and the notion of a B-constant sequence. To bring out the idea, we shall consider one example. First, recall that "$R_k(a_n)$" denotes the sequence obtained from (a_n) by rounding off each term of (a_n) to k decimal places — whenever k is a positive integer. Consider the sequence (c_n), where $(c_n) = (0.179, 0.17949, 0.179501, 0.1794999, 0.17950001, 0.179499999, \cdots)$.

Then

$$R_1(c_n) = (0.2, 0.2, 0.2, 0.2, \cdots, 0.2, \cdots),$$
$$R_2(c_n) = (0.18, 0.18, 0.18, \cdots, 0.18, \cdots),$$
$$R_3(c_n) = (0.179, 0.179, 0.18, 0.179, 0.18, 0.179, 0.18, \cdots),$$
$$R_4(c_n) = (0.179, 0.1795, 0.1795, 0.1795, 0.1795, \cdots),$$
$$R_5(c_n) = (0.179, 0.17949, 0.1795, 0.1795, 0.1795, \cdots).$$

Notice that $R_3(c_n)$ is not B-constant, whereas $\forall p[p \neq 3 \rightarrow R_p(c_n)$ is B-constant]. Indeed, $\forall p[p > 3 \rightarrow \text{B-lim } R_p(c_n) = 0.1795]$.

Let us focus our attention on the vital property possessed by (c_n), namely, $R_p(c_n)$ is B-constant whenever $p \in N$, with at most one exception. Any sequence that has this property is said to be *almost-constant*.

> **DEFINITION 5.3.3.** A sequence of decimal rationals, say (a_n), is said to be *almost-constant* iff $R_p(a_n)$ is B-constant whenever p is a natural number, with at most one exception.

You may wonder why we do not insist that $\forall p[R_p(a_n)$ is B-constant]. It is a peculiarity of the rounding-off process that compels us to permit one exception—as the preceding example points out.

To illustrate our definition, we note that the sequence $(-5.301, -5.3001, -5.30001, \cdots)$ is almost-constant.

In Section 5.4 we shall prove that a sequence is almost-constant iff the sequence *converges* in the usual sense.

> **THEOREM 5.3.3.**   Each real number is almost-constant.
>
> *Proof:*   Consider Definition 5.2.1.

We now introduce a unary operation on almost-constant sequences, which we denote by "R"; the image of an almost-constant sequence is constructed in terms of the rounding-off process and the B-limit.

> **DEFINITION 5.3.4.** Let (a_n) be any almost-constant sequence; then $R(a_n) = (e_n)$, where
>
> $$e_p = \begin{cases} \text{B-lim } R_p(a_n), & \text{if } R_p(a_n) \text{ is B-constant} \\ e_{p+1} \text{ rounded off to } p \text{ decimal places, otherwise.} \end{cases}$$

To illustrate, we consider the sequence (c_n) introduced above:

$$(c_n) = (0.179, 0.17949, 0.179501, 0.1794999, 0.17950001,$$
$$0.179499999, \cdots).$$

Clearly, $R_p(c_n)$ is B-constant whenever $p \neq 3$; furthermore, B-lim $R_1(c_n) = 0.2$, B-lim $R_2(c_n) = 0.18$, and B-lim $R_p(c_n) = 0.1795$ whenever $p > 3$. Therefore, $R(c_n) = (0.2, 0.18, 0.18, 0.1795, 0.1795, 0.1795, \cdots)$.

This important notion warrants another illustration. Let

$$(d_n) = (0.137549, 0.1375501, 0.1375499, 0.13755001, 0.13754999,$$
$$0.137550001, \cdots).$$

Then

$$R_1(d_n) = (0.1, 0.1, 0.1, \cdots),$$
$$R_2(d_n) = (0.14, 0.14, 0.14, \cdots),$$
$$R_3(d_n) = (0.138, 0.138, 0.138, \cdots),$$
$$R_4(d_n) = (0.1375, 0.1376, 0.1375, 0.1376, 0.1375, 0.1376, \cdots),$$
$$R_5(d_n) = (0.13755, 0.13755, 0.13755, \cdots),$$
$$R_6(d_n) = (0.137549, 0.13755, 0.13755, 0.13755, \cdots),$$
$$R_7(d_n) = (0.137549, 0.1375501, 0.1375499, 0.13755, 0.13755,$$
$$0.13755, \cdots).$$

It is clear that $R_p(d_n)$ is B-constant, provided that $p \neq 4$; furthermore, B-lim $R_1(d_n) = 0.1$, B-lim $R_2(d_n) = 0.14$, B-lim $R_3(d_n) = 0.138$, and B-lim $R_p(d_n) = 0.13755$ whenever $p > 4$. Hence,

$$R(d_n) = (0.1, 0.14, 0.138, 0.1376, 0.13755, 0.13755, 0.13755, \cdots).$$

Considering this example further, notice that $R(d_n)$ is *not* a real number. However, by applying the D operation, we subtly alter the terms of $R(d_n)$ so as to obtain a real number:

$$DR(d_n) = D(0.1, 0.14, 0.138, 0.1376, 0.13755, 0.13755, 0.13755, \cdots)$$
$$= (0.1, 0.13, 0.137, 0.1375, 0.13755, 0.13755, 0.13755, \cdots).$$

One should think of DR as a unary operation on almost-constant sequences. The image of (a_n) under this operation is found by first computing $R(a_n)$ and then finding the image of the resulting sequence under D. For example,

$$DR(0.179, 0.1799, 0.17999, \cdots) = D(0.2, 0.18, 0.18, 0.18, \cdots)$$
$$= (0.1, 0.18, 0.18, 0.18, \cdots);$$

and

$$DR(0.5, 0.55, 0.555, \cdots) = D(0.6, 0.56, 0.556, 0.5556, \cdots)$$
$$= (0.5, 0.55, 0.555, \cdots).$$

EXERCISES

Simplify the following sequences:
1. $R(2.3949, 2.39501, 2.39499, 2.395001, 2.394999, \cdots)$.
2. $R(25.1, 25.01, 25.001, 25.0001, \cdots)$.

3. $R(-5.301, -5.3001, -5.30001, \cdots)$.
4. $R(3.14, 3.1415, 3.141592, 3.14159265, 3.1415926535, 3.141592653589, \cdots)$.
5. $R(21.109, 21.1089, 21.10901, 21.108999, 21.1090001, \cdots)$.
6. $R(0.37549, 0.375501, 0.3754999, 0.37550001, 0.375499999, 0.3755000001, \cdots)$.
7. $DR(1.1749, 1.17501, 1.174999, 1.1750001, \cdots)$.
8. $DR(-0.4782, -0.47802, -0.478002, -0.4780002, \cdots)$.
9. $DR(0.047793, 0.0477993, 0.04779993, 0.047799993, 0.0477999993, \cdots)$.
10. $DR(0.04781, 0.04779, 0.047801, 0.047799, 0.0478001, 0.0477999, \cdots)$.
11. $DR(2.01, 2.002, 2.0003, 2.00004, 2.000005, \cdots)$.

12. Let (a_n) be almost-constant and let $DR(a_n) = (b_n)$; suppose that for a certain natural number k, $b_{k+1} = b_k + 9/10^{k+1}$. Show that $b_{k+2} \neq b_{k+1} + 9/10^{k+2}$.

13. Prove that $\forall p[R_p(a_n)$ is B-constant] provided that (a_n) is a real number.

14. Consider the conjecture: "If (a_n) is almost-constant and $R(a_n) = (b_n)$, then $\forall p[b_p = b_{p+1}$ rounded off to p decimal places]". Show, by means of a counter-example, that this conjecture is false.

15. Prove that $D(a_n)$ is almost-constant whenever (a_n) is a real number.

16. Show, by means of a counterexample, that the following conjecture is false: "Given that $(a_n) \in R, \forall k \exists m[m > k \wedge$ B-lim $R_m(a_n) = a_m]$".

5.4   The DR Operation

In this section we shall prove that DR is a unary operation on the set of all almost-constant sequences; i.e., we shall prove that DR associates an almost-constant sequence with each almost-constant sequence. Of course, R associates a sequence of decimal rationals with each almost-constant sequence; i.e., if (a_n) is almost-constant, then $R(a_n)$ certainly exists. Let $R(a_n) = (b_n)$; first we shall show that $D(b_n)$ exists. In other words, we shall show that $\forall k[D_k(b_n)$ is B-constant].

First, consider the following theorem.

THEOREM 5.4.1.   Let (a_n) be any almost-constant sequence and let $R(a_n) = (b_n)$; then $\forall p \exists q \forall m[m > q \rightarrow |a_m - b_p| < 1/10^p]$.

Proof: Let p be any natural number. There are two possibilities.

1. $R_p(a_n)$ is B-constant. Then $B_q R_p(a_n) = (b_p)$ for a suitable q. Therefore, each term of $B_q(a_n)$ differs from b_p by less than $1/10^p$, i.e., $\forall m[m > q \rightarrow |a_m - b_p| < 1/10^p]$.

2. $R_p(a_n)$ is not B-constant. Then b_p is b_{p+1} rounded off to p decimal

places. But, by the first part of this proof, $\exists t \forall m [m > t \rightarrow |a_m - b_{p+1}| < 1/10^{p+1}]$. Therefore, if m is large enough, then

$$|a_m - b_p| \leq |a_m - b_{p+1}| + |b_{p+1} - b_p| < 1/10^{p+1} + 5/10^{p+1} < 1/10^p.$$

This establishes that $\exists t \forall m [m > t \rightarrow |a_m - b_p| < 1/10^p]$. We have established Theorem 5.4.1.

This result has an immediate corollary.

COROLLARY 5.4.1.   Let (a_n) be any almost-constant sequence and let $R(a_n) = (b_n)$; then

$$\forall p \forall t [|b_p - b_{p+t}| < 1/10^p + 1/10^{p+t}].$$

Proof: By Theorem 5.4.1, $|a_m - b_p| < 1/10^p$ and $|a_m - b_{p+t}| < 1/10^{p+t}$, provided that m is large enough. Therefore,

$$|b_p - b_{p+t}| \leq |b_p - a_m| + |a_m - b_{p+t}| < 1/10^p + 1/10^{p+t}.$$

This establishes our result.

We come now to the main theorem of this section.

THEOREM 5.4.2.   Let (a_n) be any almost-constant sequence and let $R(a_n) = (b_n)$; then $D(b_n)$ exists.

Proof: Suppose that $D(b_n)$ does not exist; then there is a smallest natural number k such that $D_k(b_n)$ is not B-constant. This means that $\forall q [B_q D_k(b_n)$ is not constant and that $\forall q [B_q D_{k-1}(b_n)$ is constant]. Therefore,

(1) $\forall q \exists r \exists s [r > q \wedge s > q \wedge b_r$ and b_s agree in their first $k-1$ decimal places and differ in their kth decimal place].

Let $r = s + t$; if s is large enough, then b_s and b_{s+t} agree among the first $k-1$ digits following the decimal point and differ in the kth digit. In particular, we may think of s as being very much greater than k. But, by Corollary 5.4.1, $|b_s - b_{s+t}| < 1/10^s + 1/10^{s+t}$; intuitively, then, b_s and b_{s+t} differ by very little. It follows that b_s and b_{s+t} agree in their first $k-1$ decimal places, differ by 1 in their kth decimal place, and thereafter one consists of a block of 9's and the other a block of 0's, at least until the sth decimal place. For example, if $k = 2$ and $s = 12$, suppose that

$$b_s = 5.1400000\ 00000,$$
$$b_{s+t} = 5.1399999\ 99999\ \underset{\nearrow}{d_1} d_2 \cdots d_t.$$
$$\text{sth decimal place}$$

Notice that $|b_s - b_{s+t}| < 1/10^s + 1/10^{s+t}$. The key to this discussion is the *length* of the block of 9's occurring in b_{s+t}. We want to show that there is another term of (b_n) which agrees with b_{s+t} in the first k decimal places, and involves a longer block of 9's (indeed, by choosing our term of (b_n) suitably, we can obtain as long a block of 9's as we wish). Let us make another choice of r and s permitted by our assumption (1). Choose numbers greater than the number $s + t$ with which we have been working. For example, by (1), there are numbers S and T such that b_S and b_{s+T} agree among the first $k - 1$ decimal places and differ in their kth, and $s + t < S$. Suppose, for definiteness, that $S = s + t + 1$; then

$$b_{S+T} = 5.1399999\ 99999\ 99 \cdots 9\ \underset{\nearrow}{9} d'_1 d'_2 \cdots d'_T.$$
$$\text{$s + t$th decimal place}$$

But, for each p, $b_p = \text{B-lim } R_p(a_n)$; hence, b_p is obtained from a_m, if m is large enough, by rounding off a_m to p decimal places. In particular, if we choose m appropriately, b_{S+T} is obtained by rounding off a_m to $S + T$ decimal places, and b_{s+t} is obtained by rounding off a_m to $s + t$ decimal places. Now, the result of rounding off a_m to $S + T$ decimal places is

$$5.1399999\ 99999\ 99 \cdots 9\ \underset{\nearrow}{9} d'_1 d'_2 \cdots d'_T.$$
$$\text{$s + t$th decimal place}$$

Therefore, rounding off a_m to $s + t$ decimal places produces 5.14. This contradiction establishes Theorem 5.4.2.

It is easy to prove the following theorem.

THEOREM 5.4.3.   If (a_n) is almost-constant, then $\text{DR}(a_n)$ is a real number.

Proof: We have only to show that $\text{DR}(a_n)$ is not an N-sequence. However, the proof of Theorem 5.4.2 has already shown that this is impossible. The details are left as an exercise.

Applying Theorem 5.3.3 we obtain the following result.

THEOREM 5.4.4.   DR is a unary operation on almost-constant sequences.

5.5 Properties of the DR Operation

In this section we shall explore some of the properties of the DR operation; in particular, we shall demonstrate that our notion of an almost-constant sequence has captured the idea of a *convergent* sequence. In the following theorem we bring out a useful property of real numbers. This theorem is easily grasped by keeping in mind the intuitive idea of a real number — namely, the notion of an infinite decimal.

THEOREM 5.5.1.   Let (a_n) be any real number; then $\forall k \exists q \forall m [m > q \rightarrow$ the first k digits of a_m are not affected by rounding off a_m to more than q decimal places].

Proof: We consider the case in which (a_n) is non-negative; the remaining case is easily handled by a proof similar to the following. Let k be any natural number. It is easy to find a natural number q with the desired property. Let q be any natural number greater than k such that $a_q \neq a_{q-1} + 9/10^q$; i.e., $a_q = a_{q-1} + d/10^q$ where $d \neq 9$. Since (a_n) is a real number, q exists. Now let m be any natural number greater than q; then the first k digits of a_m are not affected by rounding off a_m to more than q decimal places. This establishes Theorem 5.5.1.

THEOREM 5.5.2. $DR(a_n) = (a_n)$ whenever $(a_n) \in R$.

Proof: Suppose the theorem is false. Then there is a real number, say (a_n), such that $DR(a_n) \neq (a_n)$. Let $R(a_n) = (b_n)$ and let $D(b_n) = (c_n)$; then there is a natural number, say k, such that $c_k \neq a_k$. But $c_k = $ B-lim $D_k(b_n)$; this means that c_k is obtained from b_t, if t is large enough, by deleting the final $t - k$ digits. Furthermore, $(b_n) = R(a_n)$; thus, $b_t = $ B-lim $R_t(a_n)$. It follows that if t and m are large enough, c_k is obtained by rounding off a_m to t decimal places, and then deleting the final $t - k$ digits of the resulting decimal rational. By Theorem 5.5.1, however, the number obtained in this way is a_k. This contradiction establishes Theorem 5.5.2.

The purpose of the following chain of theorems is to characterize directly the notion of an almost-constant sequence; we shall obtain a condition on the terms of a sequence which constitutes an acid test for our concept.

THEOREM 5.5.3. Let (a_n) be any almost-constant sequence, and suppose that $DR(a_n) = (c_n)$; then $\forall p \exists q \forall m [m > q \to |a_m - c_p| < 1/10^p]$.

Proof: Let $R(a_n) = (b_n)$; then, by Theorem 5.4.1, $\forall p \exists q \forall m [m > q \to |a_m - b_p| < 1/10^p]$. Let p be any natural number; then $|a_m - b_{p+1}| < 1/10^{p+1}$ whenever $m > q$, for a certain q. Now consider the effect of D on (b_n). For definiteness, assume $\exists k [b_k > 0]$. Then D replaces b_p by $b_p - 1/10^p$ if $b_{p+1} < b_p$ and if b_{p+1} rounded off to p decimal places is b_p; otherwise D replaces b_p by b_p. In other words, $c_p = b_p - 1/10^p$ if $b_{p+1} < b_p$ and if b_{p+1} rounded off to p decimal places is b_p; otherwise, $c_p = b_p$. [An example will clarify the preceding observation; e.g., consider $DR(3.1, 3.14, 3.141, 3.1415, 3.14159, 3.141592, \cdots)$]. Notice that if $c_p = b_p - 1/10^p$ then $b_{p+1} - (b_p - 1/10^p) \leq 9/10^{p+1}$. Now, under this circumstance,

$$|a_m - c_p| = |a_m - (b_p - 1/10^p)| \leq |a_m - b_{p+1}| + |b_{p+1} - (b_p - 1/10^p)|$$
$$< 1/10^{p+1} + 9/10^{p+1}$$
$$= 1/10^p.$$

Thus, $\exists q \forall m [m > q \to |a_m - c_p| < 1/10^p]$ provided that $c_p = b_p - 1/10^p$. In case $c_p = b_p$, then by Theorem 5.4.1, $\exists q \forall m [m > q \to |a_m - c_p| < 1/10^p]$. If $\forall k [b_k \leq 0]$, a similar argument establishes the same result. This demonstrates Theorem 5.5.3.

THEOREM 5.5.4. Let (a_n) be any sequence of decimal rationals and let (b_n) be any real number such that $\forall p \exists q \forall m [m > q \to |a_m - b_p| < 1/10^p]$; then (a_n) is almost-constant and $DR(a_n) = (b_n)$.

Proof: 1. We show that (a_n) is almost-constant. Suppose $R_p(a_n)$ is not B-constant. By assumption, there exist natural numbers $q_1, q_2, q_3, \cdots$ such that:

$$(1) \quad \begin{array}{l} b_{p+1} - 1/10^{p+1} < a_m < b_{p+1} + 1/10^{p+1} \text{ whenever } m > q_1, \\ b_{p+2} - 1/10^{p+2} < a_m < b_{p+2} + 1/10^{p+2} \text{ whenever } m > q_2, \\ b_{p+3} - 1/10^{p+3} < a_m < b_{p+3} + 1/10^{p+3} \text{ whenever } m > q_3, \end{array}$$

and so on. There is only one possibility! The terminal digit of b_{p+1} is 5 (i.e. 5 is the final non-zero digit of b_{p+1}) and $\forall t [b_{p+t} = b_{p+1}]$. Therefore, for a certain q, each term of $B_q(a_n)$ is obtained by writing down b_{p+1}, replacing the terminal digit by 4, and adjoining a string of 9's followed, possibly, by other digits; or it is obtained by writing down b_{p+1}, adjoining a string of 0's, and then, possibly, more digits. Also, the lengths of the strings of 9's or 0's increase without bound, in conformity with inequalities (1). Therefore, $B_q R_p(a_n)$ involves exactly two decimal rationals which differ by $1/10^p$; furthermore, $R_t(a_n)$ is B-constant whenever $t \neq p$. This establishes that (a_n) is almost-constant.

2. We show that $DR(a_n) = (b_n)$. Suppose $DR(a_n) = (c_n)$ and $(c_n) \neq (b_n)$. Then there is a natural number, say k, such that $b_k \neq c_k$; hence, $1/10^k \leq |b_k - c_k|$. Since (b_n) and (c_n) are real numbers, it cannot be the case, for each t, that $b_{k+t} = b_k$ and that c_{k+t} is obtained from c_k by adjoining t 9's to c_k. Therefore, there is a natural number, say t, such that $2/10^{k+t} \leq |b_{k+t} - c_{k+t}|$. But, by Theorem 5.5.3 and the first part of this theorem, $\forall p \exists q \forall m [m > q \rightarrow |a_m - c_p| < 1/10^p]$. Choosing m suitably, we have $|b_{k+t} - c_{k+t}| \leq |b_{k+t} - a_m| + |a_m - c_{k+t}| < 1/10^{k+t} + 1/10^{k+t} = 2/10^{k+t}$, i.e., $|b_{k+t} - c_{k+t}| < 2/10^{k+t}$. But $2/10^{k+t} \leq |b_{k+t} - c_{k+t}|$! This result contradicts the Trichotomy Law for the rational number system. Hence, the assumption $(c_n) \neq (b_n)$ is false; therefore, $DR(a_n) = (b_n)$. This establishes Theorem 5.5.4.

The following theorem contains an important and useful method of characterizing the two concepts of an almost-constant sequence and the image of an almost-constant sequence under DR.

THEOREM 5.5.5. (a_n) is almost-constant and $DR(a_n) = (b_n)$ iff $\forall p \exists q \forall m [m > q \rightarrow |a_m - b_p| < 1/10^p]$ and $(b_n) \in R$.

Proof: Theorem 5.5.3 and Theorem 5.5.4.

COROLLARY 5.5.1. (a_n) is almost-constant and $DR(a_n) = 0$ iff $\forall p \exists q \forall m [m > q \rightarrow |a_m| < 1/10^p]$.

THEOREM 5.5.6. Let (a_n) and (b_n) be any almost-constant sequences; then $DR(a_n) = DR(b_n)$ iff $\forall p \exists q \forall m [m > q \rightarrow |a_m - b_m| < 1/10^p]$.

Proof: The theorem asserts that the almost-constant sequences (a_n) and (b_n) have the same image under DR iff the sequence $(a_n - b_n)$ is almost-constant and $DR(a_n - b_n) = 0$. There are two parts to the proof.

1. Assume $DR(a_n) = DR(b_n) = (c_n)$. Then $\forall p \exists q \forall m [m > q \rightarrow |a_m - c_p| < 1/10^p]$ and $\forall p \exists q \forall m [m > q \rightarrow |b_m - c_p| < 1/10^p]$. Therefore,

$$|a_m - b_m| \leq |a_m - c_{p+1}| + |c_{p+1} - b_m| < 1/10^{p+1} + 1/10^{p+1} < 1/10^p,$$

provided that m is large enough; i.e., $\forall p \exists q \forall m [m > q \rightarrow |a_m - b_m| < 1/10^p]$. Applying Corollary 5.5.1, we see that $(a_n - b_n)$ is almost-constant and $DR(a_n - b_n) = 0$.

2. Assume $\forall p \exists q \forall m [m > q \rightarrow |a_m - b_m| < 1/10^p]$. Let $DR(a_n) = (d_n)$ and let $DR(b_n) = (e_n)$. Now suppose $(d_n) \neq (e_n)$; then there is a natural num-

ber, say t, such that $d_t \neq e_t$, hence $|d_t - e_t| \geq 1/10^t$. Actually, we can say much more. By Theorem 5.4.3, (d_n) and (e_n) are real numbers, so neither is an N-sequence. In terms of infinite decimals, this rules out the possibility that we are dealing with, say, $1.13999 \cdots 9 \cdots$ and $1.14000 \cdots 0 \cdots$; notice that $1.14 - 1.13 = 1/10^2$, $1.140 - 1.139 = 1/10^3$, $1.1400 - 1.1399 = 1/10^4$ and so on. We conclude that there exists a natural number s such that $s > t$ and $|d_s - e_s| > 10/10^s$. Now, if m is large enough then by Theorem 5.5.3 and our assumption

$$|d_s - e_s| \leq |d_s - a_m| + |a_m - b_m| + |b_m - e_s|$$
$$< 1/10^s + 1/10^s + 1/10^s$$
$$= 3/10^s.$$

This contradicts Theorem 5.2.3; we conclude that our assumption is false. Hence, $DR(a_n) = DR(b_n)$. This establishes Theorem 5.5.6.

COROLLARY 5.5.2.   Let (a_n) be any almost-constant sequence, and let (b_n) be any real number; then $DR(a_n) = (b_n)$ iff $\forall p \exists q \forall m [m > q \rightarrow |a_m - b_m| < 1/10^p]$.
Proof: Theorem 5.5.6 and Theorem 5.5.2.

The following theorem establishes that the question "Is (a_n) almost-constant?" can be answered by examining the terms of (a_n).

THEOREM 5.5.7. (a_n) is almost-constant iff $\forall p \exists q \forall m [m > q \rightarrow |a_m - a_q| < 1/10^p]$.
Proof: 1. Assume (a_n) is almost-constant. Let $DR(a_n) = (b_n)$. By Theorem 5.5.5, given p, we can find a natural number t such that $|a_m - b_{p+1}| < 1/10^{p+1}$ whenever $m > t$. Therefore,

$$|a_m - a_{t+1}| \leq |a_m - b_{p+1}| + |b_{p+1} - a_{t+1}| < 1/10^{p+1} + 1/10^{p+1} < 1/10^p,$$

provided that $m > t$. This establishes that $\forall p \exists q \forall m [m > q \rightarrow |a_m - a_q| < 1/10^p]$.
2. Assume $\forall p \exists q \forall m [m > q \rightarrow |a_m - a_q| < 1/10^p]$. We shall show that $R_p(a_n)$ is B-constant for each natural number p, with at most one exception. Suppose p is a natural number such that $R_p(a_n)$ is not B-constant. By assumption, there is a natural number t such that

$$\forall m [m > t \rightarrow |a_m - a_t| < 1/10^{p+2}].$$

Therefore,

$$|a_m - a_u| \le |a_m - a_t| + |a_t - a_u| < 1/10^{p+2} + 1/10^{p+2} < 1/10^{p+1},$$

provided that $m > t$ and $u > t$. In other words, any two terms of $B_t(a_n)$ differ by less than $1/10^{p+1}$. Hence, any two terms of $B_t R_p(a_n)$ differ by at most $1/10^p$. Since $R_p(a_n)$ is not B-constant, it follows that $B_t R_p(a_n)$ involves exactly two decimal rationals which differ by $1/10^p$. Finally, we must show that $R_q(a_n)$ is B-constant whenever $q \ne p$. Let k be any natural number. As before, there is a natural number, say s, such that $|a_m - a_u| < 1/10^{p+k+1}$, provided that $m > s$ and $u > s$. In other words, any two terms of $B_s(a_n)$ differ by less than $1/10^{p+k+1}$. Let a_m be any term of $B_s(a_n)$; then the digit in the $p + 1$st decimal place of a_m is either 4 or 5. Furthermore, a 4 in the $p + 1$st decimal place is followed by at least k 9's, and a 5 in the $p + 1$st decimal place is followed by at least k 0's. Also, any two terms of $B_s(a_n)$ have the same integral part and the same digits in the first p decimal places. Therefore, $R_q(a_n)$ is B-constant whenever $q < p + k$, except when $q = p$ Now suppose $q \ne p$; we can choose k such that $q < p + k$. Therefore, $R_q(a_n)$ is B-constant. This establishes Theorem 5.5.7.

COROLLARY 5.5.3. (a_n) is almost-constant if $\forall p[D_p(a_n)$ is B-constant].

To illustrate the power of Theorem 5.5.7, consider the sequence $(2.01, 2.009, 2.0001, 2.00009, 2.000001, 2.0000009, \cdots)$. Denoting this sequence by "(a_n)", it is clear that $\forall p \forall m[m > p \to |a_m - a_p| < 1/10^p]$; therefore, (a_n) is almost-constant.

The following theorem is a useful variation of Theorem 5.5.7.

THEOREM 5.5.8. (a_n) is almost-constant iff $\forall p \exists q[$any two terms of $B_q(a_n)$ differ by less than $1/10^p]$.
   Proof: 1. Assume (a_n) is almost-constant. Choose p; let q be such that $|a_m - a_q| < 1/10^{p+1}$ whenever $m > q$. Then

$$|a_i - a_j| \le |a_i - a_q| + |a_q - a_j| < 1/10^{p+1} + 1/10^{p+1} < 1/10^p,$$

provided that $i > q$ and $j > q$. In other words, any two terms of $B_q(a_n)$ differ by less than $1/10^p$.
   2. Assume $\forall p \exists q[$any two terms of $B_q(a_n)$ differ by less than $1/10^p]$.

Choose p; let t be such that any two terms of $B_t(a_n)$ differ by less than $1/10^p$. Then $|a_m - a_{t+1}| < 1/10^p$ whenever $m > t + 1$. Hence,

$$\exists q \forall m [m > q \rightarrow |a_m - a_q| < 1/10^p].$$

Therefore, by Theorem 5.5.7, (a_n) is almost-constant. This establishes Theorem 5.5.8.

We now investigate certain algebraic properties of the operations D, R, and N; we are particularly interested in the connection between the DR operation and the operations of addition and multiplication of real numbers.

THEOREM 5.5.9.   Let (a_n) and (b_n) be any almost-constant sequences; then $(a_n + b_n)$ is almost-constant and $DR(a_n + b_n) = DR(A_n + B_n)$, where $(A_n) = DR(a_n)$ and $(B_n) = DR(b_n)$.

Proof: 1. We show that $(a_n + b_n)$ is almost-constant. Choose p; by assumption, there are natural numbers s and t such that $|a_i - a_j| < 1/10^{p+1}$ and $|b_i - b_j| < 1/10^{p+1}$ whenever $i > s$, $j > s$, $i > t$, and $j > t$. Let q be the larger of s and t; then

$$|a_i + b_i - a_j - b_j| \le |a_i - a_j| + |b_i - b_j| < 1/10^{p+1} + 1/10^{p+1} < 1/10^p$$

whenever $i > q$ and $j > q$. Therefore, by Theorem 5.5.8, $(a_n + b_n)$ is almost-constant.

2. We show that $(a_n + b_n)$ and $(A_n + B_n)$ have the same image under DR. (*Note:* $(A_n + B_n)$ is almost-constant by the first part of this proof.) By Theorem 5.5.2, $DR(a_n) = DR(A_n)$ and $DR(b_n) = DR(B_n)$; therefore, by Theorem 5.5.6, $\forall p \exists q \forall m [m > q \rightarrow |a_m - A_m| < 1/10^p]$. Now choose p; there is a natural number q such that $|a_m - A_m| < 1/10^{p+1}$ and $|b_m - B_m| < 1/10^{p+1}$ whenever $m > q$. Therefore,

$$|a_m + b_m - A_m - B_m| \le |a_m - A_m| + |b_m - B_m| < 1/10^{p+1} + 1/10^{p+1} < 1/10^p$$

whenever $m > q$. Hence, by Theorem 5.5.6, $DR(a_n + b_n) = DR(A_n + B_n)$.

THEOREM 5.5.10.   Let (a_n) and (b_n) be any almost-constant sequences; then $(a_n \cdot b_n)$ is almost-constant and $DR(a_n \cdot b_n) = DR(A_n \cdot B_n)$, where $(A_n) = DR(a_n)$ and $(B_n) = DR(b_n)$.

Proof: Observe, first, that if (c_n) is almost-constant, there exists a natural number k such that $\forall m [|c_m| < 10^k/1]$. Therefore, there is a natural number, say k, such that $\forall m [|a_m| < 10^k/1 \wedge |b_m| < 10^k/1]$. We shall demonstrate that $(a_n \cdot b_n)$ is almost-constant. Choose p; then $|a_i - a_j| < 1/10^{p+k+1}$ and $|b_i - b_j| < 1/10^{p+k+1}$ whenever $i > q$ and $j > q$, for a suitable q. Therefore,

$$
\begin{aligned}
|a_i \cdot b_i - a_j \cdot b_j| &\leq |a_i \cdot b_i - a_j \cdot b_i| + |a_j \cdot b_i - a_j \cdot b_j| \\
&= |b_i| \cdot |a_i - a_j| + |a_j| \cdot |b_i - b_j| \\
&< (10^k/1) \cdot (1/10^{p+k+1}) + (10^k/1) \cdot (1/10^{p+k+1}) \\
&< 1/10^p
\end{aligned}
$$

whenever $i > q$ and $j > q$. Hence, by Theorem 5.5.8, $(a_n \cdot b_n)$ is almost-constant. The proof that $DR(a_n \cdot b_n) = DR(A_n \cdot B_n)$ is easily worked out and is left as an exercise. This completes the proof of Theorem 5.5.10.

THEOREM 5.5.11.   Let (a_n) be any sequence such that $D(a_n)$ exists; then (a_n) and $D(a_n)$ are almost-constant and $DR(a_n) = DRD(a_n)$.
Proof: (a_n) is almost-constant by Corollary 5.5.3. We show that $D(a_n)$ is almost-constant. Let $D(a_n) = (b_n)$; then b_p is obtained from b_m by deleting the last $m - p$ digits of b_m, whenever $m > p$. Therefore, $|b_m - b_p| < 1/10^p$ whenever $m > p$. Hence, by Theorem 5.5.7, (b_n) is almost-constant. We now show that $DR(a_n) = DR(b_n)$. Choose p; then $|a_m - b_{p+1}| < 1/10^{p+1}$ whenever $m > q$, for a suitable q. Therefore,

$$
|a_m - b_m| \leq |a_m - b_{p+1}| + |b_{p+1} - b_m| < 1/10^{p+1} + 1/10^{p+1} < 1/10^p
$$

whenever $m > q$ and $m > p + 1$. Hence, by Theorem 5.5.6, $DR(a_n) = DR(b_n)$. This establishes Theorem 5.5.11.

THEOREM 5.5.12.   Let (a_n) be any N-sequence; then (a_n) and $N(a_n)$ are almost-constant and $DR(a_n) = DRN(a_n)$.
Proof: By Theorem 5.5.8, any N-sequence is almost-constant. We show that $N(a_n)$ is almost-constant. Let $N(a_n) = (b_n)$; then $\forall m[|a_m - b_m| < 1/10^{m+k}]$, where k is an integer which depends upon (a_n). Choose p; then $|a_m - b_m| < 1/10^{p+1}$, provided that $m + k - 1 > p$; furthermore, $|a_i - a_j| < 1/10^{p+1}$ whenever $i > q$ and $j > q$, for a suitable q. Therefore,

$$
|b_i - b_j| \leq |b_i - a_i| + |a_i - a_j| + |a_j - b_j| < 3/10^{p+1} < 1/10^p,
$$

provided that $i + k - 1 > p$, $j + k - 1 > p$, $i > q$, and $j > q$. Hence, by Theorem 5.5.8, (b_n) is almost-constant. It is easy to see that $DR(a_n) = DR(b_n)$, for $|a_m - b_m| < 1/10^p$ whenever $m + k > p$. Hence, by Theorem 5.5.6, $DR(a_n) = DR(b_n)$. This establishes Theorem 5.5.12.

THEOREM 5.5.13. Let (a_n) and (b_n) be any real numbers; then $(a_n) + (b_n) = DR(a_n + b_n)$.
Proof:

$$
\begin{aligned}
DR(a_n + b_n) &= DRD(a_n + b_n) && \text{by Th. 5.5.11} \\
&= DRND(a_n + b_n) && \text{by Th. 5.5.12} \\
&= ND(a_n + b_n) && \text{by Th. 5.5.2} \\
&= (a_n) + (b_n) && \text{by Def. 5.2.3.}
\end{aligned}
$$

This establishes Theorem 5.5.13.

THEOREM 5.5.14. Let (a_n) and (b_n) be any real numbers; then $(a_n) \cdot (b_n) = DR(a_n \cdot b_n)$.
Proof: The proof is similar to the proof of Theorem 5.5.13.

THEOREM 5.5.15. $DR(a_n + b_n) = DR(a_n) + DR(b_n)$,   provided   that (a_n) and (b_n) are almost-constant.
Proof: Let $(A_n) = DR(a_n)$ and let $(B_n) = DR(b_n)$; then

$$
\begin{aligned}
DR(a_n + b_n) &= DR(A_n + B_n) && \text{by Th. 5.5.9} \\
&= (A_n) + (B_n) && \text{by Th. 5.5.13} \\
&= DR(a_n) + DR(b_n).
\end{aligned}
$$

This establishes Theorem 5.5.15.

THEOREM 5.5.16. $DR(a_n \cdot b_n) = [DR(a_n)] \cdot [DR(b_n)]$, provided that (a_n) and (b_n) are almost-constant.
Proof: Let $(A_n) = DR(a_n)$ and let $(B_n) = DR(b_n)$; then

$$
\begin{aligned}
DR(a_n \cdot b_n) &= DR(A_n \cdot B_n) && \text{by Th. 5.5.10} \\
&= (A_n) \cdot (B_n) && \text{by Th. 5.5.14} \\
&= [DR(a_n)] \cdot [DR(b_n)].
\end{aligned}
$$

This establishes Theorem 5.5.16.

E X E R C I S E S

1. Prove that (a_n) is almost-constant and $DR(a_n) = (b_n)$ iff $\forall p \exists q \forall m [m > q \rightarrow |a_m - b_m| < 1/10^p]$ and $(b_n) \in R$.

2. Let (a_n) be any real number between 1 and 10, and let (b_n) be any sequence of decimal rationals such that $\forall k [k \in N \rightarrow a_k \cdot b_k \leq 1 < a_k \cdot (b_k + 1/10^k)]$.

a. Prove that (b_n) is almost-constant.

b. Prove that $ND(b_n) = DR(b_n)$.

c. Prove that $(a_n) \cdot ND(b_n) = 1$.

5.6 Properties of the Real Number System

We are now in a position to demonstrate that the associative laws and the distributive law are true in the real number system.

THE ASSOCIATIVE LAW FOR +. $\forall x \forall y \forall z [x + (y + z) = (x + y) + z]$.

Proof: Let (a_n), (b_n), and (c_n) be any real numbers. Then

$$
\begin{aligned}
(a_n) + [(b_n) + (c_n)] & \\
= DR(a_n) + DR(b_n + c_n) \quad & \text{by Th. 5.5.2 and Th. 5.5.13} \\
= DR(a_n + [b_n + c_n]) \quad & \text{by Th. 5.5.15 and Th. 5.5.9.}
\end{aligned}
$$

By the same argument, $[(a_n) + (b_n)] + (c_n) = DR([a_n + b_n] + c_n)$. But $(a_n + [b_n + c_n]) = ([a_n + b_n] + c_n)$, since $+$ is associative in the rational number system. Therefore, $DR(a_n + [b_n + c_n]) = DR([a_n + b_n] + c_n)$; hence, $(a_n) + [(b_n) + (c_n)] = [(a_n) + (b_n)] + (c_n)$. This establishes the associative law for $+$.

THE ASSOCIATIVE LAW FOR $\cdot$. $\forall x \forall y \forall z [x \cdot (y \cdot z) = (x \cdot y) \cdot z]$.

Proof: The proof is similar to the proof of the associative law for $+$.

THE DISTRIBUTIVE LAW. $\forall x \forall y \forall z [x \cdot (y + z) = x \cdot y + x \cdot z]$.

Proof: Let (a_n), (b_n), and (c_n) be any real numbers. Then

$$
\begin{aligned}
(a_n) \cdot [(b_n) + (c_n)] & \\
= [DR(a_n)] \cdot [DR(b_n + c_n)] \quad & \text{by Th. 5.5.2 and Th. 5.5.13} \\
= DR(a_n \cdot [b_n + c_n]) \quad & \text{by Th. 5.5.16 and Th. 5.5.9.}
\end{aligned}
$$

By the same argument, $(a_n) \cdot (b_n) + (a_n) \cdot (c_n) = DR(a_n \cdot b_n + a_n \cdot c_n)$. But $(a_n \cdot [b_n + c_n]) = (a_n \cdot b_n + a_n \cdot c_n)$, since the distributive law holds in the rational number system. Therefore, $DR(a_n \cdot [b_n + c_n]) = DR(a_n \cdot b_n + a_n \cdot c_n)$; hence, $(a_n) \cdot [(b_n) + (c_n)] = (a_n) \cdot (b_n) + (a_n) \cdot (c_n)$. This establishes the distributive law.

Recalling the results stated on pages 174–176, we see that $(R, +, \cdot, <, 0, 1)$ is an ordered field. It remains to show that the real number system is *complete*.

THE COMPLETENESS THEOREM. *K* possesses a least upper bound whenever *K* is a nonempty set of real numbers which possesses an upper bound.

Proof: We shall construct the least upper bound of *K*. Let "$D_m(K)$" denote the set of all decimal rationals obtained from *K* by selecting the *m*th term of each member of *K*. Since *K* possesses an upper bound, it is clear that there is a largest decimal rational in the set $D_1(K)$, say d_1. Similarly, there is a largest decimal rational in the set $D_2(K)$, say d_2. In general, there is a largest decimal rational in the set $D_m(K)$, say d_m, whenever $m \in N$. Now consider the sequence (d_n). By construction, (d_n) meets the first two requirements of a real number; therefore, $N(d_n)$ *is* a real number. In fact, $N(d_n)$ is the least upper bound of *K*! Let us prove this statement. Denote $N(d_n)$ by "(e_n)". We show, first, that the real number (e_n) is an upper bound of *K*. Suppose there is a member of *K*, say (a_n), such that $(e_n) < (a_n)$; then there is a natural number t such that $10/10^t < a_t - e_t$. Now, $\forall s[|e_s - d_s| \leq 1/10^s]$ since $(e_n) = N(d_n)$. In particular, $|e_t - d_t| \leq 1/10^t$; it follows that $d_t < a_t$. But, by construction, $a_t \leq d_t$. This contradiction demonstrates that there is no real number (a_n) with the stated property. Thus, (e_n) is an upper bound of *K*. Finally, we shall show that (e_n) is the least upper bound of *K*. Suppose that (b_n) is an upper bound of *K* such that $(b_n) < (e_n)$; then there is a natural number s such that $10/10^s < e_s - b_s$. But $|e_s - d_s| \leq 1/10^s$; hence, $b_s < d_s$. It follows from this that (b_n) is not an upper bound of *K*. We conclude that (e_n) is the least upper bound of *K*. This completes our proof.

We have now demonstrated the following theorem.

THEOREM 5.6.1. $(R, +, \cdot, <, 0, 1)$ is a complete ordered field.

E X E R C I S E S

1. Prove the Associative Law for Multiplication.
2. By following through the proof of the Completeness Theorem, construct the greatest lower bound of *K*, where *K* is a nonempty set of real numbers which possesses a lower bound.
3. Let *A* and *B* be sets of real numbers such that $A \cup B = R$, $A \cap B = \emptyset$, $A \neq \emptyset$,

$B \neq \emptyset$, $\forall x [x \in A \to x$ is a lower bound of $B]$, and $\forall y [y \in B \to y$ is an upper bound of $A]$. Prove the following:

a. $\forall x \forall y [x \in A \land y < x \to y \in A]$.

b. $\forall x \forall y [x \in B \land x < y \to y \in B]$.

c. The least upper bound of A and the greatest lower bound of B are the same.

d. Either the least upper bound of A is a member of A, or the greatest lower bound of B is a member of B.

4. Suppose that (a_n) is almost-constant and $\forall t [a_t \leq a_{t+1}]$; let $K = \{x | x \in R \land \exists t [x = a_t]\}$. Prove that $DR(a_n)$ is the least upper bound of K.

5. Suppose that (α_n) and (β_n) are sequences of real numbers such that $\forall t [0 \leq \alpha_t \leq \alpha_{t+1}]$ and $\forall t [0 \leq \beta_t \leq \beta_{t+1}]$; let $A = \{x | \exists t [x = \alpha_t]\}$, $B = \{x | \exists t [x = \beta_t]\}$, and $K = \{x | \exists t [x = \alpha_t \cdot \beta_t]\}$. Assuming that A and B each possess upper bounds, prove that K possesses a least upper bound and l.u.b. $K = [$l.u.b. $A] \cdot [$l.u.b. $B]$.

6. Prove that the real number system is an extension of the rational number system.

5.7 Roots and Exponents

The Completeness Theorem is one of the most exciting theorems we have yet encountered—exciting because of its unexpected power! For this property of the real number system, when adroitly used, penetrates to the heart of many fundamental questions concerning this important number system. For example, we shall prove that any positive real number possesses a square root. This is one of the most recognized advantages of the real number system over the rational number system. The discovery by the early Greeks that there is no rational number with square $2/1$ came as a complete surprise; indeed, this discovery dealt a body blow to the mathematics of the time. It was not until the nineteenth century that mathematicians, namely Dedekind and Cantor, overcame this difficulty by constructing a complete ordered field. In fairness to the Greek mathematicians, however, it should be observed that Eudoxus worked out the basic idea of a Dedekind cut, and Archimedes developed the essential ideas of calculus.

Let us prove that there is no rational number with square $2/1$. Suppose, to the contrary, that p/q is a rational number such that $(p/q)^2 = 2/1$; then $p \cdot p = 2 \cdot q \cdot q$ in the system of integers. Now, any integer can be represented uniquely as the product of primes. Consider the *number* of 2's that are factors of $p \cdot p$; this number is even, since it is double the number of 2's that are factors of p. Similarly, the number of 2's that are factors of $q \cdot q$ is even. Hence, looking at the equation $p \cdot p = 2 \cdot q \cdot q$, we observe that the number of 2's that are factors of the left-hand side is even, while the number of 2's that are factors of the right-hand side is odd. Therefore, $p \cdot p \neq 2 \cdot q \cdot q$.

On the other hand, there is a real number whose square is $(2.0, 2.0, 2.0, \cdots)$, namely $(1.4, 1.41, 1.414, 1.4142, \cdots)$, since

$$(1.4, 1.41, 1.414, 1.4142, \cdots) \cdot (1.4, 1.41, 1.414, 1.4142, \cdots)$$
$$= DR(1.96, 1.9881, 1.999396, 1.99996164, \cdots)$$
$$= D(2.0, 2.0, 2.0, \cdots)$$
$$= (2.0, 2.0, 2.0, \cdots).$$

You accept these statements? Good! You have faith! But the time has come for a critical look at what we are doing. We have asserted that if, for each natural number n, a_n is the decimal rational whose terminal digit occurs before the $n + 1$st decimal place and is such that $a_n \cdot a_n < 2.0$ and $2.0 \leq [a_n + 1/10^n] \cdot [a_n + 1/10^n]$,

then $DR(a_n \cdot a_n) = DR(1.96, 1.9881, 1.999396, 1.99996164, \cdots)$
$$= (2.0, 2.0, 2.0, \cdots)$$

We need to prove that given any natural number p, we can choose n so large that rounding off $a_n \cdot a_n$ to p decimal places produces 2.0. No doubt you have believed this for many years; possibly, you will point out that

$$(1.41421356)^2 = 1.99999\ 99932\ 87873\ 6,$$

arguing that this demonstrates the required result for $p = 7$, and that a similar computation will demonstrate the required result for any larger value of p. Of course, it is true that direct computation verifies the result for small values of p; for example, you could easily carry out the required computations for $p = 8$, 9, and 10, determining for each value of p how large n must be. The procedure works for small values of p, but does it work for large values of p? For example, if $p = 10^6$, how large must n be? It turns out that the answer to this question is apparent once we consider the inequalities contained in the assumptions. Generalizing on the example, let us prove the following theorem.

THEOREM 5.7.1. $\forall x \exists y [0 < x \rightarrow 0 < y \wedge y \cdot y = x]$ in the real number system.

Proof: Let x be any positive real number. Let K be the set of all positive real numbers with square less than x. Clearly, K is nonempty and possesses an upper bound (prove this!). Therefore, by the Completeness Theorem (p. 192), K possesses a least upper bound, say y. By construction $0 < y$; we shall show that $y \cdot y = x$. Let $x = (x_n)$ and let $y = N(d_n)$.

Recalling the construction for the least upper bound, we see that $d_m \cdot d_m < x$ whenever $m \in N$; furthermore, $x \le [d_m + 1/10^m] \cdot [d_m + 1/10^m]$; therefore, $|x_m - d_m \cdot d_m| \le d_m \cdot [1/10^m] + d_m \cdot [1/10^m] + 1/10^{2m}$ whenever $m \in N$. But there is a natural number k such that $\forall t [d_t < 10^k/1]$. Now choose p; then $|x_m - d_m \cdot d_m| < 2/10^{m-k} + 1/10^{2m} < 1/10^p$, provided that $m > p + k$. Therefore, by Theorem 5.5.6, $DR(d_n \cdot d_n) = DR(x_n)$, and by Theorem 5.5.2 $DR(x_n) = (x_n)$. But

$$
\begin{aligned}
DR(d_n \cdot d_n) &= [DR(d_n)] \cdot [DR(d_n)] && \text{by Th. 5.5.16}\\
&= [DRN(d_n)] \cdot [DRN(d_n)] && \text{by Th. 5.5.12}\\
&= [N(d_n)] \cdot [N(d_n)] && \text{by Th. 5.5.2}\\
&= y \cdot y.
\end{aligned}
$$

Hence, $y \cdot y = x$. This establishes Theorem 5.7.1.

In the case of the example, $x = (2.0, 2.0, 2.0, \cdots)$ and $(d_n) = (1.4, 1.41, 1.414, 1.4142, \cdots)$; therefore, $k = 1$. Thus, $|2.0 - d_m \cdot d_m| < 1/10^p$, provided that $m > p + 1$. Hence, rounding off $d_m \cdot d_m$ to 10^6 decimal places produces 2.0, provided that $m > 2 + 10^6$.

By a similar argument, we can establish the following theorem.

THEOREM 5.7.2. $\forall x \exists y [0 < x \rightarrow 0 < y \wedge y \cdot y \cdot y = x]$ in the real number system.

Prove this theorem!

Perhaps you see the direction in which we are moving. But, as usual, we need to improve our notation. Suppose $a \in R$; it is convenient to denote $a \cdot a$ by writing "a^2". In general, if n is any natural number, we denote by "a^n" the number obtained by multiplying a by itself n times. We formulate this convention in a precise manner as follows: we say that $a^1 = a$, and that if we know the real number denoted by "a^n", where n is any natural number, then "a^{n+1}" denotes $a^n \cdot a$. It is a simple exercise in mathematical induction to prove that this definition has succeeded in defining a^k whenever $k \in N$.

Using this terminology, we observe that any positive real number possesses a kth root. More precisely, we present the following theorem.

THEOREM 5.7.3. $\forall x \exists y [0 < x \rightarrow 0 < y \wedge y^k = x]$ whenever $k \in N$.

Once again, this theorem is easy to prove by following through the argument given above.

Some more notation. Suppose $a \in R$, $0 < a$, $b^k = a$, and $0 < b$; then we shall refer to b as *the* kth root of a, and we shall denote b by writing "$a^{1/k}$". *Problem:* Show that the kth root of a is unique for each natural number k.

The number x which appears in the expression "a^x" is called an *exponent*. The following six theorems about exponents are easy to prove by using mathematical induction.

THEOREM 5.7.4. $[a \cdot b]^x = a^x \cdot b^x$ whenever $x \in N$ and a and b are positive real numbers.

THEOREM 5.7.5. $a^{x+y} = a^x \cdot a^y$ whenever $x \in N$, $y \in N$, and a is a positive real number.

THEOREM 5.7.6. $a^{x \cdot y} = [a^x]^y$ whenever $x \in N$, $y \in N$, and a is a positive real number.

THEOREM 5.7.7. $[a^{1/(k \cdot t)}]^k = a^{1/t}$ whenever $k \in N$, $t \in N$, and a is a positive real number.

THEOREM 5.7.8. $[a^{1/(k \cdot t)}]^{k \cdot s} = [a^{1/t}]^s$ whenever $k \in N$, $s \in N$, $t \in N$, and a is a positive real number.

THEOREM 5.7.9. $[a^{1/t}]^s = [a^{1/v}]^u$ whenever $s \cdot v = t \cdot u$, $s \in N$, $t \in N$, $u \in N$, $v \in N$, and a is a positive real number.

We wish to define the expression "a^x", where a is a positive real number and x is any number. This expression has been defined in case the exponent is a natural number. We now define "a^x" where x is an integer. There are three classes of integers — positive, negative, and 0. If x is a positive integer, then x corresponds to a certain natural number — in fact, they bear the same name; if x is considered to be that natural number, then a^x is defined. If x is a negative integer, then we say that a^x is $1/a^{-x}$. Finally, we say that a^0 is 1. Thus, "a^x" is defined for any integer x. We now define this expression for any rational number x. If x is a rational number, there are integers s and t, $0 < t$, such that "s/t" is a name of x (this means that the ordered pair (s, t) is a member of x). Then we say that a^x is $[a^{1/t}]^s$. Note that Theorem 5.7.9 assures us that the number a^x is independent of the choice of a name of x. Finally, we shall define the expression "a^x" for a real exponent. First, we suppose that x is a nonnegative real number. This means that $x = (b_n)$, where (b_n) is a sequence of nonnegative decimal rationals. Consider the set $\{c \mid \exists t[t \in N \land c = a^{b_t}]\}$. This set is nonempty and possesses an upper bound; therefore, by the Completeness Theorem, this set possesses a least upper bound, say d. Then we say that a^x is d. The remaining case, $x < 0$, is easy to treat: we say that a^x is $1/a^{-x}$.

EXERCISES

1. Prove Theorem 5.7.2.
2. Prove Theorems 5.7.4 – 5.7.9.

Prove the following propositions, where a and b are positive real numbers:

3. $[a \cdot b]^x = a^x \cdot b^x$ whenever x is an integer.
4. $a^{x+y} = a^x \cdot a^y$ whenever x and y are integers.
5. $a^{x \cdot y} = [a^x]^y$ whenever x and y are integers.
6. $[a \cdot b]^x = a^x \cdot b^x$ whenever x is rational.
7. $a^{x+y} = a^x \cdot a^y$ whenever x and y are rational.
8. $a^{x \cdot y} = [a^x]^y$ whenever x and y are rational.
9. $[a \cdot b]^x = a^x \cdot b^x$ whenever $x \in R$. (*Hint:* See Ex. 5, p. 193.)
10. $a^{x+y} = a^x \cdot a^y$ whenever $x \in R$ and $y \in R$.
11. In the real number system, a is called the *logarithm of A to base b* iff $b^a = A$; a is denoted by writing "$\log_b A$". Assuming $0 < b$, prove the following:
    a. $\log_b 1 = 0$.
    b. $\log_b [x \cdot y] = \log_b x + \log_b y$.
    c. $b^{\log_b A} = A$.

Chapter 6

The Limit Concept

6.1 The B_k and R_k Operations

In this chapter we shall bring out the intimate relationship between the concepts underlying the real number system and the fundamental notion of analysis – the limit concept. In constructing the real number system, we found that the B_k, D_k, and R_k operations penetrated to the heart of the processes involved and enabled us to master this highly complex and important number system. We shall find that operations on sequences of *real* numbers, analogous to B_k and R_k, are helpful in studying the limit concept.

We begin by defining our *blocking-out* operation on sequences of real numbers.

DEFINITION 6.1.1. Let (α_n) be any sequence of real numbers, and let k be any nonnegative integer; then $B_k(\alpha_n) = (\alpha_{n+k})$.

DEFINITION 6.1.2. Let (α_n) be any sequence of real numbers, and let k be any natural number; then "$R_k(\alpha_n)$" denotes the sequence of decimal rationals whose nth term is the $k + 1$st term of α_n rounded off to k decimal places.

Notice the use of boldface type; this is intended to help distinguish between an operation on a sequence of decimal rationals and the corresponding operation on a sequence of real numbers.

To illustrate Definition 6.1.2, let (α_n) be a sequence of real numbers, and let $\alpha_n = (a_{n,1}, a_{n,2}, a_{n,3}, \cdots)$ whenever $n \in N$. Then $R_k(\alpha_n) = (b_n)$, where b_n is $a_{n,k+1}$ rounded off to k decimal places.

For example, consider the sequence of real numbers (θ_n) such that

$$\theta_1 = (1.5, 1.55, 1.555, \cdots),$$
$$\theta_2 = (2.5, 2.55, 2.555, \cdots),$$
$$\theta_3 = (3.5, 3.55, 3.555, \cdots),$$

198

and, in general, $\theta_n = (n.5, n.55, n.555, \cdots)$ whenever $n \in N$. Then $R_2(\theta_n) = (1.56, 2.56, 3.56, \cdots, n.56, \cdots)$.

EXERCISES

Simplify the following:

1. $R_2(2 + 1/10^n)$.	5. $D_2R_3(\pi + 1/10^n)$.	9. $R_4B_2(1 - 1/10^n)$.
2. $R_4(7 + 1/10^{2n})$.	6. $D_3R_3(\pi + 1/10^n)$.	10. $B_2R_4(1 - 1/10^n)$.
3. $R_3(\pi + 1/10^n)$.	7. $D_6R_3(\pi + 1/10^n)$.	11. $R_3(5 - 1/10^n)$.
4. $B_2R_3(\pi + 1/10^n)$.	8. $DR_3(\pi + 1/10^n)$.	12. $B_3R_3(5 - 1/10^n)$.

6.2   Almost-Constant Sequences

Our purpose in this section is to characterize the notion of a *convergent* sequence of real numbers and to introduce the concept of the *limit* of any such sequence.

Let (α_n) be a sequence of real numbers; then $R_p(\alpha_n)$ is a sequence of decimal rationals. Therefore, we can make use of our notion of a B-constant sequence of decimal rationals.

DEFINITION 6.2.1.   A sequence of real numbers, say (α_n), is said to be *almost-constant* iff $R_p(\alpha_n)$ is B-constant whenever p is a natural number, with at most one exception.

To illustrate this definition, consider (θ_n), where $\theta_n = \pi + 1/10^n$ whenever $n \in N$. Then

$$R_1(\theta_n) = (3.2, 3.2, 3.1, 3.1, 3.1, \cdots),$$
$$R_2(\theta_n) = (3.24, 3.15, 3.14, 3.14, 3.14, \cdots),$$
$$R_3(\theta_n) = (3.242, 3.152, 3.143, 3.142, 3.142, 3.142, \cdots),$$
$$R_4(\theta_n) = (3.2416, 3.1516, 3.1426, 3.1417, 3.1416, 3.1416, 3.1416, \cdots),$$

and so on. It is clear that $R_p(\theta_n)$ is B-constant whenever $p \in N$. Furthermore,

$$\text{B-lim } R_1(\theta_n) = 3.1,$$
$$\text{B-lim } R_2(\theta_n) = 3.14,$$
$$\text{B-lim } R_3(\theta_n) = 3.142,$$
$$\text{B-lim } R_4(\theta_n) = 3.1416,$$

and so on. This example suggests that we introduce $\mathbf{R}$, a mapping which associates a sequence of decimal rationals with an almost-constant sequence of real numbers. Recall that B-lim $\mathbf{R}_p(\alpha_n)$ exists and is a decimal rational, provided that $\mathbf{R}_p(\alpha_n)$ is B-constant (see Definition 5.3.2).

DEFINITION 6.2.2.   Let (α_n) be any almost-constant sequence of real numbers; then $\mathbf{R}(\alpha_n) = (e_n)$, where

$$e_p = \begin{cases} \text{B-lim } \mathbf{R}_p(\alpha_n), \text{ if } \mathbf{R}_p(\alpha_n) \text{ is B-constant,} \\ e_{p+1} \text{ rounded off to } p \text{ decimal places, otherwise.} \end{cases}$$

For example, $\mathbf{R}(\pi + 1/10^n) = (3.1, 3.14, 3.142, 3.1416, \cdots)$.

Notice that $\mathbf{R}(\pi + 1/10^n)$ is a sequence of decimal rationals but is *not* a real number. Applying D (see Definition 5.2.2) to this sequence, we obtain the real number $(3.1, 3.14, 3.141, 3.1415, \cdots) = \pi$. This example shows that we can construct a real number from an almost-constant sequence of real numbers by first applying $\mathbf{R}$ and then applying D. In fact, the real number obtained in this way is the *limit* of the sequence in the usual sense.

DEFINITION 6.2.3.   Let (α_n) be any almost-constant sequence of real numbers; then $\mathbf{DR}(\alpha_n)$ is called the *limit* of (α_n) and is denoted by "$\lim(\alpha_n)$".

Considering the preceding example, notice that

$$\begin{aligned} \lim(\pi + 1/10^n) &= \mathbf{DR}(\pi + 1/10^n) \\ &= \mathbf{D}(3.1, 3.14, 3.142, 3.1416, \cdots) \\ &= (3.1, 3.14, 3.141, 3.1415, \cdots) \\ &= \pi. \end{aligned}$$

EXERCISES

Show that each of the following sequences of real numbers is almost-constant:

1. $(5, 5, 5, \cdots, 5, \cdots)$.
2. $(1, 2, 3, 7, 7, 7, \cdots, 7, \cdots)$.
3. $(2^{1/2} + 1/10^n)$.
4. $(2^{1/2} + 1/(-10)^n)$.
5. $(3^{1/2} + 1/10^n)$.
6. $(3^{1/2} + 5/10^n)$.
7. $(3^{1/2} + 1/10^{2n})$.
8. $(\pi + 5/10^n)$.
9. $(\pi + 5/10^{2n})$.
10. $(\pi + 5/(-10)^n)$.

11. Compute the *limit* of each of the above sequences.

6.3   Properties of the Limit Concept

We now develop some important properties of the mapping lim.

THEOREM 6.3.1.   Let (α_n) be any almost-constant sequence of real numbers; then $\lim(\alpha_n)$, rounded off to p decimal places, is B-lim $\mathbf{R}_p(\alpha_n)$ — whenever p is a natural number such that $\mathbf{R}_p(\alpha_n)$ is B-constant.
Proof: Examine the construction of $\lim(\alpha_n)$.

COROLLARY 6.3.1.   Let (α_n) be any almost-constant sequence of real numbers; then $\forall p \exists q$[each term of $\mathbf{B}_q \mathbf{R}_p(\alpha_n)$ differs from $\lim(\alpha_n)$, rounded off to p decimal places, by at most $1/10^p$].

COROLLARY 6.3.2.   Let (α_n) be any almost-constant sequence of real numbers; then $\forall p \exists q$[each term of $\mathbf{B}_q \mathbf{R}_p(\alpha_n)$ differs from $\lim(\alpha_n)$ by at most $1/10^p$].

COROLLARY 6.3.3.   Let (α_n) be any almost-constant sequence of real numbers; then $\forall p \exists q$[each term of $\mathbf{B}_q(\alpha_n)$ differs from $\lim(\alpha_n)$ by at most $1/10^p$].

THEOREM 6.3.2.   Let (α_n) be any sequence of real numbers; then (α_n) is almost-constant iff there is a real number, say A, such that $\forall p \exists q$[each term of $\mathbf{B}_q \mathbf{R}_p(\alpha_n)$ differs from A by at most $1/10^p$].
Proof: 1. Assume that (α_n) is almost-constant. Then $\lim(\alpha_n)$ exists and, by Corollary 6.3.2, has the required property.
2. Assume that A is a real number such that $\forall p \exists q$[each term of $\mathbf{B}_q \mathbf{R}_p(\alpha_n)$ differs from A by at most $1/10^p$]. We shall show that $\mathbf{R}_p(\alpha_n)$ is B-constant whenever p is a natural number, with at most one exception. Suppose t is a natural number such that $\mathbf{R}_t(\alpha_n)$ is not B-constant. Now consider $\mathbf{R}_{t+1}(\alpha_n)$; there is a natural number s_1 such that each term of $\mathbf{B}_{s_1} \mathbf{R}_{t+1}(\alpha_n)$ differs from A by at most $1/10^{t+1}$. Similarly, there is a natural number s_2 such that each term of $\mathbf{B}_{s_2} \mathbf{R}_{t+2}(\alpha_n)$ differs from A by at most $1/10^{t+2}$. Again, there is a natural number s_3 such that each term of $\mathbf{B}_{s_3} \mathbf{R}_{t+3}(\alpha_n)$ differs from A by at most $1/10^{t+3}$. Of course, this process can be continued. This means that, given any natural number m, we can find a natural number s such that the terms of $\mathbf{B}_s(\alpha_n)$ possess the same digits in the integral part and in the first t decimal places; furthermore, the digit in the $t + 1$st decimal place is either 4 or 5; if it is 4, then it is followed by at least m 9's, and if it is 5, then it is followed by at least m 0's. Thus, $\mathbf{R}_p(\alpha_n)$ is B-constant whenever $p \neq t$; therefore, (α_n) is almost-constant. This establishes Theorem 6.3.2.

COROLLARY 6.3.4.   Let (α_n) be any sequence of real numbers; then (α_n) is almost-constant iff there is a real number, say A, such that $\forall p \exists q$[each term of $\mathbf{B}_q(\alpha_n)$ differs from A by at most $1/10^p$].

THEOREM 6.3.3.   Let (α_n) be any sequence of real numbers; then $\lim(\alpha_n) = A$ if $\forall p \exists q$[each term of $\mathbf{B}_q(\alpha_n)$ differs from A by at most $1/10^p$].

Proof: We must show that there is just one number, say A, such that $\forall p \exists q$[each term of $\mathbf{B}_q(\alpha_n)$ differs from A by at most $1/10^p$]. Suppose there are two real numbers with this property, say B and C. Then there is a natural number k such that B and C differ by more than $1/10^k$. But there is a natural number r such that each term of $\mathbf{B}_r(\alpha_n)$ differs from B by at most $1/10^{k+1}$, and there is a natural number s such that each term of $\mathbf{B}_s(\alpha_n)$ differs from C by at most $1/10^{k+1}$. Let q be the larger of r and s; then each term of $\mathbf{B}_q(\alpha_n)$ differs from B and from C by at most $1/10^{k+1}$. But this is possible only if B and C differ by at most $2/10^{k+1}$. This contradiction demonstrates that $B = C$. We are now ready to prove that $\lim(\alpha_n) = A$. Applying Corollary 6.3.4, we see that (α_n) is almost-constant. Therefore, by Corollary 6.3.3, $\lim(\alpha_n) = A$. This establishes Theorem 6.3.3.

COROLLARY 6.3.5.   Let (α_n) be any sequence of real numbers; then $\lim(\alpha_n) = A$ if $\forall p \exists q$[each term of $\mathbf{B}_q(\alpha_n)$ differs from A by less than $1/10^p$].

Note that Theorem 6.3.3 contains a useful criterion for checking that a given real number is the limit of a given sequence. This theorem is also of great technical importance, since it can be used to establish additional properties of lim.

Problem: Prove that $\lim(\alpha_n) = 0$ iff $\forall p \exists q[\mathbf{B}_q \mathbf{R}_p(\alpha_n) = (0)]$.

6.4   A Useful Technique

The technique for computing the limit of a given almost-constant sequence is based on the following four theorems.

THEOREM 6.4.1.   Let (α_n) and (β_n) be any almost-constant sequences of real numbers; then $(\alpha_n + \beta_n)$ is almost-constant and

$$\lim(\alpha_n + \beta_n) = \lim(\alpha_n) + \lim(\beta_n).$$

THEOREM 6.4.2.   Let (α_n) and (β_n) be any almost-constant sequences of real numbers; then $(\alpha_n \cdot \beta_n)$ is almost-constant and

$$\lim(\alpha_n \cdot \beta_n) = [\lim(\alpha_n)] \cdot [\lim(\beta_n)].$$

THEOREM 6.4.3.   Let (α_n) and (β_n) be any almost-constant sequences of real numbers; then $(\alpha_n - \beta_n)$ is almost-constant and

$$\lim(\alpha_n - \beta_n) = \lim(\alpha_n) - \lim(\beta_n).$$

THEOREM 6.4.4.   Let (α_n) and (β_n) be any almost-constant sequences of real numbers such that $\lim(\beta_n) \neq 0$ and $\forall t[\beta_t \neq 0]$; then (α_n/β_n) is almost-constant and

$$\lim\left(\frac{\alpha_n}{\beta_n}\right) = \frac{\lim(\alpha_n)}{\lim(\beta_n)}.$$

Recall that the operations $+$, $\cdot$, $-$, $\div$ on sequences are defined as follows: $(\alpha_n) + (\beta_n) = (\alpha_n + \beta_n)$, $(\alpha_n) \cdot (\beta_n) = (\alpha_n \cdot \beta_n)$, $(\alpha_n) - (\beta_n) = (\alpha_n - \beta_n)$, and $(\alpha_n) \div (\beta_n) = (\alpha_n/\beta_n)$; thus, Theorem 6.4.1 states that the limit of the sum of two almost-constant sequences is the sum of the two limits; Theorem 6.4.2 states that the limit of the product of two almost-constant sequences is the product of the two limits; Theorem 6.4.3 states that the limit of the difference of two almost-constant sequences is the difference of the two limits; and Theorem 6.4.4 states that the limit of the quotient of two almost-constant sequences is the quotient of the two limits, provided the conditions of the theorem are met.

To see just how these theorems help us find the limit of a given almost-constant sequence, observe that if we can express the given sequence as the sum, say, of two sequences whose limits we know, then Theorem 6.4.1 enables us to compute the limit of the given sequence. For example, the sequence $(5 + 1/10^n)$ is the sum of the almost-constant sequences (5) and $(1/10^n)$, whose limits are 5 and 0, respectively. Therefore, $\lim(5 + 1/10^n) = 5 + 0 = 5$. Similarly,

$$\lim\left(\frac{5}{10^n}\right) = \lim\left(5 \cdot \frac{1}{10^n}\right) = [\lim(5)] \cdot \left[\lim\left(\frac{1}{10^n}\right)\right] = 5 \cdot 0 = 0.$$

We shall prove the above theorems in a moment; first, let us express symbolically the criterion for establishing that a given real number is the limit of a given sequence of real numbers. By Corollary 6.3.5, $\lim(\alpha_n) = A$ iff $\forall p \exists q$ [each term of $\mathbf{B}_q(\alpha_n)$ differs from A by less than $1/10^p$]. Therefore, $\lim(\alpha_n) = A$ iff $\forall p \exists q \forall n [\alpha_{q+n}$ differs from A by less than $1/10^p$], and so $\lim(\alpha_n) = A$ iff $\forall p \exists q \forall n [|\alpha_{q+n} - A| < 1/10^p]$; hence $\lim(\alpha_n) = A$ iff $\forall p \exists q \forall n [n > q \rightarrow |\alpha_n - A| < 1/10^p]$. We shall use this form of Theorem 6.3.3 to establish the theorems of this section. Since the absolute-value function is involved here, let us recall its properties: if M and N are any numbers, then

$$|M + N| \le |M| + |N| \quad \text{and} \quad |M \cdot N| = |M| \cdot |N|;$$

from the first of these, we easily deduce that $|M| - |N| \le |M - N|$.

We shall now prove the four theorems stated above.

Proof of Theorem 6.4.1: Suppose $\lim(\alpha_n) = A$ and $\lim(\beta_n) = B$; we shall prove that $\forall p \exists q \forall n [n > q \rightarrow |\alpha_n + \beta_n - (A + B)| < 1/10^p]$. Let p be any natural number; then there is a natural number r such that $|\alpha_n - A| < 1/10^{p+1}$ whenever $n > r$, and there is a natural number s such that $|\beta_n - B| < 1/10^{p+1}$ whenever $n > s$. Let q be the larger of r and s; then $|\alpha_n - A| < 1/10^{p+1}$ and $|\beta_n - B| < 1/10^{p+1}$ whenever $n > q$.

Hence,

$$\begin{aligned}
|\alpha_n + \beta_n - (A + B)| &= |(\alpha_n - A) + (\beta_n - B)| \\
&\le |\alpha_n - A| + |\beta_n - B| \\
&< 1/10^{p+1} + 1/10^{p+1} \\
&< 1/10^p,
\end{aligned}$$

provided that $n > q$. This establishes that $\forall p \exists q \forall n [n > q \rightarrow |\alpha_n + \beta_n - (A + B)| < 1/10^p]$; we conclude that $(\alpha_n + \beta_n)$ is almost-constant and $\lim(\alpha_n + \beta_n) = A + B$.

Proof of Theorem 6.4.2: Suppose $\lim(\alpha_n) = A$ and $\lim(\beta_n) = B$; we shall prove that $\forall p \exists q \forall n [n > q \rightarrow |\alpha_n \cdot \beta_n - A \cdot B| < 1/10^p]$. First, we note that there is a natural number, say k, such that $|A| < 10^k$ and $|B| < 10^k$. We have seen in the proof of Theorem 6.4.1 that if p is any natural number, then there is a corresponding natural number q such that $|\alpha_n - A| < 1/10^{p+k+1}$ and $|\beta_n - B| < 1/10^{p+k+1}$ whenever $n > q$. Hence,

$$\begin{aligned}
|\alpha_n \cdot \beta_n - A \cdot B| &= |\alpha_n \cdot (\beta_n - B) + B \cdot (\alpha_n - A)| \\
&\le |\alpha_n| \cdot |\beta_n - B| + |B| \cdot |\alpha_n - A| \\
&< |\alpha_n| \cdot (1/10^{p+k+1}) + |B| \cdot (1/10^{p+k+1})
\end{aligned}$$

$$< (|A| + 1/10^{p+k+1}) \cdot (1/10^{p+k+1}) + |B| \cdot (1/10^{p+k+1})$$
$$< 1/10^{p+1} + 1/10^{2p+2k+2} + 1/10^{p+1}$$
$$< 1/10^{p},$$

provided that $n > q$. This establishes that $\forall p \exists q \forall n [n > q \rightarrow |\alpha_n \cdot \beta_n - A \cdot B| < 1/10^p]$; therefore, $(\alpha_n \cdot \beta_n)$ is almost-constant and $\lim(\alpha_n \cdot \beta_n) = A \cdot B$.

Proof of Theorem 6.4.3: Suppose that $\lim(\alpha_n) = A$ and $\lim(\beta_n) = B$. But $(\alpha_n - \beta_n) = (\alpha_n) + (-\beta_n)$, and, by Theorem 6.4.2,

$$\lim(-\beta_n) = [\lim(-1)] \cdot [\lim(\beta_n)] = (-1) \cdot B = -B.$$

Therefore, the sequence $(\alpha_n - \beta_n)$ is almost constant and $\lim(\alpha_n - \beta_n) = \lim(\alpha_n) + \lim(-\beta_n) = A + -B = A - B$.

Proof of Theorem 6.4.4: Suppose that $\lim(\alpha_n) = A$, $\lim(\beta_n) = B$, $B \neq 0$, and $\forall t[\beta_t \neq 0]$. We shall prove that the sequence (α_n/β_n) is almost-constant and $\lim(\alpha_n/\beta_n) = A/B$. First, we prove that the sequence $(1/\beta_n)$ is almost-constant and $\lim(1/\beta_n) = 1/B$. Note that there is a natural number, say k, such that $1/10^k < |B|$. Since $\lim(\beta_n) = B$,

$$\exists q \forall n [n > q \rightarrow |\beta_n - B| < 1/10^{p+2k+1}].$$

Hence,
$$\left| \frac{1}{\beta_n} - \frac{1}{B} \right| = \frac{|B - \beta_n|}{|B| \cdot |\beta_n|} < \frac{10^{-p-2k-1}}{|B| \cdot (|B| - 10^{-p-2k-1})}$$
$$< \frac{10^{-p-2k-1}}{10^{-k} \cdot (10^{-k} - 10^{-p-2k-1})}$$
$$= \frac{1}{10^{p+k+1} \cdot (10^{-k} - 10^{-p-2k-1})}$$
$$= \frac{1}{10^{p+1} - 10^{-k}}$$
$$< 1/10^{p},$$

provided that $n > q$ where q is suitably chosen (see the proof of Theorem 6.4.1). Therefore,

$$\forall p \exists q \forall n [n > q \rightarrow |\frac{1}{\beta_n} - \frac{1}{B}| < 1/10^p];$$

hence, the sequence $(1/\beta_n)$ is almost-constant and $\lim(1/\beta_n) = 1/B$. We are now in a position to prove Theorem 6.4.4. Observe that $(\alpha_n/\beta_n) = (\alpha_n) \cdot (1/\beta_n)$; hence,

$$\lim\left(\frac{\alpha_n}{\beta_n}\right) = [\lim(\alpha_n)] \cdot \left[\lim\left(\frac{1}{\beta_n}\right)\right] = A \cdot \frac{1}{B} = \frac{A}{B}.$$

This establishes Theorem 6.4.4.

The following theorem is concerned with the sequence (α_n/β_n) in case $\lim(\beta_n) = 0$.

THEOREM 6.4.5. $\sim[\lim(\alpha_n) = 0] \wedge \lim(\beta_n) = 0 \wedge \forall t[\beta_t \neq 0] \rightarrow (\alpha_n/\beta_n)$ is *not* almost-constant.

Proof: $\sim[\lim(\alpha_n) = 0]$ means $\sim\forall p \exists q \forall n[n > q \rightarrow |\alpha_n| < 1/10^p]$; i.e., there is a natural number, say t, such that $\forall q \exists n[n > q \wedge 1/10^t \leq |\alpha_n|]$. Suppose (α_n/β_n) is almost-constant; then there is a natural number k such that $|\lim(\alpha_n/\beta_n)| < 10^k$. But $\exists q \forall n[n > q \rightarrow |\beta_n| < 1/10^{k+t}]$, since $\lim(\beta_n) = 0$. Therefore, $\forall q \exists n[n > q \wedge 10^k = [1/10^t] \cdot 10^{k+t} < |\alpha_n/\beta_n|]$. It follows that $\lim(\alpha_n/\beta_n) \leq -10^k$ or $10^k \leq \lim(\alpha_n/\beta_n)$; this contradicts our assumption that $|\lim(\alpha_n/\beta_n)| < 10^k$. This establishes Theorem 6.4.5.

Theorem 6.4.5 is important largely because of the following corollary, which is useful in analysis.

COROLLARY 6.4.1.   If the sequence (α_n/β_n) has a limit, and if $\lim(\beta_n) = 0$, then $\lim(\alpha_n) = 0$.

Proof: We know that if (α_n) and (β_n) are any sequences, then the proposition "$\sim[\lim(\alpha_n) = 0] \wedge \lim(\beta_n) = 0 \rightarrow (\alpha_n/\beta_n)$ has no limit" is a tautology. In other words, this proposition is true no matter what the truth-values of its components are. Thus, assuming the truth-values asserted in the hypothesis of the corollary forces us to the conclusion that the proposition "$\sim[\lim(\alpha_n) = 0]$" is false. Hence, we conclude that $\lim(\alpha_n) = 0$.

E X E R C I S E S

Use the technique of this section to show the following:

1. $\lim\left(\dfrac{1}{n} + \dfrac{1}{n^2}\right) = 0$.

2. $\lim\left(\dfrac{n+1}{n^2}\right) = 0.$

3. $\lim\left(\left[1 + \dfrac{1}{n}\right]^2\right) = 1.$

4. $\lim\left(\dfrac{4 + 4/n + 1/n^2}{2 + 1/n}\right) = 2.$

5. $\lim(\pi + 2/n) = \pi.$

6. $\lim(2^{1/2} + 5/10^n) = 2^{1/2}.$

7. Given that $\lim(\alpha_n) = A$, $\lim(\beta_n) = B$, and $\lim(\gamma_n) = C$, prove that:
$$\text{(i) } \lim(\alpha_n + \beta_n + \gamma_n) = A + B + C,$$
$$\text{(ii) } \lim(\alpha_n \cdot \beta_n \cdot \gamma_n) = A \cdot B \cdot C.$$

8. Given that $([\alpha_n]^{1/2})$ is almost-constant and that $\lim(\alpha_n) = A$, prove that $\lim([\alpha_n]^{1/2}) = A^{1/2}.$

9. a. In order to compute $\pi^{1/2}$ rounded off to p decimal places, to how many decimal places must π be rounded off?

  b. Assuming that (α_n) is almost-constant and $\alpha_n \geq 0$ for each n, show that $([\alpha_n]^{1/2})$ is almost-constant.

10. Given that $\lim(\alpha_n) = A$, show the following:

  a. $\lim\left(\dfrac{A^2 - \alpha_n^2}{A - \alpha_n}\right) = 2 \cdot A.$

  b. $\lim\left(\dfrac{A^3 - \alpha_n^3}{A - \alpha_n}\right) = 3 \cdot A^2.$

  c. $\lim\left(\dfrac{A^{1/2} - \alpha_n^{1/2}}{A - \alpha_n}\right) = \dfrac{1}{2 \cdot A^{1/2}}$, provided that $\alpha_n \geq 0$ for each n and $A > 0$.

11. a. Given that $\lim(\beta_n) = B$ and $\lim(\alpha_n - \beta_n) = L$, show that $\lim(\alpha_n) = B + L.$

  b. Given that $\lim(\beta_n) = B$ and $\lim(\alpha_n + \beta_n) = M$, show that $\lim(\alpha_n) = M - B.$

  c. Given that $\lim(\alpha_n - \beta_n) = L$ and $\lim(\alpha_n + \beta_n) = M$, show that
$$\lim(\alpha_n) = \dfrac{L + M}{2} \quad \text{and} \quad \lim(\beta_n) = \dfrac{M - L}{2}.$$

12. Prove that $\lim(\alpha_n) \leq K$ if $\lim(\alpha_n)$ exists and $\forall t[\alpha_t \leq K].$

13. Prove that $K \leq \lim(\alpha_n)$ if $\lim(\alpha_n)$ exists and $\forall t[K \leq \alpha_t].$

14. Prove that $\lim(\alpha_n) \leq \lim(\beta_n)$ if both limits exist and $\forall t[\alpha_t \leq \beta_t].$

15. The sequence (β_n) is said to be a *subsequence* of (α_n) if (β_n) can be obtained from (α_n) by deleting specified terms of (α_n). For example, $(1, 3, 5, 7, \cdots)$ is the subsequence of $(1, 2, 3, 4, \cdots)$ obtained by deleting alternate terms; and $B_5(\alpha_n)$ is the subsequence of (α_n) obtained by deleting the first five terms of (α_n). Show that if (β_n) is any subsequence of (α_n) and if $\lim(\alpha_n)$ exists, then $\lim(\beta_n) = \lim(\alpha_n).$

16. Construct a sequence (α_n) and a subsequence of (α_n) such that the subsequence possesses a limit, although (α_n) does not.

17. Suppose that (β_n) is a subsequence of (α_n) and that (γ_n) is the subsequence of (α_n) obtained by deleting the terms appearing in (β_n). Prove that $\lim(\beta_n) = \lim(\gamma_n) = L \rightarrow \lim(\alpha_n) = L$.

18. The sequence (α_n) is said to be *bounded* iff there is a real number K such that $\forall t[|\alpha_t| < K]$. The sequence (α_n) is said to be *monotonically increasing* iff $\forall i \forall j[i < j \rightarrow \alpha_i \leq a_j]$. Prove that (α_n) possesses a limit if (α_n) is bounded and monotonically increasing. (*Hint:* Show that the least upper bound of the set of terms of (α_n) is the limit of (α_n).)

19. The sequence (α_n) is said to be *monotonically decreasing* iff $\forall i \forall j[i < j \rightarrow \alpha_j \leq \alpha_i]$. Prove that (α_n) possesses a limit if (α_n) is bounded and monotonically decreasing. (*Hint:* Consider the sequence $(-\alpha)$.)

20. A sequence is said to be *monotonic* iff it is monotonically increasing or is monotonically decreasing. Show that each bounded sequence possesses a monotonic subsequence. (*Hint:* Consider the sequence $(\alpha_{q_1}, \alpha_{q_2}, \cdots)$, where α_{q_1} is the largest term of (α_n), α_{q_2} is the largest term of $B_{q_1}(\alpha_n)$, and so on.)

21. Prove that each bounded sequence possesses an almost-constant subsequence.

APPENDIXES

Appendix 1

Cardinal Numbers

In discussing the important number system known as the *natural number system,* there are two widely used approaches: the *axiomatic* approach and the *constructive* approach. As we have seen, the famous Italian mathematician Peano used the former approach; here, we shall consider the latter approach.

The basic ideas behind the constructive approach were worked out by Frege in the mid-nineteenth century, and were later rediscovered and popularized by Russell. We now consider the contribution of Frege and Russell to the problem of constructing the natural numbers. First, recall that a natural number is certainly a mathematical object; since it is convenient to represent a mathematical object by a set, we shall try to represent each natural number by a set. For example, following Russell's approach, let us construct the natural number 2. We begin with a question. At an intuitive level, what is meant by saying that a set, say S, has *exactly* two members? Well, S has exactly two members iff there are objects, say a and b, such that $a \neq b$ and $S = \{a, b\}$. It is easy to characterize this condition formally.

DEFINITION. S has exactly two members iff

$$\exists x \exists y \forall z [(x \in S \land y \in S) \land (z \in S \rightarrow z = x \lor z = y)].$$

Notice that "having exactly two members" is a property that some sets possess and some sets do not possess. For example, $\{\text{moon}, \text{sun}\}$ has exactly two members, whereas $\{\text{moon}, \text{sun}, \text{earth}\}$ does not.

The idea of Frege and Russell is this: having defined what we mean by saying that a set has exactly two members, we can characterize *twoness,* the essence of the natural number 2, by gathering together all possible

Reprinted from A. H. Lightstone, *The Axiomatic Method: An Introduction to Mathematical Logic,* © 1964, by permission of Prentice-Hall, Inc., Englewood Cliffs, N. J.

instances of *twoness*. In other words, let us collect together all sets with exactly two members; we obtain the class

$$\{S|S \text{ is a set and } S \text{ has exactly two members}\},$$

which Russell called a *bundle*. Thus, by the natural number 2, we mean this very class — the bundle formed by gathering together the sets that have exactly two members. This means that "2" is a name of the class of all sets which possess exactly two members.

DEFINITION. $2 = \{S|S \text{ is a set and } S \text{ has exactly two members}\}$.

It follows that a set, say M, has exactly two members iff $M \in 2$. In the same way, "3" is a name of the class of all sets that have exactly three members; "4" is a name of the class of all sets that have exactly four members; and so on.

In this way, Russell and Frege succeeded in constructing the natural numbers in terms of sets; indeed, they found it easy to introduce the notion of adding one — the successor operation — and were able to show that the Peano Postulates hold true in their system. This meant they had succeeded in constructing the rudimentary *system* of natural numbers which Peano had assumed to exist and had taken as the starting point in his program for developing the number systems of mathematics.

Furthermore, Frege and Russell were able to generalize their procedure in a simple and effective manner, thereby obtaining cardinal numbers. As follows, the idea is to introduce an equivalence relation on sets (we have already considered this notion; see Definition 4.1.5).

DEFINITION. $A \equiv B$, where A and B are sets, iff there exists a one–one mapping of A onto B.

It is easy to see that this binary relation is reflexive, symmetric, and transitive; this is left as an exercise.

Next, we consider the class of all sets equivalent to a given set. Let A be any set and consider $\{S|S \text{ is a set} \wedge S \equiv A\}$; we shall call this class a cardinal number, and, in particular, we shall say it is the cardinal number of A; we shall denote it by writing "$\overline{\overline{A}}$".

DEFINITION. $\overline{\overline{A}} = \{S|S \text{ is a set} \wedge S \equiv A\}$.

Clearly, $A \in \overline{\overline{A}}$; also, if $B \in \overline{\overline{A}}$, then $\overline{\overline{B}} = \overline{\overline{A}}$.

Notice that 2 is a cardinal number; indeed, each natural number is a cardinal number. To see that we have generalized the notion of a natural number, we must show that there is a cardinal number which is not a natural number. Consider the set of all natural numbers, which we shall denote by "N". What about the cardinal number of N, namely $\overline{\overline{N}}$? Let us show that $\overline{\overline{N}}$ is not a natural number, i.e., $\overline{\overline{N}} \notin N$. It is easy to prove, by using the Peano Postulates, that each natural number, say $\overline{\overline{A}}$, has the property that $B = A$ whenever $B \equiv A$ and $B \subset A$. But $\overline{\overline{N}}$ does not have this property. Consider the set $\{2n \mid n \in N\}$; clearly, $\{2n \mid n \in N\} \subset N$ and $\{2n \mid n \in N\} \neq N$. Furthermore, $\{2n \mid n \in N\} \equiv N$, as is easily seen. This demonstrates that $\overline{\overline{N}}$ is not a natural number.

The cardinal number $\overline{\overline{N}}$ is of great importance. As we have seen, N has the property that it is equivalent to one of its proper subsets. Any set which has this property is said to be *infinite,* whereas a set which is not infinite is said to be *finite.* The cardinal number of an infinite set is said to be a *transfinite* cardinal. The transfinite cardinal $\overline{\overline{N}}$ is assigned the special name "$\aleph_0$" (read "aleph zero"), where "$\aleph$" is the first letter of the Hebrew alphabet. Any set whose cardinal is $\aleph_0$ is said to be *denumerable* or *enumerable.*

THEOREM.   The set of all positive rational numbers is denumerable.

Proof: We construct a mapping, μ, of the positive rational numbers onto N, which has the following properties. Let a/b and c/d be any two positive rational numbers in lowest terms (where $a, b, c,$ and d are positive integers); first, we require that $\mu(1/1) = 1$; next, we require that

$$\mu(a/b) < \mu(c/d) \text{ if } a + b < c + d$$

and

$$\mu(a/b) < \mu(c/d) \text{ if } a + b = c + d \wedge a < c.$$

Clearly, there are many mappings possessing these properties (e.g., $\mu(1/2) = 10$). Therefore, we impose one more condition on μ:

$$\mu(c/d) = 1 + \mu(a/b) \text{ if } \mu(a/b) < \mu(c/d) \wedge \sim\exists x[\mu(a/b) < \mu(x) < \mu(c/d)].$$

Applying our three conditions, we see that

$$\mu(1/1) = 1, \quad \mu(1/2) = 2, \quad \mu(2/1) = 3, \quad \mu(1/3) = 4, \quad \mu(3/1) = 5,$$

and so on. This means that the positive rationals can be listed as follows:

$$1/1; \ 1/2, 2/1; \ 1/3, 3/1; \ 1/4, 2/3, 3/2, 4/1; \ 1/5, 5/1;$$

and so on. It is clear that each positive rational has an image in N, under μ, which can be computed by extending the above list until the given positive rational is reached. Furthermore, since our list has no end, each natural number is the image of one (and only one) positive rational number; in fact, the positive rational whose image is a given natural number, say 1,000,000, can be computed by writing out the first million entries in the above listing of the positive rationals. This demonstrates that μ is a one–one mapping of the positive rationals onto N.

COROLLARY. $N \times N \equiv N$, where N is the set of all natural numbers.

Proof: Apply the method of the proof of the preceding theorem.

THEOREM. Suppose $A \subset B$ and A is infinite; then B is infinite.

Proof: We shall construct a proper subset of B, equivalent to B. Since A is infinite, there is a proper subset of A, say A_1, such that $A_1 \equiv A$. Let λ be a one–one mapping of A_1 onto A; we show that $A_1 \cup (B - A) \equiv B$. Let

$$\mu(a) = \begin{cases} a \text{ if } a \in B - A, \\ \lambda(a) \text{ if } a \in A_1. \end{cases}$$

Then μ is a one–one mapping of $A_1 \cup (B - A)$ onto B; since $A_1 \cup (B - A)$ is a proper subset of B, we have established that B is infinite.

COROLLARY. The set of all real numbers is infinite.

Proof: This set possesses a denumerable subset.

THEOREM. The set of all real numbers is *not* denumerable.

Proof: Suppose that the set of all real numbers is denumerable; then there is a one–one mapping of this set onto N, say ν. Given $i \in N$, let x be the real number such that $\nu(x) = i$. Since each real number can be represented as an infinite decimal, let $x = a_i.d_{i1}d_{i2}d_{i3} \cdots d_{in} \cdots$, where each d_{ij} is a digit and a_i is the integral part of x. Now, construct the real number $0.d_{11}d_{22}d_{33} \cdots d_{nn} \cdots$. We transform this real number as follows: replace each d_{kk} by 5 if $d_{kk} \neq 5$; otherwise, replace d_{kk} by 4. By construction, the resulting real number differs from each $a_i.d_{i1}d_{i2}d_{i3} \cdots d_{in} \cdots$; thus, we have constructed a real number which has no image in N under the mapping ν. Contradiction! This establishes our theorem.

Let "c" denote the cardinal number of the set of all real numbers; we have shown that $\aleph_0 \neq c$. Thus, there are at least two transfinite cardinal numbers; as a matter of fact, there is an infinite number of transfinite cardinal numbers. To investigate this question, we need a method of comparing cardinal numbers. We begin by establishing the following theorem.

CANTOR–BERNSTEIN THEOREM. $A \equiv B$ whenever A possesses a subset A_1 and B possesses a subset B_1 such that $A \equiv B_1$ and $B \equiv A_1$.

Proof: Let μ be a one–one mapping of A onto B_1, and let ν be a one–one mapping of B onto A_1. In general, given any set C and any mapping λ, we shall denote $\{\lambda x \mid x \in C\}$ by writing "λC". We now use the given mappings μ and ν to construct additional subsets of A and B, as follows:

$$A_1 = \nu B, \quad A_2 = \nu B_1, \quad A_3 = \nu B_2, \quad \cdots,$$
$$B_1 = \mu A, \quad B_2 = \mu A_1, \quad B_3 = \mu A_2, \quad \cdots.$$

In general, $A_{n+1} = \nu B_n$ and $B_{n+1} = \mu A_n$ whenever $n \in N$. Clearly, $A_{n+1} \subset A_n$ and $B_{n+1} \subset B_n$ whenever $n \in N$. Let $t \in A$; either $\forall n [t \in A_n]$ or there is a natural number j such that $t \bar{\in} A_j$. Hence,

(1) $$A = \bigcap_{n \in N} A_n \cup (A - A_1) \cup \bigcup_{n \in N} (A_n - A_{n+1});$$

clearly, $\bigcap_{n \in N} A_n$ and $(A - A_1) \cup \bigcup_{n \in N} (A_n - A_{n+1})$ are disjoint. Similarly,

(2) $$B = \bigcap_{n \in N} B_n \cup (B - B_1) \cup \bigcup_{n \in N} (B_n - B_{n+1});$$

again, $\bigcap_{n \in N} B_n$ and $(B - B_1) \cup \bigcup_{n \in N} (B_n - B_{n+1})$ are disjoint. Let

$$A^* = (A - A_1) \cup \bigcup_{n \in N} (A_{2n} - A_{2n+1})$$
$$A^{**} = \bigcup_{n \in N} (A_{2n-1} - A_{2n})$$
$$B^* = (B - B_1) \cup \bigcup_{n \in N} (B_{2n} - B_{2n+1})$$
$$B^{**} = \bigcup_{n \in N} (B_{2n-1} - B_{2n}).$$

Then $A = \bigcap_{n \in N} A_n \cup A^* \cup A^{**}$ and $B = \bigcap_{n \in N} B_n \cup B^* \cup B^{**}$. But $\mu A^* = B^{**}$ and $\nu B^* = A^{**}$; therefore, $A^* \equiv B^{**}$ and $B^* \equiv A^{**}$. Finally, we shall show that $\bigcap_{n \in N} A_n \equiv \bigcap_{n \in N} B_n$. Suppose $a \in \bigcap_{n \in N} A_n$, i.e., $\forall n [a \in A_n]$; then $\forall n [\mu a \in B_n]$, and so $\mu a \in \bigcap_{n \in N} B_n$. In other words, with each member of $\bigcap_{n \in N} A_n$, say a, we can associate a unique member of $\bigcap_{n \in N} B_n$, namely μa. Since μ is a one–one mapping of A onto B_1, we know that no member of $\bigcap_{n \in N} B_n$ is used twice as an image. Furthermore, no member of $\bigcap_{n \in N} B_n$ is omitted; to see this, suppose that $\mu a_1 \in \bigcap_{n \in N} B_n$ and that $a_1 \bar{\bar{\in}} \bigcap_{n \in N} A_n$. Then, there is a natural number j such that $a_1 \bar{\bar{\in}} A_j$. Hence, $\mu a_1 \bar{\bar{\in}} B_{j+1}$, and so $\mu a_1 \bar{\bar{\in}} \bigcap_{n \in N} B_n$. Contradiction! This establishes that $\bigcap_{n \in N} A_n \equiv \bigcap_{n \in N} B_n$. In view of (1) and (2), it now follows that $A \equiv B$. In particular, we can construct a one–one mapping of A onto B, say λ, as follows:

$$\lambda a = \begin{cases} \mu a \text{ if } a \in \bigcap_{n \in N} A_n \cup A^*, \\ b \text{ where } vb = a, \text{ if } a \in A^{**}. \end{cases}$$

This establishes the Cantor-Bernstein Theorem.

Expressing this result in the language of cardinal numbers, we have the following corollary.

COROLLARY. $\bar{\bar{A}} = \bar{\bar{B}}$ whenever A possesses a subset A_1 and B possesses a subset B_1 such that $\bar{\bar{A}} = \bar{\bar{B}}_1$ and $\bar{\bar{B}} = \bar{\bar{A}}_1$.

This corollary suggests a natural way of comparing cardinal numbers, i.e., of introducing a *less than* relation on cardinal numbers.

DEFINITION.   Let A and B be any sets; we shall say that $\bar{\bar{A}} < \bar{\bar{B}}$ iff

$$\exists B_1 (B_1 \subset B \wedge A \equiv B_1) \wedge \sim \exists A_1 (A_1 \subset A \wedge B \equiv A_1).$$

Clearly, $<$ is transitive but not symmetric and not reflexive. Let A and B be any sets; there are four possibilities:

(1) $\exists B_1 (B_1 \subset B \wedge A \equiv B_1) \wedge \exists A_1 (A_1 \subset A \wedge B \equiv A_1)$; then $\bar{\bar{A}} = \bar{\bar{B}}$.
(2) $\exists B_1 (B_1 \subset B \wedge A \equiv B_1) \wedge \sim \exists A_1 (A_1 \subset A \wedge B \equiv A_1)$; then $\bar{\bar{A}} < \bar{\bar{B}}$, by definition.
(3) $\sim \exists B_1 (B_1 \subset B \wedge A \equiv B_1) \wedge \exists A_1 (A_1 \subset A \wedge B \equiv A_1)$; then $\bar{\bar{B}} < \bar{\bar{A}}$, by definition.
(4) $\sim \exists B_1 (B_1 \subset B \wedge A \equiv B_1) \wedge \sim \exists A_1 (A_1 \subset A \wedge B \equiv A_1)$; $\bar{\bar{A}}$ and $\bar{\bar{B}}$ are not comparable.

It turns out that, under a certain hypothesis known as the Axiom of Choice, (4) is impossible. We shall not prove this here; rather we content ourselves with stating the hypothesis involved.

THE AXIOM OF CHOICE. Let I be any nonempty set, and let S_a be a nonempty set whenever $a \in I$. Then there exists a set C such that $\overline{\overline{C \cap S_a}} = 1$ whenever $a \in I$; symbolically, $\exists C \forall a [C$ is a set $\wedge (a \in I \rightarrow \overline{\overline{C \cap S_a}} = 1)]$.

We observed previously that there exist infinitely many transfinite cardinal numbers. This proposition rests upon the following theorem.

THEOREM. The cardinal number of any set is less than the cardinal number of the set of all subsets of the given set.

Proof: Let A be any set, and let $S = \{T | T \subset A\}$. Clearly, there is a subset of S equivalent to A, namely $\{\{a\} | a \in A\}$. This means that $\overline{\overline{A}} = \overline{\overline{S}}$ or else $\overline{\overline{A}} < \overline{\overline{S}}$ (see (1) and (2) above). Suppose $\overline{\overline{A}} = \overline{\overline{S}}$. Then there exists a one–one mapping of A onto S, say μ. Let $a \in A$; then either $a \in \mu a$ or $a \overline{\in} \mu a$ (recall that μa is a subset of A). Consider the subset of A, say T, formed as follows: $T = \{a | a \in A \wedge a \overline{\in} \mu a\}$. Whether or not T is empty, by assumption there is a member of A, say a_1, such that $\mu a_1 = T$. There are two cases:

Case 1. $a_1 \in T$. Then $a_1 \in \mu a_1$; hence, by the construction of $T, a_1 \overline{\in} T$. Contradiction! This means that Case 1 is impossible.

Case 2. $a_1 \overline{\in} T$. Then $a_1 \overline{\in} \mu a_1$; hence, by the construction of $T, a_1 \in T$. Contradiction! This means that Case 2 is impossible.

We conclude from this argument that a_1 does not exist. Hence, each mapping of A into S must leave out at least one member of S. Thus, there is no one–one mapping of A onto S. We have demonstrated that A is *not* equivalent to S; we conclude that $\overline{\overline{A}} < \overline{\overline{S}}$.

The following definitions are aimed at developing a notation for the cardinal number of the set of all subsets of a given set—in terms of the cardinal number of the given set.

DEFINITION. Let A and B be any sets; then $A^B = \{\mu | \mu$ is a mapping of B into $A\}$.

DEFINITION. Let $\overline{\overline{A}} = a$ and $\overline{\overline{B}} = b$; then we shall denote the cardinal number of the set A^B by writing "a^b", i.e., $a^b = \overline{\overline{A^B}}$.

THEOREM. Let A be any set, and let $S = \{T | T \subset A\}$. Then $\overline{\overline{S}} = 2^a$, where $a = \overline{\overline{A}}$.

Proof: Given a subset of A, say T, either $a \in T$ or $a \overline{\in} T$ whenever $a \in A$. Therefore, $\{T | T \subset A\} \equiv \{\mu | \mu$ is a mapping of A into $\{0, 1\}\}$; hence, $\overline{\overline{S}} = 2^a$.

It is easy, now, to see that there are infinitely many transfinite cardinal numbers. Applying the two preceding theorems, we see that $m < 2^m$ whenever m is a cardinal number. In particular, $\aleph_0 < 2^{\aleph_0}$, $2^{\aleph_0} < 2^{(2^{\aleph_0})}$, and so on. Thus, given any transfinite cardinal number, there is a larger transfinite cardinal number.

E X E R C I S E S

1. Use quantifiers to define the notion of a set that has:
   a. exactly one member,   c. exactly four members,
   b. exactly three members,   d. no members.
2. Prove that $\equiv$ is reflexive, symmetric, and transitive.
3. Let m' denote $\overline{\overline{M \cup \{x\}}}$, where $\overline{\overline{M}} = m$ and $x \overline{\in} M$.
   a. Show that $1' = 2$ and $2' = 3$.
   b. Show that the set of all finite cardinal numbers (i.e., cardinal numbers which are not transfinite) together with the unary operation $'$ and the special cardinal number 1 satisfy the Peano Postulates.
4. Addition is defined as follows: $a + b = \overline{\overline{A \cup B}}$ whenever $\overline{\overline{A}} = a$, $\overline{\overline{B}} = b$, and $A \cap B = \emptyset$.
   a. Show that $a + b = b + a$ whenever a and b are cardinal numbers.
   b. Show that $1 + \aleph_0 = \aleph_0$. (*Hint:*   Consider $\{x\} \cup N$, where $x \overline{\in} N$.)
   c. Show that $\aleph_0 + \aleph_0 = \aleph_0$. (*Hint:*   Consider $\{2n - 1 | n \in N\} \cup \{2n | n \in N\}$.)
5. Multiplication is defined as follows: $a \cdot b = \overline{\overline{A \times B}}$ whenever $\overline{\overline{A}} = a$ and $\overline{\overline{B}} = b$.
   a. Show that $a \cdot b = b \cdot a$.
   b. Show that $2 \cdot \aleph_0 = \aleph_0$.
   c. Show that $\aleph_0 \cdot \aleph_0 = \aleph_0$.
6. Show that $(2^{\aleph_0})^{\aleph_0} = 2^{\aleph_0}$.
7. Show there is no such thing as the set of *all* sets.
8. "$\leq$" is defined as follows: $a \leq b$ iff $a < b$ or $a = b$, whenever a and b are cardinal numbers.
   a. Show that $\overline{\overline{A}} \leq \overline{\overline{B}}$ iff $\exists B_1(B_1 \subset B \wedge A \equiv B_1)$.
   b. Show that $a = b$ iff $a \leq b$ and $b \leq a$.
9. Prove that $\aleph_0$ is the smallest transfinite cardinal number (i.e., show that A is finite whenever $\overline{\overline{A}} < \aleph_0$).

Appendix 2

The Complex Number System

Our purpose here is to outline some of the features of the complex number system. The idea is to construct an extension of $(R, +, \cdot, 0, 1)$ in which the proposition $\exists x[x \cdot x = -1]$ is true. In the following, we shall denote real numbers by lower-case Roman letters.

Consider the algebraic system $(R \times R, +, \cdot, (0,0), (0,1))$, where $+$ and $\cdot$ are binary operations on $R \times R$ defined as follows: $(a,b) + (c,d) = (a+c, b+d)$ whenever (a,b) and (c,d) are members of $R \times R$, and $(a,b) \cdot (c,d) = (ac - bd, ad + bc)$ whenever (a,b) and (c,d) are members of $R \times R$.

We shall call members of $R \times R$ *complex numbers,* and we shall call $(R \times R, +, \cdot, (0,0), (0,1))$ the *complex number system.* It is easy to prove that the algebraic system $(R \times R, +, \cdot, (0,0), (1,0))$ is a field.

Now, consider the set of complex numbers $\{(a,0) | a \in R\}$. Notice that

$$(a,0) + (b,0) = (a+b, 0) \qquad \text{and} \qquad (a,0) \cdot (b,0) = (ab, 0)$$

whenever $a \in R$ and $b \in R$. Let μ be the one–one mapping of R onto $\{(a,0) | a \in R\}$ such that $\mu a = (a,0)$ whenever $a \in R$. Using μ, it is easy to see that the complex number system is an extension of the real number system with $<$ deleted.

It is customary to regard a complex number as an expression "$a + bi$", where a and b are real numbers and $i^2 = -1$. Let us see how this accords with our presentation. First, let us agree to denote the complex number $(a,0)$ by "a"; next, let "i" denote the complex number $(0,1)$. But $(0,1) \cdot (0,1) = (-1,0)$; thus, $i^2 = -1$. Furthermore, if (a,b) is any complex number, then

$$(a,b) = (a,0) + (0,b) = (a,0) + (b,0) \cdot (0,1) = a + bi.$$

This demonstrates that the idea that a complex number is an ordered pair of real numbers is equivalent to the idea that a complex number is an expression "$a + bi$".

Furthermore, it is easy to establish that $\forall x \exists! y[x \neq 0 \rightarrow x \cdot y = 1]$; i.e., if $(a, b) \neq 0$, then there is a unique complex number (c, d) such that $(a, b) \cdot (c, d) = 1$. Indeed, $c = a/(a^2 + b^2)$ and $d = -b/(a^2 + b^2)$. By using this fact, it is easy to demonstrate the following theorem.

THEOREM. $(R \times R, +, \cdot, 0, 1)$ is a field.

Next, we observe that given any nonzero complex number (a, b), there are unique real numbers r and θ, where $r > 0$ and $0 \leq \theta < 2\pi$, such that $a = r \cos \theta$ and $b = r \sin \theta$ (indeed, $r = \sqrt{a^2 + b^2}$, and if $a \neq 0$, then $\tan \theta = b/a$, whereas if $a = 0$, then $\theta = \pi/2$). Thus, $a + bi = r[\cos \theta + i \sin \theta]$; this is called the *polar form* of the complex number (a, b).

It is convenient to multiply complex numbers in polar form. It is easy to establish that if $a_1 + b_1 i = r_1[\cos \theta_1 + i \sin \theta_1]$ and $a_2 + b_2 i = r_2[\cos \theta_2 + i \sin \theta_2]$, then

$$[a_1 + b_1 i] \cdot [a_2 + b_2 i] = r_1 r_2 [\cos(\theta_1 + \theta_2) + i \sin(\theta_1 + \theta_2)].$$

From this result, we have the following theorem by mathematical induction.

DE MOIVRE'S THEOREM.   Let n be any natural number; then $[a + bi]^n = r^n[\cos n\theta + i \sin n\theta]$, provided that $a + bi = r[\cos \theta + i \sin \theta]$.

Finally, we observe that De Moivre's Theorem enables us to compute nth roots of nonzero complex numbers. Indeed, we can establish the following result.

THEOREM.   Let (a, b) be any nonzero complex number, and let $(a, b) = r[\cos \theta + i \sin \theta]$. Then, for each natural number n, there are exactly n distinct complex numbers z such that $z^n = r[\cos \theta + i \sin \theta]$; these complex numbers are:

$$r^{1/n}\left[\cos \frac{\theta + 2k\pi}{n} + i \sin \frac{\theta + 2k\pi}{n}\right], \qquad k = 0, 1, 2, \cdots, n - 1.$$

To illustrate this result, we compute the three third roots of the complex number 2. Now $(2, 0) = 2[\cos 0 + i \sin 0]$; therefore, the third roots of 2 are

$$2^{1/3}[\cos 0 + i \sin 0], \quad 2^{1/3}[\cos \frac{2\pi}{3} + i \sin \frac{2\pi}{3}], \quad 2^{1/3}[\cos \frac{4\pi}{3} + i \sin \frac{4\pi}{3}];$$

namely,

$$2^{1/3}, \quad 2^{1/3}[-1/2 + i\sqrt{3}/2], \quad 2^{1/3}[-1/2 - i\sqrt{3}/2].$$

We now state a result known as the Fundamental Theorem of Algebra.

THEOREM. Let n be any natural number and let $z_0, z_1, \cdots, z_{n-1}, z_n$ be any complex numbers where $z_n \neq 0$; then there is a complex number, say z, such that

$$z_n \cdot z^n + z_{n-1} \cdot z^{n-1} + \cdots + z_1 \cdot z + z_0 = 0.$$

For a proof of this key result, see R. Redheffer, "The Fundamental Theorem of Algebra", *The American Mathematical Monthly*, 64 (1957), 582–585.

References

Arnold, B. H., *Logic and Boolean Algebra,* Englewood Cliffs, N. J.: Prentice-Hall, 1962.

Halmos, P. R., *Naive Set Theory,* Princeton, N. J.: Van Nostrand, 1960.

Johnson, R. E., *First Course in Abstract Algebra,* Englewood Cliffs, N. J.: Prentice-Hall, 1953.

Landau, E., *Foundations of Analysis,* New York: Chelsea, 1951.

Lightstone, A. H., *The Axiomatic Method: An Introduction to Mathematical Logic,* Englewood Cliffs, N. J.: Prentice-Hall, 1964.

Roberts, J. B., *The Real Number System in an Algebraic Setting,* San Francisco: Freeman, 1962.

Rudin, W., *Principles of Mathematical Analysis,* New York: McGraw-Hill, 1953.

Stabler, E. R., *An Introduction to Mathematical Thought,* Reading, Mass.: Addison-Wesley, 1953.

Suppes, P., *Introduction to Logic,* Princeton, N. J.: Van Nostrand, 1957.

Waismann, F., *Introduction to Mathematical Thinking,* New York: Harper, 1959.

Wilder, R. L., *Introduction to the Foundations of Mathematics,* New York: Wiley, 1952.

Index

223